Henry Ritchie

The Fusing
of the
Ploughshare

Dedication

Dedicated to
Those who served in the volunteer
Yeomanry Regiments and to the Gunners
who rendered the Royal Artillery such a
powerful authority on the Battlefields

The Fusing of the Ploughshare

By Henry R. Ritchie

From East Anglia to Alamein
The Story of a Yeoman at War

First published in 1987 by
Henry Ritchie
Marks Hall
Margaret Roding
Dunmow, Essex, England

Photoset by Grainer Photosetting Ltd., Southend-on-Sea, Essex.

Printed in Great Britain at The Bath Press, Avon

3rd Edition 1990
ISBN 0 9513164 0 0

Editors Note

As one of those soldiers who were but a small piece in the vital history of the Western Desert Campaigns, I was very conscious of the privilege being accorded to me in being invited to edit this book. Few stories can match the detailed authenticity of the gallantry and the humour and the sadness of this narrative.

Henry Ritchie served with the Gunners throughout the Desert campaigns from the first lightning strike by General Wavell in December 1940 to the great battles of Alam Halfa and Alamein in the winter of 1943. He is a member of the Rats of Tobruk Association and is one of the relatively few who saw through and survived the whole of the 242 day Tobruk Siege — the longest siege in British military history.

Since the war Henry Ritchie has worked tirelessly for his comrades as Chairman of his Branch of the Yeomanry Association and his love of Farming and the Land has led him to high offices in the Agricultural Industry.

Leonard E. Tutt,
Knightsfield,
Welwyn Garden City,
Herts.

For Ernestine (Tina)
With Love

and to dear

Julian and Caroline
William and Belinda
Saffron and Tania

With the hope and prayer that they will
grow up in a Land where war shall be no
more.

From The Author

"The Fusing of the Ploughshare" is offered as a humble contribution to the story of East Anglian rural life and the Gunners during the war. The war years were among the hardest of my life but they were also full of the richest experiences that life can give. It is easy to indulge in self centred sentimentalism but it has to be said that the raw experiences and the deeply cherished friendships forged during the war years have a measure of value worth more than all the gold in the Rand.

The British as a nation are quite used to early disasters in our wars. Much of this has been due to cheese-paring defence policies. Those of us who fought in the Western Desert in the early years know exactly what was implied when it was said that the British anti tank rifle was only of any use if you climbed on the enemy tank, opened the turret and shot the driver! It is the duty of those of us who fought on the lowest level of the sharpest end to ensure that the politicians never let this happen again.

Henry R. Ritchie
Marks Hall,
Margaret Roding,
Dunmow,
Essex.

About The Author

His grandparents came down from Scotland in the late 19th Century and he is the third generation of his family to farm in Essex.

Henry Ritchie is a Nuffield Foundation Scholar and is a member of the Court of the University of Essex. He has travelled widely and has been involved in Trade Missions for the Export Council to Canada, New Zealand, Australia, Iran and the U.S.A. He has been President of the Essex Agricultural Society, Honorary Director of the Essex Show and Chairman of the Essex County Branch of the National Farmers Union. He has served on many national committees and is also a member of the Minister of Agriculture's Advisory Panel and of the Panel of the Agricultural Land Tribunal.

In earlier years he was a well known point to point rider and was a recognised judge of Livestock at the R.A.S.E., the Royal Highland and the Smithfield Shows.

During the war, after returning to England after serving for five years in the Middle East, he became a lecturer in Field Gunnery on the staff of the 4th Training Regiment near Aldershot. He is Deputy Lieutenant of the County of Essex.

Henry Ritchie is married with three children and his relaxations are golf and bridge.

PHILIP SHAW, M.B.E., M.R.A.C.,
Agriculture House,
Chelmsford,
Essex.

Acknowledgements

My first thanks go to Len Tutt, a desert and Tobruk veteran who now writes and broadcasts for the BBC, for so willingly taking on the task of editing this book.

I am indebted to Ray Fullerton, another desert comrade, for his painstaking work in providing the artistry and design work for the superb jacket cover and also for the drawings, maps and illustrations.

I must express my warm gratitude to Sir Richard Butler, D.L., past President of the National Farmers Union for his kind help and co-operation, and also to Major General Mervyn Janes C.B., M.B.E., and Lieutenant Colonel Alan Nicholls O.B.E., M.C., (both experienced desert leaders) for their tremendous support and assistance. Four "Desert Rats" Geoffrey Pyman M.B.E., Victor Hammick, Johnny Richardson and Charley Perry M.M., read and commented on the book pre-publication and I am very indebted to them.

I am very grateful to Philip Shaw M.B.E. for his tremendous assistance and to Jeremy Beale for sharing his expertise as a publisher.

I would particularly like to thank Colin Bonham of Grainger Photosetting for guiding me along the path of book production. To Ken Rumbold, Federal Vice President of the Rats of Tobruk Association and to Bob Procter of the Liverpool Branch and to Ken Rankin who wrote "Top Hats in Tobruk" I extend my warmest thanks for their willing help.

Mr Terence Charman of the Imperial War Museum traced for me the names of the two Scottish pipers of the 2nd Battalion Black Watch that we all heard from the gun position on the morning of the breakout from Tobruk in November 1941, and I am most grateful.

The Fusing of the Ploughshare

'The Fusing of the Ploughshare' is the story of an East Anglian farm worker who, as a volunteer, joins the colours of a Territorial Yeomanry Regiment before the Second World War and serves on the guns throughout the dark days of the Desert Campaigns in North Africa.

The account in the earlier chapters of East Anglian farming life is beautifully paced and written. It makes compulsive reading and abounds with fine descriptive passages and glistens with humour.

The course of the war in North Africa is faithfully followed and most of the military units mentioned in this book are actual regiments or formations.

Many desert veterans will recall with nostalgia the wide and lonely spaces and the heat of the desert sun.

Contents

CHAPTER ONE

The Rearing and the Schooling

CHRIST, I WAS riled with Reg and Weaver. I know they were my brothers, but neither one of them was fit to jump off a bale of straw. It happened it was my seventh birthday, and they were bunging stones at my jam jar of tadpoles which stood on the top of the water butt. If it didn't come that Reg, who was eight and a half, was bigger than me I'd have kicked him. I could have clouted my younger brother, Weaver, but then Reg would have clocked me one and, as like as not, Dad would have leathered the lot of us.

Reg stood there in his cut down trousers and with his bouncey freckled face all screwed up. He had a wrinkled sock turned down over one boot, and two garters of thin white elastic pulled up over his other leg. He had basin crop hair and gappy teeth, and always pulled the peak of his flat cap over his right ear. Christ, I hated Reg. I reckon he was backward.

Weaver was as bad. He was like a snotty nosed spaniel at heel and did what Reg told him. Weaver stood there, wearing one of his mother's woolly hats, and looking at his boots. He had a face like a moon in a bike tyre with mud all over his ripped jersey and a water mark round his neck.

I shouldn't think anyone had worse brothers, you couldn't trust them to spread a molehill, and they wouldn't make an errand boy between them.

'I'll tell on yer,' I said.

'If yer do,' said Reg 'we'll chuck yer in the pond.'

Just then my mother came up straight from the wash tub, sleeves rolled up, hair flying and apron tied round the middle. We could see she was on the warpath.

'If you boys haven't got nothing better to do than stand about,' she said, 'you can go and get two pails of water from the pump.' My mother took in washing and we were always stomping over to the old iron handled pump and carrying up pails of water. It was enough to pull your arms out of their sockets.

Let's face it Mum had been brought up to rough it. She worked double hours and never seemed to have a minute. To tell you the truth, she was a drudge to herself. But I'll say this for her. Even though my mother sometimes went out with wrinkled stockings, ankle boots and a tea cloth round her head, none the more for that, she kept the yard tidy, had rods for the curtains and she wouldn't have anything on tick. Dad always said 'She done what she could'.

* * * *

It was the winter of 1927, the year after the General Strike, and farming in West Suffolk was in a bad way. Farms were being sold for three or four pounds an acre,

1

and there were ructions about the tythe that was being paid to the clergy. The price of corn hit rock bottom and gallons of milk were being poured down the drain. Someone said that the Stour was like running whitewash. The farmworkers were uneasy, and the furrows were getting further from the hedge.

My father was second horseman for Wilfred Jessop, a self made grey haired man of 58 who farmed four hundred acres of chalky boulder clay between Ipswich and Bury. Well, I say 'chalky boulder clay', but two fields had sandy seams and sticky patches, and fifteen acres behind the church was heaviest pug.

Mr. Jessop was a splay mouthed man with florrid cheeks and watery eyes and he walked with small steps, more like a city man than a long stepping heavy land farmer. He played poor and there was often more than one rent in his jacket, but they reckoned that he was worth three or even four thousand pounds.

Although Mr. Jessop left school when he was thirteen, he was long headed and had plenty up top and, when he went to markct, he often came in on a side wind and outdid the dealers. Not many farmers got the better of that crafty needle witted lot, particularly when they worked a ring and wouldn't bid against each other. I've heard tell of Mr. Jessop getting someone to run his shorthorn steers up against the dealers but then sometimes he came unstuck and then didn't sell, and he had to bring his cattle, clotted with market dung on their rumps, back home. The dealers were up to all the tricks and, after market, they gathered in the 'Plough and Sail' to have another little private auction and straighten things up.

The dealers were known among the farmers as 'The Forty Thieves' and one of the head ones was Spider Joslin the pig higgler. Spider was a slippery double tongued hard case if ever there was one. He was full of sharp practice and, the day before market, he made sure that his pigs were kept short of water and then he gave them several pailfuls just before they went on the scales. He'd have stuck a cork in their backsides if he knew how to keep it in. It was well known that, after market, Spider spent time with some of the market women from the cheap jack stalls. They would adjourn to Spider's decrepit wooden bucked lorry which he always parked behind the fat lamb pens.

According to my father, who sometimes took a couple of Mr. Jessop's stall fed bullocks into market in the horse drawn cattle float, whatever the Forty Thieves got up to in the Live Stock market was nothing to what come to happen in the monthly horse sales. My father said that what went on there would shame the Devil and you may lay a penny that the dealers and dicers and didicoys busied themselves when there were fish to fry.

If a nag was tardy and sluggish like an afternoon hinny they'd jigger it up with a drench of nicotine, beer and henbane, and happen it was too lively and on the free side, they'd give it a bellyful of boiled barley and warm water. Othertimes a sharp horse would be given a pint mix of oil of ben and oil of burdock, and father said that he had seen a thoroughbred kicker go tame as a rabbit. He didn't reckon any of the dealers was straighter than a woman's bent hairpin.

★   ★   ★   ★

The small cottage where we lived and where, come to that, me and my brothers were born, was walled and ended in black tarred weatherboard. If the cottage had been put up on the market I doubt whether it would have made fifty quid. It had small lattice windows, a thatched roof and a nailed up front door.

The thatch was riddled with sparrows' nests and, at nesting time, small blue eggs and naked baby sparrows splotched on to the brick garden path under the roof overhang. It kept the cat busy. It beat me why Mr. Jessop didn't have wire netting fixed over the roof to keep the sparrows out but, being it was a tied cottage, the likes of we had to be content.

I suppose that the weeds that grew on the thatch kept the cottage warm in the winter and cool in the summer but, after a rain or a heavy dew it would start dripping. Drip, drip, it got on your tits with its plash and sputter. Why they never put eaves troughs on a thatch roof I shan't ever know, but, if they had, we should have had a lot more rainwater in the water butt, and that would have come in handy, and we shouldn't have had to go carting water from the pump for Mum's washing all day long. Downstairs the cottage had one musty smelling front room which was hardly ever used, a kitchen with an open black iron stove and a round tin bath leaning against the wall, and a small scullery which smelled of potato peelings and lifebuoy soap. Upstairs, two small low ceilinged bedrooms.

Mum and Dad slept in one room and me, Reg and Weaver slept on the floor in the other. The chipped white enamel slop bucket stood in the corner and there was hardly room to stand the candle.

The bucket privy was half way down the garden path and it was a tidy step if you got took short. My father tarred the outside every three years but that didn't keep the draught out. It was wonderful cold out there in the winter and there were mouse turds everywhere. They came for the newspaper for nests. Behind the privy stood the tin roofed woodshed with sawdust and wood chippings lying ankle deep on the dirt floor. Part of Dad's wages was wood and a home made wooden sawbench for log cutting stood in the middle of the shed together with the oak butt chopping block with its whole surface notched and scored by thousands of cuts and slashes and from the countless years of chopping faggots and splitting logs with the sharp cutting blade of the bill.

Resting on two six inch nails, which had been hammered in over the door, was my father's axe, honed and sharpened on the whetstone. Dad said that anyone could shave with it but us boys were not allowed to touch it. Three big string tied bunches of over wintered onions hung on the cross beam and a couple of wire snares and a rusty mole trap were looped round a wooden peg in the far corner of the shed.

The cottage had a tidy sized vegetable garden. It was long and narrow and a high blackthorn hedge, which harboured blackfly and weevil, grew all around it. To tell you the truth the garden lay damp because it didn't get enough sun. Dad always dibbled in a few winter cabbage and early lettuce but, three years out of four, come the Spring, the slugs and the rabbits had put paid to most of them and I've seen the time when my father was driven spare to see wood pigeons getting wound into his winter cabbages. It was a struggle. The spring carrots nearly always

got the carrot fly and, even though Dad dragged a bran bag soaked in parrafin up and down the – rows, they didn't want much thinning out I can tell you. Dad said that gardening was a worse gamble than pitch and toss. The only thing that came close to profit every year was the rhubarb. The sticks were as big as your arm and you may depend we piled the hoss dung on that.

*   *   *   *

A lot of time was taken up thinking and talking about the farm horses. The stables were the heart of the farm and the horses were the kingpins. My father looked after four. Their names were Prince, Watchman, Blossom and Sedgemoor, and I can tell you this, that years later, when my father had his second stroke and he didn't know even my mother, when the doctor said 'Can you remember the names of your horses?', he whispered three of them, so his brain wasn't completely gone.

Prince and Watchman were purebred five year old black shire geldings and they could have been registered in the Stud book of the Shire Horse Society. They both stood seventeen two and must have weighed close on a ton apiece. You'd certainly know about it if one of them stepped on your harvest corns. They were a matchy pair and no mistake, although Watchman had a shade more white round his fetlocks. The main trouble with Prince and Watchman was that they both carried a bit too much feather for heavy land and, after a day's ploughing in the winter, they'd bring in the best part of half a hundredweight of clay and mud on their legs, and they had to be ridden round and round the green weeded pond for over five minutes to wash if off. But my father wouldn't hear a word against them.

Blossom was a three parts Clydesdale bay mare with a short docked tail and a wicked eye. She was rising four and she stood square and was a good mover and, when she was in the mood and she was put on the harrows or the hay tedder, she'd step out all day. She'd been covered by the travelling stallion and, with a bit luck, she would foal in early April so that the foal could be weaned before harvest.

Sedgemoor was got by a Suffolk stallion on a Clydesdale mare. He was a rich colour chestnut gelding but he was old and broken winded. The vet had filed his teeth and his legs were greasy. He was only good for doing a bit of light dung-cart or for pulling the pole on the turntable that drove the corn stack elevator. I once heard Mr. Jessop say to my father 'I reckon old Sedgemoor will have to go John,' and my father said 'He'll do another year to two yet.' And so he did.

The horses were given their early morning feed at a quarter past six every morning. When they were at work they were fed twelve pounds of oats a day and sixteen pounds of hay, and there was always a lump of rock salt in the manger. My father's horses never went to work without their manes being braided up and their tails plaited, and they always had a bit of ribbon round the forelock. When he did a road job, he got out the brasses.

Most of the winter before Christmas, when the ground wasn't too wet or iron hard from the frost, the horsemen spent at plough. On a full day's ploughing the horsemen walked the best part of eleven miles but, none the more for that, they reckoned that ploughing was the best job of the lot as you were left on your own and did your three quarters of an acre and nobody hazed you. Well, I tell you that, but the tale was told that Sam Hoggett, one of the other horsemen, had reined up on the headland one day to have a quiet spit and a draw when Mr. Jessop rode up on his horse. Mr. Jessop said 'Sam, I don't mind you having a rest but I don't like to see the horses standing still.' Sam hadn't got a lot to say to that.

Mr. Jessop wanted his day's work and we heard tell that he had told some of the other farmers that, you never want to have a tin roof over your stables as a knats piss shower sounds like a heavy thunderstorm and you'll never get your horsemen out of the stable on a wet morning.

Although there was a foreman on the farm Mr. Jessop was always in the stables at half past six to give orders to the horsemen. He would say to my father 'Do yew goo dungcart John' or 'Do yew goo plough.'

Sunday afternoons when the horses weren't out to grass, we would go with my father along to the stables and watch him lead the horses, one at a time, down to the long iron water trough. For a treat he would let us lead Sedgemoor and, as Sedgemoor was old and quiet, Dad would sometimes put us boys on his back.

On these occasions my father would be decked out in his Sunday suit. He'd paid two years' harvest money for it. The suit was a dark grey and made of best pheasant eye cord with a high cut coat and a waistcoat which was buttoned up almost to the neck. The trousers were narrow legged with a deep fly flap in the front which fastened on to two bone buttons just below his belt. It must have been hot in the summer because my father always wore the waistcoat with its dangling watch chain, over his collarless shirt. He reckoned that anyone who wore a check suit on a Sunday was low class and common but he didn't let on because Mr. Jessop always wore a check suit and a tartan tie on Sundays.

*   *   *   *

My two brothers and me all went to the village school at Newton Green. It was Church of England and the classrooms stank putrid, what with the ink and the plasticine and half the kids breaking wind and all. Too many senna pods, greens and unripe apples, that was the trouble. It was bad enough in the classrooms but the stink round the privy and urinals at the far end of the playground would make a polecat cry. It was enough to put you off your beaver. The bucket only got emptied once a week and the boys' trough nailed on to the tarred brick wall didn't get much weak disinfectant wasted on it either.

The fumes off the leaky old anthracite stove, set on a thin concrete slab in the middle of the classroom, were enough to choke you to death, but some of the kids were coughing and spluttering half the time anyway. They could have done with some goose grease and camphorated oil. Several of them never seemed to have a handkerchief, and their jersey sleeves were really snotty. It's a wonder we learned anything.

As it was a Church school you may depend we had to learn our catechisms and all that dottle and moonshine. I believe this and I believe that, and lead us not into temptation. We were strongly told that if we yielded to temptation God would come down on us like a ton of bricks. Our teacher, Miss Bonner, tarted herself up and went to Church every Sunday. We reckoned that as it was a Church of England school, if she didn't go to church she'd get wrong with the vicar.

Once a year, round about currant time, one of the local parsons came round and tested us for Religious Knowledge. We all stood in a semi-circle in the class-room while the parson sat at Miss Bonner's desk and asked questions about God and Jesus. To tell you the truth, I always got in a bit of a how d'ye do about religion, what with the Red Sea and the Dead Sea and John this and John that, I reckon there must have been two thousand Johns.

None the more for that, one day when the parson came to test us and it was my turn to answer the question, I had a really big deal. The parson asked,

'Who made the World?' and I said

'Please sir, God made the World.'

It was a bit of luck being asked that one and Miss Bonner, who had been mouthing the answers behind the parson's back, looked something relieved.

The biggest swot in the school was Charity Bright. She not only knew the names of all the disciples but always came top in arithmetic. She was always telling tales on the boys and brought Miss Bonner plums and flowers. She would never play conkers and hopscotch with us and looked down her stupid little nose when we played with our tops in the road. Charity was a prissy twit who never peed her draws.

I was half tidy at English, though I say so myself, and the lesson I liked best was English composition. I used to like making up stories and one day I wrote a composition of six pages about a fox being hunted and all, and Miss Bonner said 'That's very good Albert,' and she read it out to the whole class, and then she sprung a surprise I hadn't bargained for and said 'You have a feeling for words.'

One day during my second year at school, the Rural Dean came to mark the register. He was a fat, flop mouthed old boy with a dew drop nose. He was very ancient. We reckoned he must have been about a hundred. He had no teeth and when he said anything he piffed and blew. We reckoned that anyone standing downwind would think that April was come. We called him 'Humguffer' and he drove an old blue Trojan with solid tyres. After old Humguffer had called the register he said that, as it was Empire Day, we could have a half holiday.

So we ran home and had an early dinner of bread, marge and fat bacon and then Reg, Bert Piggot and Sweedy Cheeseman asked me to go along with them after sparrow's nests.

Mr. Jessop gave us a penny a nest, so we rustled round the barn and the stables and the cart shed and got over thirty. Half of the nests had eggs in them but we knew that the sparrows would be back building again in a day or two.

By the time we had been round the buildings it was close on half past two and Reg, who had been swinging on the horse yard gate and was now sitting on the shaft of a cart that stood by the woodpile, said 'Let's play "parcels".' Sweedy, Bert and me, already getting bored, perked up and said 'Let's.'

Sweedy slid off home to fetch a shoe box, and Reg sent me off to get some binder string and brown paper and, in twenty minutes we were all back in the cartshed.

Reg then made up the parcel. He put a brick in the shoe box, wrapped the brown paper round it and then tied it up with string. Then Reg tied about fifteen yards of string to the parcel and we took it down to the main road. We laid the parcel on the edge of the road about two feet from the kerb, covered up the string with sand and dust from the gutter and took the string through the hedge. We all lay down behind the hedge and Reg had hold of the end of the string.

Well, after about ten minutes a red bull nosed Morris with a capless steaming radiator, slowly chugging and firing on three, came round the corner. 'Christ,' said Reg 'I'm buggered if it isn't old Catsmeat.' Catsmeat Mobbs was the butcher from Lower Barnston and he delivered meat round the villages. He had once been fined for selling bad meat. We wouldn't ever let him hear us call him 'Catsmeat' because he was a strong old boy and did his own slaughtering, and it didn't take much to put him out. Catsmeat had done his rounds and was off to see about a sow for sausages.

Well, sure enough, Catsmeat saw the parcel and stopped his old Morris twenty yards on. He cautiously opened the door and climbed out into the road. He gave a crafty sideways look up and down the road and then trotted back to the parcel. He bent down and was just about to pick it up when Reg gave a sharp tug and the parcel shot into the ditch. You should have seen Catsmeat's face. He was looking broody as a bull. Talk about a lefthanded smile. He soon saw what was going on and started to come round the end of the hedge, and you could see he was something riled. He started to run after us but we were soon half way along Sheepcote Bottom. Catsmeat soon gave up and we lay down in the long grass and cow mumble and laughed like drunk starlings. We didn't go straight home and Reg climbed up an old knotted ivy covered elm and got a couple of magpies eggs, and then we pole jumped over the narrow part of the river.

When we got home about five o'clock my father was waiting for us and, standing beside him was Catsmeat Mobbs. They had put two and two together and Catsmeat was hopping about like an old ewe with footrot.

My father's belt was like a horses bellyband and when he undid the buckle we knew we'd get a leathering we wouldn't forget in a hurry. But 'parcels' was a hellupin good game none the more for that, and no one can't say any different.

*   *   *   *

There were four school holidays a year; Easter, Harvest, Potato Picking and Christmas. During the Potato holidays my brothers and I used to go along and help my mother. My mother was a good picker and picked straight into her apron instead of into a pail or a basket like the other women. Sometimes she scrapped up sixty bags in a day, but she didn't always fill the bags too full and then the foreman would come round and shake a couple of bags down and say 'Another apronfull in these two bags Mrs. Cooper.' The silly old sod, he always was a master's man.

The best time of the year was during the long summer harvest holidays, when the horsemen were cutting the corn and the binders were chucking out the sheaves in long yellow rows. Reg, Weaver and me would each have an ash stick and stand on the corners so we could watch two sides. We were after rabbits and when they ran out they couldn't get up much speed with the sheaves lying about, and we were often able to run them down in the stubble. Weaver wasn't much good at anything else but he could certainly run down a rabbit, and I've never seen anyone happier than Weaver when he caught one. He would grin for half an hour.

When the harvest gang were carting corn in the field and the horses were leaning into their collars moving the waggon from trave to trave, my father would sometimes give me a leg up on to the horse's back. My feet didn't reach the shafts but I sat there between the hard wooden topped saddle and the leather collar. I had a bran bag to sit on and I held on tightly to the hames so I shouldn't slide off. To tell you the truth, sitting up there six feet off the ground, with the inside of my knees sticky with horse's sweat, I felt like the Lord of the Harvest.

The full harvest gang was four men in the field and four on the stack and one or two driving away according to the distance from stack to field. I've seen the time when there were shindigs among the men as to who should work in the field, who should go on the stack, and who should pitch and who should load. Most of the men reckoned that it was better to be in the field because when you were pitching the sheaves you were standing on firm ground, but, on the stack you were falling all over the shop and there was always a chance of ending up on the wrong end of your two tined fork. You had to look slippy with a sheaf coming off the elevator every three seconds. About the worst place to be was in the pitch hole in a dutch barn on a hot windless day. The sun hit the tin roof, and there was very little air. Talk about sweat. The men in their flannel shirts and thick cord trousers lost as much lard as the horses.

*　　　*　　　*　　　*

Sometimes we watched the pigs, particularly when the ginger coated Tamworth boar was riding an old sow outside the red tiled stonewall pigsty. Charlie, the pigman, used to say to us that the boar was getting up on the old sows back to see what he could see and then he was getting out his pencil and writing it down. Charlie was a comical customer and no mistake and times without number we creased ourselves with laughing.

I hark back to one day in late Spring. It wasn't a proper wet day but it looked like coming on to wet. Fred said 'Wot makes it rain is they ode wircless waves.' It was school holiday time and we were in the old thatched barn. Some of the men were dressing clover seed on the Bobbie and others were sorting out rat gnawed corn sacks and hanging those that didn't need repair on a swinging pole which hung from a beam on two ropes, to keep the rats from nesting. Mr. Jessop was proud of his sacks which had stencilled on them in bold black letters

J. H. JESSOP
FARMER
NEWTON MANOR

Next door in the mixing barn we could hear Charlie and Sam getting on at each other and having a 'set to' about Charlie's pigs and Sam's horses.

Charlie's pigs had the scour and Sam, who was re-tying the twine round the knees of his trousers, said 'Charlie, them ode pigs of yourn do stink suthin pourin'.'

Charlie said 'They don't stink no wuss than your ode hosses stalin all over the stable floor.'

'Strike a light,' said Sam. 'With your stinky ode pigs I don't reckon you'd smell a poxy ode rat with rotgut what had lived fourteen years in the sewer. Anyways, I can't stand about here argufying with you.'

'I don't know about argufying,' said Charlie, waving his shovel 'but I reckon about all you do round here is stand about. The way you slomp and poddle about here it's a wonder you don't git perished with cold. You allus was all shuffle and no "do". For all the good you do about the place Sam you ought to be stood orf and sent to the knacker's yard.'

Sam sucked his teeth and chawed at his old clay pipe and said 'You do take on Charlie, you're a pesky obstopolous ode sod and you barney on like you got out of bed back'ards. You ain't wuth a shovelful of hoss dung.'

As Charlie hunched his shoulders and picked up his buckets to feed his weaners he called out over his shoulder 'Sam, you're an everlastin' ode flandangle. I don't reckon you're hardly all there. You ought to be put away or done in.'

We had to laugh the way they carried on.

*   *   *   *

My father always kept two pigs at the bottom of the garden. They were fed on scraps, swill and chat potatoes. He bought two weaners from Mr. Jessop twice a year and when they were seven months old he sold one and we ate the other, whether there was an R in the month or not. When the pig was killed my mother used to be up to her elbows in the steaming guts which lay all over the scullery. It was enough to put you off your grub I can tell you. I recollect one year when the pig lay all over the kitchen that my mother dished up pork for supper and none of us fancied it. My mother then said 'Well then you can just have taters,' and she tipped the full saucepan of potatoes, which had been boiled with their skins on, slap in the middle of the wooden table and we sat round and helped ourselves, using our fingers. They weren't too bad with salt and marge.

Another time I recollect my father bought the two pigs from Mr. Jessop and, as usual, one of them was the runt of the litter but the other one, although undergrown, was middling to fair and wasn't too dusty at all. The next day at school I boasted in front of some of the older boys and said 'Dad's got two bloody good pigs,' and then after a bit of thought about the runty one, I said 'but one ain't a mucher.' I know that was a daft thing to say and it creased the older boys and when they wanted to take the mick out of me all they had to say was 'Dad's got two bloody good pigs but one aint a mucher.'

When my brother Reg was thirteen what he wanted more than anything else was a pair of long trousers. Mr. Jessop paid tuppence for a rat's tail and Reg found a couple of old rusty gin traps and reckoned that if he could catch enough rats he would be able to have his long trousers. Reg got half handy at setting his traps in an old drainpipe or in the runs where the rats came down for water, but, although he used to get up early to look at his traps, he never did earn enough to buy a pair of long trousers up to the time he left school.

CHAPTER TWO

Bachus Boy

WHEN I WAS fourteen I left the village school and my father got me a job up on the farm. The Guvnor said I could be Bachus Boy. The Bachus boy worked a lot of the time outside the back door of the farmhouse chopping wood, whacking carpets on the clothes line and breaking up lumps of coal with a seven pound hammer. Every winter two of the horsemen were sent to Ipswich railway yard with their creaking tumbrils to collect three tons of steam coal. Some of the lumps were four times as big as your head so they had to be broken up for the farmhouse fires and for the kitchener. I've never seen anything so hungry for coal as the kitchener with its ovens and its dampers and its roaring flues. I reckon that some days in the winter, when there was a strong drawing wind, it burnt the best part of a hundredweight.

My first job every morning was to go round to all the wooden slatted floor hen houses which were dotted round the inlying meadows, to let the hens out and chuck them a few handfulls of corn, then in the afternoon I had to collect the eggs from the nest boxes which were crawling with lice and redmite. If there were any broodies, I stuck them in the broody coops till they came back into lay.

The worst thing about looking after the chickens was that I had to shut the hens up at night. They never went in until it was nearly dark and sometimes in Summer this was close on ten o'clock. There's nothing more cantankerous or stupid than a chicken at shutting up time. They hang about outside the pop hole making that senseless garpy noise in their throats and wander from one side of the pophole to the other, and then they will just stand there staring at you out of the corner of one eye. If you wave your arms about to hurry them up they will run under the hen house. It's enough to drive you up the wall and, times without number, I've had a mind to leave them out and let a fox bite their stupid heads off. But then I'd have got wrong in the morning.

*   *   *   *

On Monday mornings I started work at half past six to fill the great iron copper, which stood in the farm wash house, with water from the soft water butt. I then lit the fire in the firebox underneath to get up steam before Mrs. Gussett came in at 8 o'clock to do the washing. Mrs. Gussett, the farm's washwoman, lived in Barton Parva some three miles away and she pedalled to work on an ancient rusty three wheeler. She always wore a large hat, however windy, tacked down with a red headed hat pin. She sat up high on the three wheeler with her hands tightly gripping the handlebars. Her eyes were fixed straight ahead and she used most of

12

the road. Pedalling must have been hard work on a blustery day, and when Mrs. Gussett arrived at the farm house you may depend that she let us know whether it was a head or a tail wind.

After Mrs. Gussett had spuggled the sheets and nightdresses and table cloths and other trappings round the copper with a four foot ash stick and pressed everything through the wooden rollered mangle, the washing was hung up on a line between two Worcester Pearmains to dry.

Mrs. Gusset was a robust, red faced woman with a big bosom and legs like gateposts. When she carried the wrung washing out to the line, clothes pegs in her string bag and her fat arms round the heavy wicker basket which rested on her flabby stomach, she put me in the mind of a plump well fed steam roller with a giant bicycle basket tied to the front of the engine.

On Tuesdays Mrs. Gussett returned to the farm house to iron the laundry she had washed the day before. This was done in the hot steamy kitchen, and talk about a sizzle when she spat on the flat irons.

*　　*　　*　　*

During that first year I was paid twelve bob a week. Gobstoppers were four a penny and Woodbines were fourpence for ten and, by the time I had given Mum six bob for my keep I wasn't able to save a lot.

There were a couple of skivvies in the farm house and, every morning they had to see that the fires were lit, that the range was blackleaded and that the front step was whitened.

The eldest one was Maud. Maud was a big boned girl with a flat nose and a boss eye, and she wouldn't stand a lot of nonsense when I cheeked her. I've seen her let fly at me more than once with the kitchen broom.

Ernie Pitt, who delivered the bread in the baker's boneshaker, used to hang around Maud and one Sunday afternoon I saw him walking her down by the river. I reckon Ernie was after something and Maud may have made him prick up his ears but it would be a wonder he was so lucky and didn't have to wean his thoughts away. He always said she kept done up and there wasn't much promise.

The other skivvy was Lilly. Lilly was a brassy bit of stuff with straight legs, long black hair and a nice little bum. I could go for Lilly but, when the two girls got together they cackled like leghorns in a run.

Most of the young blokes in the village were after Lilly, and I've seen the time when Bert Hogg, 'Wheeler' Perkins and Alfie Cakebread would wait outside the farm back entrance with their bikes on a Sunday afternoon, waiting for Lilly to come out on her half day off. They all wore their Sunday caps and their faces shone like threepenny bits as they always shaved on Saturday night. When Lilly came out with her bike they rode with her along Highbarns Lane ringing their bicycle bells. They were like a brow faced bunch of cock sparrows round a hen.

But Lilly was a good girl and didn't let any of the boys get fresh with her. Leastways, that's what we thought.

I reckon we were wrong in a big way because just after Christmas, Lilly's mother told her friend Mrs. Goss, who helped clean the school, that Lilly was under the doctor and in the pudden club.

The news struck the village all of a heap and everyone was in a mortal flutter. Some of the village boys' mothers were worried spare.

It turned out a week later that it was young Morris Crabtree. Morris was one of the gang that came round with the steam ploughs. According to Lilly's mother, Morris had had Lilly twice in the four wheeler brake van and once in the cartshed. The steam ploughs were only on the farm for three days, so Morris hadn't wasted a lot of time. Lilly's father, who was bullock man at Long Barton Hall, said that Morris would have to marry Lilly or pay her seven and six a week. The farm boys in the village had a good laugh about it when they rode their bikes round the Green, but I reckon they wished they'd had a chance.

CHAPTER THREE

Blossom Kicks up Rough

ALTHOUGH I HAD been Bachus Boy for over a year, I had always been bent on being a horseman like my father and, one day when I was fifteen and a half, the foreman Ambrose Pigeon came across the field when I was giving the hens their early morning feed, and he said 'Albert, you can go and do harrows behind the drill.' So I said 'What horse shall I take Ambrose?'. He said 'You had better take Blossom.'

Well, Blossom wasn't the favourite horse on the farm by a long chalk. She also wasn't too handy to harness up and the foreman knew that and all, but that was Ambrose all over.

So I chucked the rest of my pailful of wheat to the point of lay pullets, saw the Light Sussex hens in the slatted floor broody coop had got water, and walked over to the stable.

I lifted the flat iron latch on the stable door, made sure to shut the door behind me, and went down the two steps into the harness room. Blossom's head collar hung on a stout wooden peg over the tin lined crushed-oat bin. I couldn't reach it properly so I stood on an upturned bushel and lifted the heavy collar over my head so that the wide end lay on my shoulders and walked into the stable. I hadn't allowed for the width of the collar and I managed to knock down the medicine horn, a curry comb and half a beaker of linseed oil, and this all made a sharp rattling clatter on the stone floor. I could see that Blossom didn't think much to that. She had a wall eye and looked at me as cunning as you like. She knew as well as I did that I hadn't put a collar on her before and that I was sort of nervous.

Blossom was leaning on the nearside partition with her arse tight up against the kicking post. As I wanted to get up on her near side to put her collar on, I spoke to her sharpish and said 'Git over there then Blossom.' But old Blossom never moved. So, with the collar still round my neck, I gave her a bit of a shove with the flat of my hand but she just tossed her head and stood there leaning on the partition rail and looking at me out of the corner of her wall eye. The cantankerous old cow. So I thought 'Well I dunno,' and squeezed up on her off side. It is towering awkward standing on the off side and taking off the halter when the buckle is on the nearside. The halter was tied on to a wooden block through a tethering ring and in no way can the collar be put on without first taking off the halter. As I wasn't getting much forrader I climbed up into the manger dragging the heavy old collar up behind me. In my pocket I had a few split beans so I took out half a handful and held them under Blossom's muzzle and said, tender and broadhearted like, 'Here you are Blossom, good gal Blossom.' But Blossom just laid back her ears and threw up her

15

head and, with flaring nostrils, damned nearly hit the bracket on the architrave.

Well, after a bit, I did manage to get the halter off and, still standing in the manger, I picked up the collar to put over Blossom's head. Blossom seemed to have a shade more favourable turn of mind so I started to push the collar up over her ears. I reckon this was what she must have been waiting for because when I was leaning half out of the manger with the collar, Blossom took two sharp steps backwards and I fell out of the manger arse over tit. Christ, was my shoulder sore. The racket and jangle properly scared old Blossom and, if it hadn't been shut, she'd had been through the stable door.

Just then Ambrose came up and he was looking as cunning as a didicoy with a rabbit in his pocket. He said 'Well Albert, that's the headest way I've seen a horse harnessed yet.' The foreman always was a clever sod, and I'd like to have layed a docking iron across his ear. He told the other men that I couldn't get the collar on and, of course, they laughed and didn't know any better. So I thought 'One day I'll get even with Ambrose and I'll teach him not to be so cunning.'

Well, it happened that over in Middle Hagbush Field there was thirty five acres of sugar beet, drilled in twenty four inch rows. They had come up a bit patchy and the day-men were chopping them out. What they were supposed to do was to leave a plant every ten inches and chop out the rest with their long handled hoes. It has been a dry old Spring and the hares and weevils and cut worms had already done a fair bit of thinning of the stand.

When Ambrose gave his orders to the men he said 'Leave 'em ten inches apart where they are thick and leave 'em closer together where there 'ent any.' So after that, when I wanted to be a bit cocky, I would say to the men 'Leave 'em thicker where there 'ent any.' The younger men used to laugh but I never let the foreman hear me.

*   *   *   *

Although I had a bad start, after a time I got half handy with the horses and, when I did a bit of harrowing or rolling, I did my best to keep it straight, and one day the Guvnor came round when I was rolling a bit of winter wheat and he said 'Albert, you are making a good job of that — straight as the North Road.' The Guvnor never set great store by praise so having that said to me was better than being barked at or braided.

Although I say it myself, I had a decent pair of shoulders on me and I could swing a couple of fifty six pound weights up on to the loft. One day Sam said to me 'Albert, I reckon if you had a mind to you'd be able to clap that pair of weights over your head.' Sam saying that, pleased me even though I knew he was edging me on.

So by the time I was seventeen and a half I was as good as any man and my wages were put up to twenty two and six.

CHAPTER FOUR

The Tractor

ONE DAY AFTER harvest there was a hell of a spill and pelt among the men. A new Fordson tractor stood in the yard and, apart from the Foreman, no one had been told that it was coming. The tractor had been delivered while we were at beaver, it was painted bright blue and had great iron spade lugs on the wheels. Standing next to the tractor, with grease running out of its axles, was a Ransome two furrow plough. The shining steel plough breasts gleamed in the Autumn sun.

Well, that properly set the farm alight, that did. Everyone had come up to look at the tractor and plough. The horsemen laughed and said that tractors weren't any bloody good and my father said 'It aint worth two bob for scrap.'

Sam Hoggett said he wouldn't drive a tractor for a thousand pounds and Fred, one of the daymen, pleased the horsemen when he said 'and another thing – the horses don't eat when they are working.' Well, I knew that Fred was so old that he was about when the threshing machine was known as the Fantackle and Chogger, so I very nearly said 'and tractors don't eat anything when they are standing still,' but I never said it because I knew that everyone was something uneasy as to who was going to drive the tractor.

Next morning I had just tipped a cartload of loose straw in the bullock yard and was shaking the straw around with a two tine fork, when Ambrose came up and leaned on the thick end of the gate.

'Albert,' he said 'I want a word with you.'

'What about?' I said.

Ambrose in belt and braccs, blew his nose with his fingers, and drew his hand up his trouser leg. He then straightened up and stuck his thumbs in the armholes of his waistcoat and said 'The Guvnor reckons you'd better have the tractor.'

Well, you could have knocked me down with a bit of horse ribbon.

'Ambrose,' I said 'You wouldn't be wherritting me would you?' (I wouldn't have put it past him, the sorny old sod.)

'No,' said Ambrose, 'that's what the Guvnor said.'

I didn't know what to think and I was all of a blether. I was given to airy thoughts because, in my mind's eye, I'd always had a fancy to drive a tractor. To tell you the truth, when I went back to littering the bullocks, I was so edgy that my hands were all of a shake like an aspen.

After beavers the Guvnor came out in his pork pie and breeches and gaited boots, and told me that the Ford man had just telephoned to say that he would be coming out during the afternoon to show me how to drive the tractor, and that the man from Ransomes was coming out the next morning to show me how to set the plough. Christ, I was a damn sight more pleased than that artful thimble rigger, Spoiler Crow, when he sold over twenty lurcher caught rabbits one Friday night outside the 'Dog and Duck'.

*   *   *   *

Every weekday morning, while the dew was still cold on the browning grass, I topped up the tractor tank with paraffin from the green painted two wheel bowser, checked the oil and water, and greased up the plough. By ten past seven I was ready to start work.

Hour after hour, from seven o'clock in the morning till seven at night, I would turn the cold ribbons of soil as the plough sundered and quartered the brown earth. The days passed by through the tail end of Autumn and its sunset afterglow, into the grey day-worn late winter afternoons and the gathering darkness of nightfall.

It was a wonderful feeling ploughing there all on my own on the cold dark evenings with the tractor lights shining on the glistening stubble. I wore a thick khaki overcoat with string tied round the middle, and thick woollen mittens.

I was clocking up a fair bit of overtime as the Guvnor wanted all the ploughing done by Christmas so that the furrows lay high and open to take the hard frost in the New Year. Nothing did the heavy clay soil more good than a real stinger of a frost, so that the thaw would break up the great hard clods into a fine tilth for the seedbeds in the Spring.

When I got home at night my coat and overalls reeked of oil and paraffin and my ears were still drumming from the endless clack and roar of the Fordson engine, and the grinding clatter of the gearbox. Sometimes my under shirt was so dirty that I had to take it off at night.

I was particular about the tractor and I changed the oil regular, kept the air filters clean and, as it was Winter, always drained out the radiator water at night. Even though I say it myself I could set the plough so that no one could tell which were the pair of furrows, as they matched in so well together. The Guvnor was always going on about burying the trash. He didn't want to see any straw or weeds on top of the ploughing. So I made sure that I had a couple of skimmers set well forward of the mouldboards and they were set just deep enough to turn the top inch and a half into the bottom of the furrow. I was ploughing more in a day than a horseman ploughed in a week, and the Guvnor said that next year he might put me in for the District Ploughing Match.

The horsemen were still stirred up and were always letting on about the tractor being stinky and noisy and that it frightened the horses.

The best thing was that I got given the same wages as the horsemen and although my father used to yarp on about the tractor, he was pleased that I was getting on, and my mother was pleased because I was able to give her another four shillings a week for my keep.

And that must have been the winter of 1938.

CHAPTER FIVE

The Visitor

IN THE SPRING of 1939 I drilled the Spring barley and the sugar beet with the Smythe, and I'd pulled down two fields of plough for planting potatoes and one way and another, with all the cultivations, I was working a long day.

I got home late one night and was just starting my supper when a car drew up outside the house and this was soon followed by a sharp knock on the back door. My mother quickly put my supper back in the oven, straightened a few cushions, stuck my father's half glass of beer behind the flowers and went to the door. When she came back she said 'There's a man outside, Albert, and he wants to see you.'

'Does he look like a policeman?' I said.

'Could be,' said my mother.

It was two months since I had had a pheasant out of the wood and I had only taken a lemonade bottle of engine oil out of the tractor shed for Ernie Mill's motor bike to do him a favour. Anyway Ernie had brought me half a bag of cement from the building site.

The man at the door looked a bit of a toff to tell you the truth. He wore a brown trilby hat and one of those fancy jackets with a couple of splits up the arse end. Hacking jackets I think they call them. His cavalry twill trousers were really narrow. Narrow bottomed trousers looked soppy and ridiculous, I like twenty twos myself. On his feet were a pair of broguey looking brown shoes, and in no way had they been kept short of cherry blossom.

'Mr. Albert Cooper?' enquired the man.

'Yes,' I said.

'I am Captain Adams from the West Suffolk Yeomanry and I am given to understand that you drive a tractor. We are looking for drivers for our Territorial Regiment and I wondered if you would care to join us?'

'I don't know about that,' I said, 'I can't say I know much about the Territorial Army.'

'Well,' said Captain Adams, 'All you have to do is to come to the Drill Hall on Tuesday evenings and do a total of forty drills a year. As you are an agricultural worker you could do most of the drills in the winter and at times when you weren't busy.'

Well I didn't know what a drill was to start with and I knew he wasn't talking about our old Smythe seed drill.

'And if you do a three hour drill,' went on Captain Adams, 'it counts as two drills.'

19

He seemed a decent bloke but to tell the truth I didn't know too much what he was talking about.

'What is more,' continued Captain Adams, 'if you attend forty drills in a year, you get a bounty of five pounds.'

Now he was talking, he certainly was. I pricked up my ears when he talked about five pounds a year I can tell you, especially as I was saving up for a motor bike.

'Well,' I said, 'I shall have to have a word with my Mum and Dad.'

'Yes, you do that Mr. Cooper, and I will call back at the same time next Friday.'

I must say I reckoned he was a real gentleman when he called me 'Mr. Cooper'. My mother and father had been listening, you can be sure of that, so when I went back into the kitchen my mother, who was cutting thick slices off the loaf, wasn't looking too happy, I can tell you.

'You don't want to join the Territorial Army,' she said, 'you keep well away from that, two of my brothers were killed in the last war, they were army barmy. You never knew your Uncle Horace and your Uncle Geoff, not much older than you they were. Don't you have anything to do with it.'

'There won't be any war or fighting to do,' said my father. 'They only want Albert to go along to the Drill Hall and drive a tractor or something. Albert doesn't want to work all the time, and joining the Territorial Army might bring him out a bit.'

'Well, I don't know I'm sure,' said my mother. She always said that.

At any rate, to cut a long story short, when Captain Adams came back the next Friday I said I'd join. Captain Adams shook me warmly by the hand and said that I could report at the Drill Hall in Middlesham the next Tuesday evening and he would sign me on personally. He certainly was a real gentleman shaking me by the hand and all.

My mother was toying with the back door key and said, 'I hope you know what you are doing Albert, you're carrying on like you're watery headed.'

CHAPTER SIX

Albert Becomes a Military Man

THE NEXT TUESDAY evening I had an early tea and put on my grey sports jacket with built up shoulders, and my wide bottomed grey flannels which I hadn't worn more than half a dozen times. It had been a showery day so I rolled up my old mac and tied it on the racing handlebars of my bike. I then pulled on a pair of rubber leggings that Charlie lent me and which he used when he was washing down the sows for mange before they went into the farrowing crates, and set off for Middlesham, some three miles away. I didn't really want to put cycle clips over my silver greys, lest it creased the bottoms, but it would have been a lot worse if they'd got oil on them from the chain.

Pedalling up the hill into Middlesham I did just have half a thought that I might turn round and go back home. Then I thought of the five pounds, and the motor bike.

Middlesham was a pretty little market town with narrow streets, thirteen pubs and obliging shopkeepers. Market day was on a Friday and the cattle, sheep and pig pens were in the High Street where cattle had been known to stray into the shops. On market days a lot of farmers and dealers would stand around the pens from ten o'clock onwards. The market had been on the go for over a hundred years, and had only been closed twice for foot and mouth. At the bottom of the High Street by the Corn Exchange the road skewed round to the right up to the small recreation ground. Behind this there was a large piece of waste ground where people brought their dogs to romp and piddle. On the north side of the piece of waste ground stood the Middlesham Drill Hall.

I leaned my bike against the side wall of a weazened and scrubby sweet shop underneath a poster advertising Black Cat Virginia cigarettes. I hung my leggings and clips on the cross bar and walked towards the Drill Hall main gates.

The Drill Hall itself was a big ugly old red brick building with a grey slated roof and not too many windows. On the outside of the building near the main gate, and facing the road, was a big painted signboard and, emblazoned in rich colours of royal blue and gold lettering were the words 'THE 51st (WEST SUFFOLK YEOMANRY) REGIMENT ROYAL HORSE ARTILLERY'. Opposite the Drill Hall on the other side of the parade ground was a large shed with a corrugated iron roof and two massive sliding doors. The doors were open and I could see two green painted lorries inside, and what I thought were the heavy wheels and the long lethal barrel of a gun.

I walked cautiously up to the main gate. A tall fellow with a thin moustache, and kitted out in breeches and puttees, and with one stripe on his arm, was marking off names on a clipboard.

'Good evening corporal,' I said.

'I'm not a corporal,' he said, 'What's your name?'

'Albert Cooper,' I said.

'Right Cooper, go inside that main door in the Drill Hall and ask for Sergeant Pettigrove.'

It didn't strike me as much of a welcome, considering I was expecting Captain Adams to be looking out for me.

Gathering myself together I crossed the damp open parade ground heedful and wary yet hoping to take on the casual look that I didn't care a straw, like a cowboy in the movies.

Stepping gingerly through the heavy green door into the Drill Hall I got taken unexpected by a loud voice calling out 'Hullo Albert, you old bugger.'

Standing by the wall and next to a large coloured diagram of the workings of the internal combustion engine was Vincent Parsons. He had his hands in his pockets and was grinning all over his face. Vincent was a year older than me and the same age as my brother Reg. We had all been at school together and I remembered Vincent, who used to muck about in class, being told by Miss Bonner that he was rough and immature, and more than once she'd wrung him by the ear. I hadn't seen Vincent for three years and he now lived with his father, who worked for the Council. His mother had gone off with a ganger for the River Board when Vincent was ten.

'Hullo Vincent,' I said, 'what brings you here?'

'Just signing on,' said Vincent.

'Stop talking,' said a loud voice behind us, 'take your hands out of your pockets and follow me.'

We looked round and there was this salt faced customer in service dress uniform. His trousers had the way of having been pressed with a steam roller and he wore three stripes on each of his well creased sleeves. He seemed highly intent on giving us the rough edge of his tongue. Like two scolded blown upon Bachus boys, we followed the three stripes across the wide clattering drill hall.

'Sergeant Pettigrove I shouldn't wonder,' whispered Vincent.

'I thought so,' I said. 'He seems an unfriendly sod and he doesn't want to start shouting at me to stop talking. I haven't signed on yet.'

'You'd better make your mind up sharpish then,' said Vincent, 'before you get put on sanitary orderly duty, cleaning out the officers' bog.'

As we approached the cramped battery office I could see, sitting behind a flat wooden trestle table, a civilian clerk and Captain Adams. I gave Vincent a nudge. 'That's Captain Adams,' I said, 'I know him, he's been to our house and he's a real gentleman.'

Sergeant Pettigrove told us to stand in front of the table and to stand to attention. He saluted Captain Adams and said, 'Cooper and Parsons sir.' 'Thank you sergeant,' said Captain Adams, and then he turned to the civilian clerk and said 'Deal with these two will you.' Well, I didn't know what to think. Here was

Captain Adams who seemed unaware that he had shaken me warmly by the hand three days before. I was properly taken in. I could have been a total stranger.

The youngish dark haired clerk took out his glasses, polished them, and pulled out two forms from one of the narrow drawers of a tall green painted filing cabinet.

'What's your full name?' he asked.

'Albert Kitchener Cooper,' I said.

'Any relation?'

Another smartarse, I thought. How could I help it if I was born just after the war, at least it was better than 'Jellicoe.'

'Where were you born?'

'Newton Green, near Middlesham,' I said.

'Where will he die?' said Sergeant Pettigrove, being cunning.

'Probably Newton Green,' said the clerk.

'Much more likely be Belgium. He don't want to live for ever,' said Sergeant Pettigrove artfully. Yes, I thought to myself, the Territorial Army has definitely been oversold.

The forms were all filled in and signed, and Captain Adams spoke for the first time.

'Right Cooper,' he said, 'you will be a driver, and you Parsons will be a gunner. Sergeant take them over to the Q.M. and get them some overalls.'

I don't know why Sergeant Pettigrove walked so quickly. There seemed plenty of time. Vincent said 'I reckon he doesn't want to be late for his supper.'

At the Quarter Master's stores the storeman threw us a pair of secondhand overalls apiece, for which we signed twice.

'Look after them,' said Sergeant Pettigrove, 'they're the King's property.'

'I can let them have some mess tins,' said the storeman.

'In that case,' snapped Sergeant Pettigrove, who was clearly getting bored, 'they'd better have them.'

'Now,' said Vincent, holding the mess tins over his head, one in each hand, 'we have at last got something to fight with. Hit the kraut in the crotch with this one and then bang him on the head with the other one.' 'A comedian, I see.' said Sergeant Pettigrove, wide buttoning his bloodless lips. 'You may give Adolf Hitler the squitters but I can tell you that as far as I'm concerned, Gunner Parsons, you are an idle soldier and you are distinctly agitating my nervous system.'

*   *   *   *

'Whoever designed these bloody trucks,' said Lance Bombardier Henry Leathers, 'ought to be stripped naked and dropped on the North Pole.' It was a raw wet April day, and with Lance Bombardier Leathers at my side as my driving instructor, I was learning to drive the Fifteen Hundredweight Bedford. We were both cold and soaked through and the rain continued to sheet into the cab. There was nothing to stop it.

The Bedford Fifteen Hundredweight had no windscreen and the wind was tearing at the small canvas sidescreens which served as doors. The roof of the cab was also made of green canvas and, in rain, it would gather up to two gallons of water. Every time the truck hit a bump or a piece of rough road the water would bucket from the roof down into the cab. The Bedford Fifteen Hundredweight was known throughout the army as 'The pneumonia wagon'.

'I was drier on my Fordson with a sack over my shoulders,' I said. This was my fourth driving lesson and as we splashed by Hintlesham Hall, Lance Bombadier Leathers said, 'You're getting on well Albert and you will be able to take this truck out on the drill order next Sunday, and next week I'll ask if I can put you on one of the Quad gun tractors.'

*   *   *   *

I was beginning to get the idea as to how an artillery regiment functions and one drill night in late May, Lieutenant Kershaw, who was easily the brightest of the younger officers, lectured us in the Mess Hall. When Lieutenant Kershaw walked into the room, Sergeant Pettigrove brought us all to attention, eyed us all with disfavour, and said, 'And I don't want no more noise.'

Lieutenant Kershaw said, "Please sit down,' placed his cap on the table and lit a cigarette. 'You may smoke, if you wish,' he said. I was sitting beside Vincent Parsons and he said, 'I've got some matches, Albert, if you've got some fags.' Vincent was apprentice to a plasterer and after he had paid his father for his keep he was tight for cigarette money.

'An Artillery regiment,' begun Lieutenant Kershaw, 'when at full strength, has twenty four guns. These are split into three batteries of eight guns each, and each battery is divided into two troops of four guns. The regimental commander is a colonel, a battery commander is a major and a troop commander is a captain. The troop commander has at least two other officers to assist him either at the gun position or at the observation post. Someone also has to be in charge of the waggon lines, to which all vehicles retire when the guns are in action.'

'Each gun is commanded by a gun sergeant and, within each troop there are specialists, signallers, gunners and drivers, all with special jobs to do.'

'As you will know, this regiment is equipped with the new twenty five pounder guns. These guns will fire a twenty five pound shell a distance of ten thousand yards with great accuracy.'

'You can all be assured that the twenty five pounder is the finest gun in the world and far superior to any gun in the Germany army.'

'Hullo,' I thought, 'A little bit of bullshit here. I can't see the Jerries, who made those bloody great long range guns during the last war, being so far behind.'

'I hope,' continued Lieutenant Kershaw, 'that you don't get the impression that because the gun has a range of ten thousand yards, that the gun positions are ten thousand yards behind the lines. In fact, you are much more likely to find yourselves slap up behind the infantry or a regiment of tanks. The advantage of having guns with a long range is that you are then able to fire shells well into the enemy's lines of armour and attack, not only the enemy infantry, but also the enemy's own gun positions.'

'Seems a bit one sided at the moment,' said Vincent in a soft peddle, 'it is possible to imagine that if our guns are well forward behind the infantry, that they could be easily shelled by the enemy.'

'That, Gunner Parsons,' I said in mock authority, 'is careless talk.'

'Up you,' said Vincent, stretching his vocabulary.

'Before the guns are brought into action,' went on Lieutenant Kershaw, 'the Battery commander will go forward and liaise with the infantry commander and will examine the zone of fire, both on the ground and on the map. He will then establish an observation post from which he can observe targets. As the O.P. is usually within view of the enemy, as few men as possible go near it, and movement there is carefully restricted.'

'Each battery commander, or O.P. officer, can then, by using his prismatic compass and a rangefinder, compute the angle and distance to the target and orders can then be passed by telephone or wireless, back to the guns.'

Ernie Chapman, one of the signal section, who was also sitting in the back row, said 'When you are in action, the average life expectancy for a signaller, when he is maintaining the telephone line to the O.P., is nine minutes.'

'That,' said Cedric Andrews, who was battery mechanic, 'is bloody ridiculous. In fact you signallers are more likely to crap yourselves to death than get killed in action.'

'And you so called mechanics,' said Ernie, 'are well known as the scruffiest sods in the army. You're all brainless buggers and aren't fit to wipe a bloody windscreen.'

Tiffy Andrews didn't think much of that as he not only worked in a garage, but had been trained at Fords. He had got a certificate and all.

'Right, pay attention at the back there,' shouted Lieutenant Kershaw, and he smacked his swagger cane on his trousers. Then he looked straight at me and said, 'Now Gunner Cooper, what does GPO stand for?'

'Gun Position Officer,' I said.

'And what is the O.P.?'

'Observation Post sir.'

'And how many guns are there in a regiment?'

'Twenty four sir,' I said.

'Good,' said Lieutenant Kershaw.

'Bloody knowall, that's what you are,' said Vincent, 'I shouldn't wonder if a clever bugger like you wasn't straightway put in for Field Marshall, I'll get some fugging brasso for your halo.'

CHAPTER SEVEN

The Practice For War

MY MOTHER SAID 'Albert, you seem proper tethered to your Territorials. You haven't missed a week, and you're right saddled on, and the blackberry bushes round the garden want cutting back.'

It's true enough that most Tuesday evenings saw me biking into the Drill Hall and, by the last week in June I had learned to handle the 4×4 Field Artillery Tractors that were used for towing the guns.

They were queer looking contraptions with a peculiar shaped body with a sloping rear deck, and the whole of the frame was covered in metal sheeting. They looked bullet proof but, to tell you the truth, I believe I could have pushed through it with a two tine fork. We were to discover, in the years that lay ahead, that the metal sheeting wouldn't balk a pigmy shell splinter.

The roomy cab contained seats for five or six men of the 25 pdr. gun detachment. The gun commander, usually a sergeant, sat alongside the driver. In the roof, over the gun commander's seat, was a metal covered hatch and by opening the hatch and standing on his seat, the gun commander could look out, and was able to keep an eye on the Troop Leader and also on his own gun and limber.

The massive winch over the rear differential had a pulling power of over 8,000lbs and there was room to store a large quantity of shells and charges in lockers built into the rear deck.

These vehicles were known as 'Quads' and, although designed by Guy Motors, they were nearly all built at the Morris-Commercial Works at Birmingham. The Quad was noisy, it had a top speed of about thirty five miles an hour and, on anything but a good road, gave the gun detachment a rough ride.

Every few weeks, usually on a Sunday, the full Regiment of gunners, signallers, drivers and specialists, in their lorries and light vehicles, would move out of the Drill Hall Gun Park into the surrounding district, on manoeuvres.

A full scale exercise was arranged for one weekend after the hay was in. That early July morning I arrived at the vehicle park well before breakfast time. A solitary thin ray of the early morning sun filtered through the chequer work of the dark tangle of leaves on the trees bordering the gun park. I checked the petrol, oil and water levels of my quad and cleaned the windscreen and side windows with my mother's chamois leather, before letting the engine tick over for a few minutes. Our troop sergeant major, Sandy Evans, had told me that I was to drive the quad attached to Number One gun of 'A' Troop.

I knew all the men in the sub section under their gun sergeant, Harold Reeve.

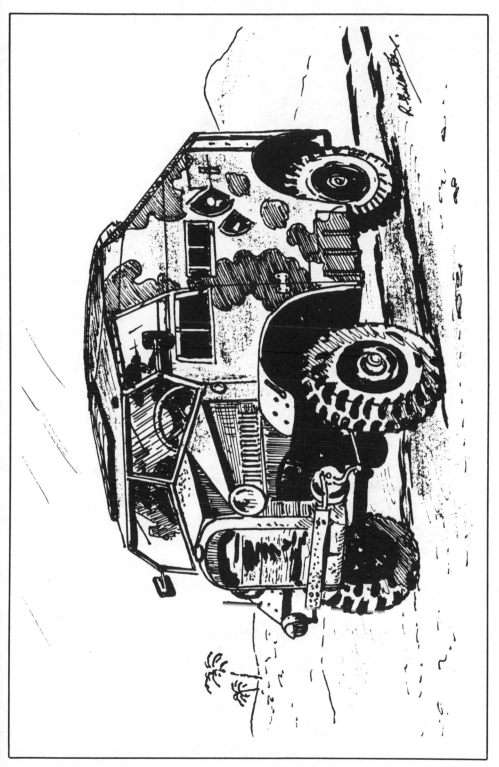

Sergeant Harold Reeve was foreman of a gang of local steel erectors which built dutch barns, and farm buildings with heavy steel stanchions and framing, and with roofs of big six corrugated asbestos. He was a married man with two children, and had been a territorial for six years.

The gun layer on Number One gun was Lance Bombardier Philip Underwood, who was a shoe salesman for Freeman Hardy and Willis. He was dark haired and cultivated a neat moustache. His girl friend, Nora, who was movie mad, said that Philip was the dead spit of Ronald Coleman. He had won a scholarship to the Grammar School, and was the best gun layer in the Troop. There were three gunners, all aged nineteen, which completed the detachment.

Gunner Siggy Buckenham was an ex farm worker who now earned more money digging holes for the Electricity Board. He was short and stocky with a bit of a stoop from long hours bending over his shovel.

Gunner Kevin Porter was a well built, good hearted young farmer who worked on his father's small holding two miles from Martlesham Heath.

The third gunner was Malcolm Burgess who had started work as an errand boy to a butcher in the Bealings. The butcher had been pleased with Malcolm and had trained him to cut up meat, and also to serve in the shop. Malcolm was also responsible for the maintenance and cleaning of the stainless steel steam cooking plant.

By a quarter to eight everyone had drawn their haversack rations, the gunners were in their seats behind me, and Sergeant Reeve was standing up on his seat with his head and shoulders through the hatch, watching for the signal from the Troop Leader, Lieutenant Kershaw, to start up and move off. The time honoured signal to start up was a clockwise circular motion with the right hand even though every vehicle had a self starter.

Apart from a few residents on their way to early Communion, there were very few people about at that time on a Sunday morning as we drove up through the High Street. The Livestock market had been swept clean and washed down since the Friday market day, and the windows of the closed shops on the west side of the street shimmered in the early morning sun.

At the top of the High Street a Don R sat on his motor bike to hold up any civilian traffic while we turned right handed and headed out towards the green fields of heavy headed standing wheat, and the fresh looking hay fields which had now been cleared of the first cut. Some of the fields of early sown Winter Barley were showing signs of beginning to turn.

The scheme for the Exercise that day was that gun positions should be occupied in Alton Park and, from there, the signal lines were to be run out over the crest and down the far side of the hill by the Church which was near the proposed site of the Observation Post. From a small clump of low bushes, some two hundred yards from the Church, a good view could be had of the falling ground towards the river and the main road which ran alongside. Most of this lower area was held by the 'Enemy'. We were playing at soldiers and no mistake.

Alton Park was the residence of the Colonel and he lived there with his wife, who came from one of the top County 'Brewery' families, and their two sons, one fourteen and one twelve, both of whom were away at Eton. Colonel Buchanan-Spooner and his father, and grandfather, had been to Eton, and it was unthinkable that Master Jeremy and Master Titus should be educated anywhere else.

The big house itself had grey limestone walls and a stone tiled roof with dormer windows which were cloaked with ivy and creeper. There was a half timbered stable block a hundred feet away on the west side and, in front of the house, on the south side of a twelve feet high, closely clipped yew hedge, was a magnificent rose garden which was now a blaze of colour. Mrs. Buchanan-Spooner was very keen on her roses and had been persuaded to become President of the local Horticultural Society.

According to Philip the house had two main drawing rooms. 'Don't talk daft,' said Siggy, 'who would want two drawing rooms?' Siggy's house was like ours, with only a front room and a kitchen.

'Well,' said Philip, 'they say there is a Blue Drawing Room and a Further Drawing Room, and behind the house there is the Buttery.'

'Buttery?' said Siggy, 'Is that where they make the butter?'

'Don't be bloody stupid,' said Philip impatiently, 'they make the butter in the dairy. The buttery is where the provisions are kept, and they say that the Colonel keeps over a dozen different liqueurs there.'

'I thought liqueurs were kept in the wine cellar,' said Kevin.

'You've all got a lot to learn,' said Philip.

'I reckon then,' said Siggy enquiringly, 'there's plenty of money about.'

'Money,' replied Philip with an absolute certainty, 'they're fugging rolling in it.'

Most of our inside information about the Colonel and his family came from Jim Spragg, the Colonel's batman. Jim had worked for the Colonel as gardener handyman since he left school and then, when the groom was sacked for swearing in front of Mrs. Buchanan-Spooner, Jim took over the horses. The Colonel was Master of Foxhounds, and Jim would ride and look after the second horse on hunting days, and bring the other one home.

Jim also helped the head keeper to bring in the stubbles and push out the spinneys on shooting days. He took the left of the line of beaters, carrying a white flag to help keep the other beaters in line.

All the guns knew not to shoot foxes, although Jim didn't hold with the opinion of certain hunting people that the more foxes there were, the greater the number of pheasants.

The Head keeper certainly didn't hold with that either and he snared the odd fox when the young reared pheasant poults were let out of their runs. Alton Park was one of the best shoots in Suffolk and they would reckon to bag between seven hundred and a thousand pheasants on their 'big' days.

Jim had heard the head keeper say that the last time they had their big day, that on the best drive the Colonel had schemed for the High Sheriff, who was reckoned to be one of the best shots in the County, to have the 'Kings Stand' on the corner of Dukes Wood. Sure enough the pheasants poured out of that corner, and the High Sheriff who Jim said could knock the eye out of a gnat at 80 yards shot forty three in under ten minutes, and that kept the 'pickers up' more than busy. The head keeper said that they all reckoned that the Colonel would get a Buckingham Palace Garden Party out of that.

Jim Spragg also told us that, on shooting days, the beaters had beer and mince pies in the cart lodge. They sat round on oil barrels, straw bales and bags of fertilisers, and had three crates of beer between them. Jim said that he liked the 'Tenants' day' best, but the tenants were only allowed to shoot a few old cocks at the end of the season.

Siggy Buckenham said, 'I can't think why they use beaters and expensive Purdey guns to shoot pheasants, when anyone can catch a pheasant by dangling a stuffed raisin on the end of a fishing line, or by knocking them off their perches at night with a spotlight fitted on the silencer of a four-ten.'

*   *   *   *

The A troop gun position was at the bottom of the deer park and the gunners carried out several dummy practice shoots while the quads were taken back some three hundred yards into a little beech spinney beside the lake. Here the drivers pulled camouflage nets over the quads and then walked over to the guns to take part in gun drill with the gunners. Harold Reeve had taught me to lay a gun and, during the later part of the morning, he allowed me to sit in the layers seat and set up the gun when the orders came through from the O.P. As was so often the case in artillery exercises in England, one of the fixed R.O's (reference objects) for laying the gun was a Church spire.

At just after one o'clock orders came through to 'Stand easy'. We pulled out our haversack rations and stood round the gun, eating great thick wads of bread and cheese, and drank half cold tea out of our mess tins.

'I thought,' said Kevin, tackling a large piece of dry crust, 'that the cooks would have provided us with smoked salmon and some thinly cut cucumber sandwiches.'

'I wish I was having my Sunday dinner at home,' said Malcolm Burgess. 'The Guvnor always gives me a decent bit of meat at the end of the week, and a bit of sirloin done rare and roast potatoes and peas would be just the ticket, and for afters I wouldn't say no to a plateful of suet pudding smothered in treacle.'

It was at that moment that the A Troop wagon line officer, Second Lieutenant the Honourable Charles Hester-Hewitt, walked up. The Honourable Charles looked young enough to still be in the school classroom. He was the Colonel's nephew and, according to Philip Underwood, he must have come straight off a course in man management, because he said, 'Have the men got their dinner Sergeant Major?'

'Yes sir,' said Sandy Evans.

'Good, then I'll go "acrorse" to the mess. I *do* feel I might be late.'

When he had gone Philip mischievously said, 'Albert are you going "acrorse" to the mess?'

'Have you noticed,' said Kevin, 'how that twerp keeps saying "I *do* feel? I do feel this and I do feel that?"'

'I know what we'll do,' said Philip Underwood, 'We'll form a Royal Society for the Men who *do* feel.'

*   *   *   *

Late that afternoon, when the regiment was returning back to base, I felt really proud sitting up there driving my own quad with a full complement of gunners aboard and with the gun and limber in tow close behind.

The convoy, with its strange looking quads and guns, and with a stream of trucks with pennants flying, always brought the villagers out into the road.

Kevin said, 'I shouldn't be surprised if my sister, Julie, and some of the girls aren't on the brim of the cricket field at Slades Green.'

Julie Porter was seventeen and worked behind the counter at Joslins the Chemists in Middlesham, and I'd seen her a couple of times with Kevin, and the second time, when she smiled at me, I thought that she was prettier than Norma Shearer, but I hadn't got the nerve to ask her to come out with me.

The hill through the pretty little village of Slades Green was very steep and the convoy was crawling along in bottom gear like a pregnant funfair on the move. Halfway up the hill near the Green itself, Kevin suddenly said, 'There's Julie with Bev and Pam.'

The three girls were waving and peering into the cabs of the quads. Julie was waving a red scarf. Sitting up there driving my quad I felt a lot more sure of myself and, to tell you the truth, a bit lightheaded. When we drew level with the girls I slid back my window and shouted, 'Hullo Julie, will you come to the pictures with me on Saturday night?' As they say, the fat was in the fire. I thought sure that Julie would say no but she shouted back 'I don't mind if I do,' and then she ran a little way alongside the Quad and called out, 'I'll be outside the Odeon at six.' That properly set me on fire that did, talk about blowing the coals. You see I really fancied Julie, I reckoned she had class, and I hadn't taken a girl out before.

*   *   *   *

The early peas had been picked, the cocksfoot seed was nearly ready to be bindered, and the first batch of ewes had been dipped against fly strike. I'd taken Julie to the Odeon four times and we'd walked the fields a couple of fine weekends. Christ, I was properly gone on her. My mother said, 'Albert, you're a doting rattle minded giddy head and you're acting like a crack brained loose screw.'

My brother Reg said, 'Albert, you're carrying on like a duck in thunder.'

'Don't you start Reg,' I said. 'Don't you start.'

I had to admit that I was like a clock that had just been fully wound. Julie was the best thing that had happened to me in nearly eighteen years.

*   *   *   *

One hot Saturday afternoon in July I turned out in my cricket flannels for Newton Green. The match was at home on the green and we were playing Middlesham second eleven. All the members of the Middlesham team had biked over on their Raleighs and Hercules and Rudge Whitworths, but their scorer, Ephraim Trotter, had ridden over on his red and silver Matchless motor bike.

Newton Green won the toss and decided to bat. The opening batsmen were in and I was padded up ready to go in first wicket down. I sat down on the wooden form beside Ephraim, who had just recorded two leg byes, and I said to him 'How's the bike running then Ephraim?'

'Like a bird,' said Ephraim, 'I touched sixty on the way here, but the missus keeps on at me to buy a bike and sidecar so I can take her out Sundays.'

'If you want to sell your Matchless, I might be interested,' I said.

'How much'd you give me?'

'Six quid,' I said.

'Give me seven and she's yours,' said Ephraim.

'Looks as if she'll soon want a new tyre on the back,' I said.

'I shan't take less than seven,' said Ephraim.

There was an appeal for LBW and the umpire raised his finger. I straightened my cap and picked up my bat and gloves.

'I'll give you six and a half,' I said, standing up. Ephraim wrote very carefully in the scorebook under the 'How out' column 'LBW', and under the 'Bowler' column he wrote 'G. Clements', and under 'Runs' he wrote '6'.

'All right,' said Ephraim, 'you can have it Sunday, you're a tightfisted, close handed bugger, and I hope you get a bloody duck.'

*   *   *   *

My mother twittered on about the Matchless being dangerous and all, but it certainly turned Julie on. At first when we went out for a spin and she was riding pillion, she grabbed tight hold of my jacket. But after a couple of times she sat there straight as you like with her hands behind her back. Every now and then she would rub her chin on my shoulder just so I knew she was there. She wore a little green jacket and a red and white silk scarf. She was July sun tanned and as brown as a berry, and her long soft chestnut hair streamed in the wind. Christ, I was proud of Julie. Did I say Julie was prettier than Norma Shearer? Julie was prettier than Myrna Loy, Greta Garbo and Joan Crawford put together.

I reckon my mother was a bit jealous of Julie and the way I was gone on her, but my father took to her no end and Julie asked him to show her round the horses one Sunday. That pleased Dad.

One morning, just after nineses, Sam Hoggett was carrying a bag of chaff down to his horses, and I was taking a five gallon drum of engine oil up to the tractor shed. Sam said 'See you're courtin' then Albert and have took a shine to Julie Porter.'

'Shouldn't be surprised,' I said, without stopping.

'See she doesn't run you around and lead you on,' he said.

'If she does Sam,' I said, 'you'll be the first to know.'

Julie's mother thought that Julie was a bit on the young side to be going steady but, just before harvest I was issued with a brand new uniform, complete with service dress jacket with regimental buttons and lanyard, an S.D. cap and badge, and a pair of Bedford cord Khaki R.H.A. breeches and puttees. On the top of this pile of uniform in the Q.M. stores was a wide leather belt with a large brass buckle, and a pair of long chrome spurs. Although we were a regiment of motorised artillery they couldn't forget the horses, and I half fancied myself with spurs.

I took the whole lot home and laid it out on the kitchen table. My mother brought out the brasso from the cleaning cupboard under the stairs and made me up a button stick from a piece of stiff cardboard, and my father went over to the stables and brought me back a tin of his special leather polish.

It took four hours to shine everything up. The belt had five coats of polish and I boned my boots with cherry blossom and spittle, rubbing it in with a toothbrush handle till the toecaps shone like mirrors. My mother ironed my puttees and blancoed the lanyard. My regimental buttons and cap badge, burnished with brushes and metal polish, glittered in the soft glow of the tall brass table lamp.

It was nearly midnight, but my mother and father hadn't gone to bed as they were waiting to see me in the uniform, and when I came out of the kitchen into the front room to show them, my father said, 'Albert, you look as smart as a peacock,' my mother said, 'You look a proper soldier now.' I could see that she had wet eyes.

On the way to the drill hall on the following Tuesday, I called at Julie's house to show her my uniform. Julie's mother seemed real partial to me and gave me a glass of elder flower wine. I reckoned that as far as Julie's mother was concerned I could hang my cap up behind the door. When Julie and I were alone in the scullery, Julie gave me a little kiss and said 'Albert you look smashing. I'm very proud of you.'

*   *   *   *

Half a dozen of us were grouped round a table in the Drill Hall. It was a map reading class and our instructor was Lieutenant Kershaw. We had looked at the symbols for churches, railways, woods and bridges, and were following the line of the three hundred feet contour when Battery Sergeant Major Watts bore up. He saluted Lieutenant Kershaw and said 'Gunner Cooper is to report to the Battery Office sir, the B.C. wants to see him.

'Off you go then Cooper,' said Lieutenant Kershaw.

I followed BSM Watts into the Battery Office and the Battery Commander, Major Rupert Coleman was sitting behind the cluttered office table. 'King Cole' had a thin nose, a heavy moustache and bushy eyebrows. I'll bet he had a clean shirt every day of his life. He was a real gentleman and County to the bone and he didn't shout and carry on like some of the junior officers. He sometimes had the habit, when he was listening to you, of looking at his feet. He may have been a little deaf and he was slightly stooped and round shouldered. He had won over twenty point to points, and had been upended when leading at the last fence on a hobdayed eight-year-old in the Military Gold Cup at Sandown. We were not sure whether his stoop and round shoulders were from riding chasers, or because he spent a lot of time looking at his feet.

'Gunner Cooper sir,' said BSM Watts.

I came to attention and gave a tight salute.

'Good evening Cooper,' said Major Coleman, spreading his arms over the table and peering over his horn rimmed glasses.

'Good evening sir,' I said.

'Cooper,' went on Major Coleman, 'I am hearing good reports of your work and your keenness here, and Mr. Kershaw has recommended that you should be made up to Lance Bombadier. What do you say to that?'

'Thank you very much sir,' I said.

'You may collect your stripes from the Q Stores before you go home, and get your mother to sew them on for you,' said Major Coleman.

'Yes sir,' I said.

'And another thing Cooper.'

'Yes sir?'

'Always remember you're an N.C.O.'

'Yes sir,' I said.

I was blessed well over the moon, and I knew that Julie would be pleased and all.

CHAPTER EIGHT

The Darkening Hours

EVERYWHERE THERE WAS grim talk of war. Hitler was screaming the place down and Germany seemed to be going off the handle.

By the second week in August I had everything on the old International Harvester binder ready to start cutting the winter wheat. All the fingers on the cutter bar had been replaced and I had removed all the worn sections on the knife and had rivetted on the new ones. The canvasses and straps had been repaired and patched at the saddlers in Middlesham and the heavy balls of binder string had arrived from the merchants. On the 9th of August Mr. Jessop said 'Albert, I think we'll make a start.'

Mr. Jessop was one of those farmers who liked to be the first to start harvest. 'You'd better have Jake on the binder' he said.

Jake Dash certainly wasn't much good in the harvest field for anything other than sitting on the binder seat, and occasionally raising or lowering the cutter bar with the ratchet handle. He must have been seventy and his hobnails were getting heavy. He should have been on the pension. He spent most of the winter and spring months digging out ditches and wet spots, and unblocking drain outlets. Old Jake was never happier than when he was letting a bit of water off the land with a long helved spade. Sometimes in the Autumn he would cut a few hazel springels for thatching. He was thin as a bird's leg and you wouldn't wonder he was so thin if you saw the little bit of bread and cheese that he brought in his grub bag, to eat with his onion. We used to say when we sat up against the hedge at beavers with our dinner bags and bottles of cold tea, 'Jake, you don't eat enough to feed a sparrer'. So Jake wasn't a wonderful lot of good on the binder but he was able to bang the tin over the straw table when the binder threw out loose sheaves. If the string on the knotter got tangled or a sprochet or chain on the binder broke, then Jake was like a man with no arms and no legs. I shouldn't think he ever had a spanner in his hand.

Round about the middle of August there was still a lot of this war talk going on, and one night when I came in a bit late from work I found my mother and father having a bit of an up and a downer.

My mother, who was twittering round the room, said 'I don't see how Mr. Chamberlain is going to stop a war.'

'Don't talk so silly Mum,' said my father. 'It stands to reason there won't be a war, the Prince of Wales will see to that.'

'I don't know what the Prince of Wales had got to do with it,' said my mother. 'You always were a Prince of Wales man. Anyway he isn't the Prince of Wales any longer, he's gone off somewhere with that bloody woman.'

'Well,' said my father, getting his tobacco pouch off the mantlepiece, 'he didn't go over to Germany and see old Hitler for nothing, and you don't want to believe all you read in the papers.'

'Anyway,' said my mother, doing up her apron, 'don't forget that Albert's in the Territorial Army and if there's a war he will most likely have to go.'

'Don't you worry about that,' said my father. 'They wouldn't send the Territorials abroad, they've got plenty of soldiers in the regular army for that. The Territorials are for Home Defence, and anyway Albert wouldn't have to go as he works on the land.'

'Well I lost two brothers in the last war and they worked on the land,' said my mother.

'Most likely they volunteered,' said my father, 'but it would be different if we have another war. We've got to have food you see, and they wouldn't allow any farmworkers to stay in the Army. Anyway I'll go out and pick a few peas before it gets dark.'

The days of the next two weeks, ranged with anxious suspense and straining for news, hung fire and smouldered in heavy gaited flatness. But, by the end of that heavy sluggish month of August, almost half of the grain harvest was safely stowed either in the neat round stacks in the rick yard, or tightly packed into the high red tin covered Dutch barn.

On the last day of the month the harvest gang pitched and carted the row upon row of shocks of string tied sheaves from the twenty-three acres of High Barn Field.

The great roped on loads were being carried in the swaying, creaking wagons, with their shrunk on iron wheel rims, direct to the threshing tackle which was stationed next to the black boarded barn above the pond.

The noble coal fired steam engine seemed to be all brass and levers as it spilled out hot coals from the ash box. The engine was like a portly grandfather scolding his family through the hissing steam as it drove the screaming belts and racing pulleys of the chuntering barnwork through clouds of dust.

By the end of the day the high quality milling wheat from High Barn Field was thrashed and sacked, and it stood in the barn two sacks high. A sack of corn weighed 18 stone, and the yield came out at twenty-six hundredweight an acre, so the Guv'nor should be pleased even if he didn't say so. Fred, who had tied string round his trouser bottoms to stop the mice and rats from running up his legs, said 'Well we shan't need no thatching pegs for that lot.'

*   *   *   *

The rhythm and steady turn of harvest bided even and peaceful, but my mind was far from easy with the talk of war. As the binder gathered and shed the belly tight sheaves on to the sharp glistening stubble there was a tingling sensation of eager crisis in my bones and a tight feeling of turmoil, like frothy chaff, sloughed in my stomach. My heart was beating high. I knew that war must come and that I would be part of it.

On the Thursday Jake was giving me a hand to pack the binder on to its carriage so that we could draw it through the narrow gateways, when we heard a swelling roar of aircraft which drew our eyes to the sky. Three of the new R.A.F. Hawker Hurricane fighters, in tight formation, flew at speed across the blue summer sky, heading south.

That night searchlight beams scythed the darkness around Ipswich and the coast.

* * * *

On the morning of 1st September the wireless announced that the Germans were attacking Poland, and many Polish cities, including Warsaw, were being bombed.

I had biked home with dad for beavers and, as he washed his hands at the sink he said, 'Well, one thing, the Germans won't bomb us.'

'What is there to stop them?' I said.

'Secret weapons,' said my father, pulling on the roller towel and giving one of his cunning looks.

'What have you heard about secret weapons?' I asked. We all wanted to believe there was one.

'They say,' said my father, 'that those small installations that are protected with chain link fencing and barbed wire down the East Coast are secret weapons.'

I slowly shook my head from side to side. 'No,' I said, 'that's the Observer Corps and all they have inside there are two telephones.'

'That shows all you know,' said my father. 'Sam's daughter, that cleans the Council Office, says that they are military sites and contain secret ray machines which will beam in on any approaching aircraft.'

'And what's that supposed to do to the aircraft?' I said.

'It mucks up the ignition and makes the engine cut out.'

'It's right what Dad says,' said my mother, 'Mrs. Butcher told me the same thing,' and she slammed the door and went off to look at her quince jam.

This cock and bull story about the secret ray weapons was only one of the rumours.

* * * *

The next morning my mind was restless and aquiver with the short odds of war. Flurries of excitement ran through as I drove my tractor and bindered the corn. When I walked through the door at beavers my mother said, 'Have you heard the news?' 'No,' I said. 'It's just come through from Warsaw that the Polish cavalry have raided across the East Prussian frontier in a counter attack, and have beaten up the Germans.'

'What?' I said. 'Charging tanks on bloody horses. That's just propaganda. It's just the sort of thing our officers would do but, as far as charging tanks with cavalry is concerned, the Polskis might just as well shoot their bleeding horses and eat them.'

'Well that's what is says on the wireless, and they don't tell lies on the wireless. Have some more greens Albert.'

'This is a good bit of rabbit pie Mum,' I said. I could see that she was fret for me and had cooked something special.

*   *   *   *

It was the third of September and cutting the Spring oats, which had plenty of company in the shape of docks, thistles and crows onions, had been left to last. Ambrose said that the Guv'nor wanted the oats cut short as we hadn't made too much good hay and the oats straw would come in handy for fill-belly winter feed for the cattle. The oats were long in the straw and in a tangle, and about a third of the field was laid flat. It was a plague of a job getting the corn in the laid patches to run up the canvasses and, no matter how I set the binder, some of the ears were at the butt end and in no way could I get tidy sheaves. I was ashamed to be making such an untidy job. Every two or three hundred yards we were having to stop and clear the blocked canvasses. I was in a bad temper and Jake on the binder was floundering about and tetchy. We were both riled at the binder, but it wasn't the machine's fault because it was never designed to cope with a jumbled and ravelled crop like this.

All the time my mind was thrown out of gear by the approaching wrack and havoc which would swamp and engulf our lives.

I wondered about Julie and me. Christ, I wondered.

The news during that morning was that the ultimatum to Germany had expired and that Britain and France had declared war on Germany.

*   *   *   *

When I reached home from work that night, I stood up my motor bike in the shed, went in through the scullery door and found my mother busying herself in the kitchen. She was just putting the potatoes back in the oven and was looking none too happy, I can tell you.

'Albert,' she said, 'I don't know what to think. Hurry up and wash and come and have your supper.'

'OK Mum,' I said, 'but don't worry.'

'You're one to talk,' she said. 'I told you this would happen.'

I could see that my mother was being a plague to herself and was like a rankled broody pothering round a hen coop.

'I know mum,' I said, hanging up my cap on a nail behind the door, 'but the Navy will be able to blockade the Germans and starve them out. I shouldn't be surprised if they don't surrender within six months.'

She put the oven cloth on the table and came across to me and said, 'Mrs. Easter has just cycled down from the post office and she says that a telephone call has come through from your Regimental Headquarters ordering you to report to the Drill Hall as soon as possible.'

'Well I shan't be going till tomorrow morning,' I said. 'They are going to be a bit stuck up at the farm if I don't give them a hand to bring the last few loads in.'

'You must tell your Regimental Headquarters,' said my mother firmly, 'that you can't report to the Drill Hall as you have to help get the rest of the harvest in.'

'I dare say they will manage the harvest without me,' I said, 'and I reckon they'll just say at the Drill Hall that there is a war on and they didn't give me an army stripe to spuddle about on a farm tractor. Anyway Mum,' I said, 'don't forget that I am a fully paid up Lance Bombadier and the Generals stand no chance of winning the war without me.'

'This isn't a laughing matter,' said my mother, giving the fruit in the preserving pan a stir, 'and you are just a ha'p'orth of piddle in the ocean. You'd be doing a sight more good staying on the farm than playing about with those lorries and guns. Anyway, the men have taken the harvest on contract and you'll be letting them down.'

Just then my father came in and threw his thin summer working jacket over the back of the chair. 'Albert,' he said, 'I've just been talking to the Guv'nor and he says that you won't have to go as you are in a reserved occupation. He says that everyone on the farm is in a reserved occupation, and that you would be doing a damn sight more good if you stay at home.'

'That's what Mum says,' I said. 'But I reckon I'll have to report at the Drill Hall in the morning.'

I didn't sleep too well that night and, although I was tired from harvest, I was all churned up with the news and I thought of war and my famous regiment, and in the early hours when sleep at last came I dreamed of the firing of the guns.

*   *   *   *

In the morning I was up at six and went downstairs into the kitchen. My mother, with hair in curlers, was mashing the tea, and my father was just coming through the door after emptying out the tin basin of dirty washing water onto the nettles in the ditch.

'Dad,' I said, 'I shan't be going up to the farm, but if they don't keep me at the Drill Hall I shall come back and give them a hand with the harvest in the afternoon.' My mother was fussing around all the time I was having breakfast and said three or four times, 'I don't know, I'm sure,' and I said, 'Mum, stop hazing around, you're like a bluebottle in a milk can.'

'Albert,' she said, 'you've no right to be going to the Drill Hall when they need you on the farm.'

'Mum,' I said, 'you know I've had orders to report and if I don't go, as like as not I'll be shot.'

She pulled an old coat over her shoulders to take some scraps out to the chicken run. 'Albert,' she said, 'I don't know what's come over you. You put me in mind of having run off your senses.' She fumbled at the latch, stomped out and banged the door to.

CHAPTER NINE
Lingering Time

I PULLED IN at the Drill Hall at Middlesham at just after nine o'clock and stood up the Matchless in the little corrugated iron shed behind the gun park. Crossing the gun park I met Sergeant Reeve who said, 'Morning Albert, everyone is to report to the Adjutant in the Sergeants' Mess.'

I joined a short queue where the adjutant, Captain Hodgson, and the Battery Clerk, Bombardier Benson, were checking everyone in. Standing behind me was Siggy Buckenham and he said, 'Hullo Albert, have you seen the enemy?'

'What, Sergeant Pettigrove?' I said.

'No,' said Siggy. 'The beastly Germans, the filthy Hun and the Nazi swine. They say we'll be off to France in about a quarter of an hour so I hope you've brought your sandwiches.'

Sergeant Pettigrove, who had been hovering around, said 'When you have all reported to Captain Hodgson transfer yourselves to the Q stores and draw a tin hat, a gas mask and a rifle, and at eleven hundred hours there will be a muster parade on the battery car park.'

There was no doubt that Sergeant Pettigrove, who had been in the regular army for fifteen years, was enjoying the war. He stamped from one foot to the other and he shouted at gunners to 'sort yerselves out and stick yer elbows in'. He was a pain in the arse and no mistake.

*　　*　　*　　*

At the K Battery muster parade as we stood lined up on the gun park, Major Coleman warned us against possible enemy air attack. 'It is believed,' he said, 'that the Germans have massed large formations of enemy bombers ready to bomb London, and it can be expected that a proportion of the enemy raiders will fly in over the east coast. All ranks will be issued with rifles and ten rounds of .303 ammunition. You will be split into groups of twelve under a sergeant who will coordinate the fire when the enemy aircraft come within range.' Stan Palmer whispered to Roderick Lee, 'Which part of the plane should we aim for Roderick?' Roderick, who had had a pheasant or two in his time said, 'If a plane is at fifteen thousand feet, and it's flying at two hundred and fifty miles an hour, give it a lead of a hundred and twenty five yards and you'll hit the pilot right between his bloody ears.'

Major Coleman was addressing us again. 'Don't look up if there is a dogfight overhead,' he said, 'because Hurricanes and Spitfires fire several hundred rounds a second and what goes up has to come down.'

Gunner Bell, one of the cooks who stood in the back row, nervously said, 'Listen, I can hear planes.'

'Don't be bloody stupid Ding Dong,' said Philip Underwood, 'that's Elsie Pratt, the greengrocer's missus, backing her old Railton out of the garage. She always gives it too much acceleration and rides the clutch. Women never ought to be allowed anywhere near a bloody car.'

During the late morning, an air raid siren wailed eerily in the far distance. As from the eye of a bellweather, other sirens joined in with their screaming banshees. The loud, dreary high pitched moan was like the dirge of a ghost's death song.

'I'll lay they're after Ransomes,' said Vincent Parsons. Someone else said they thought they could hear bombs. 'Car doors,' said Kevin.

Before the rifles had been seized from the armoury, the all clear had sounded.

Little we did know then that, within twelve months, our guns and gun positions would be savagely attacked by hordes of enemy bombers. There would be no warning sirens and there would be no 'all clear'.

*   *   *   *

Sergeant Pettigrove stood straight as a king post on the edge of the gun park. He tucked his stick under his armpit and glared disapprovingly at the working gunners as they cleaned and polished and burnished.

'Pick up your mugs and mess tins and fall in for tiffin,' he shouted. We marched everywhere. We marched to the cookhouse, we marched to gun drill, we marched to the sick bay, and we marched to church parade. Philip Underwood said, 'I shouldn't want my Nora to see me marching up the street in baggy shapeless fatigues and carrying a tin mug in one hand and a mess tin in the other. It's demeaning, they do it deliberately.'

*   *   *   *

Kevin, Philip and myself were all billeted in Middlesham with Mr. and Mrs. Dunn, who lived in a three bedroomed semi-detached house in Station Road. Mr. Dunn was a retired dental mechanic and both he and Mrs. Dunn were kindly and cheerful, and they always gave us supper.

Mr. and Mrs. Dunn wouldn't hear of us helping with the washing up and so most evenings, after we had placed all the dirty things in the sink, we would journey round some of the Middlesham pubs. I'd hardly ever been in a pub before and I'd never drunk so much beer. We just sat in the corner with our R.H.A. shoulder flashes and no sooner had we downed one pint, than some civilian would plonk another one in front of us. We hardly paid for a drop. The time would come when a small bottle of warm, or even very hot beer would become a rare and welcome luxury, but right now the civilians vied with each other to ply us with cigarettes and drink.

As we walked back to our billets through the dark grey streets, feeling mellow and a trifle befuddled, it was hard to believe that there was a war on, yet there hung in the air that high stirred feeling that we could all be plunged into a deep world of hammering convulsion and shifting sands.

On the 17th September Russia invaded Poland, and that evening I slipped home for a few hours. I had told Lieutenant Kershaw that it was my birthday and he wrote me out an overnight pass.

'Happy birthday Bombardier Cooper,' he said. 'How old are you?'

'Eighteen,' I said.

'You're old enough to get killed overseas now,' he said with a smile.

'Sergeant Pettigrove says he thinks I'll meet my end in Belgium,' I said. 'He reckons that when I am driving my quad across Belgium, all the time cocking an eye over the hedge to see if the Belgium ploughmen have got their furrows straight, that I shall drive straight into a telegraph pole.'

'I've got a feeling that you won't be going to Belgium,' said Lieutenant Kershaw.

I had let my parents know that I should be coming home on my birthday, and my mother had two young partridges in the oven for supper. They had been given to my father by Mr. Jessop who had said, 'Here's a brace of frenchman John for when Albert comes home. I can't make out where all the English have gone. We hardly see one nowadays. They're not as hardy as the red legs.'

'There's more meat on them frenchies than on the brownies,' said my father.

Mr. Jessop then said, 'I'd like to have a word with Albert when he comes home.'

'I'll let you know,' said my father.

*   *   *   *

Mr. Jessop drove up in his old green Wolsley at just after a quarter to eight, and tapped on the back door. My father let him in and Mr. Jessop said, 'Evening John,' as he wiped his boots on the clean corn sack which lay on the brick floor. 'I shouldn't be surprised if there isn't a frost tonight.'

'Have to expect 'em now,' said my father. 'It's well past Michaelmas.'

My father led Mr. Jessop straight into the front room.

'What does he want Mum?' I said.

My mother was putting the remains of the birthday cake in the cake tin and she said, 'You'll see Albert.'

My father called out, 'Albert, Mr. Jessop wants a word with you.' I stood up, folded the *Daily Mirror* and laid it on the sideboard beside the rosette that my father had won with Watchman in the 'turn out class' at the carnival. I had to bend down to save knocking my head on the low lintel over the doorway, and stepped into the room. Mr. Jessop was sitting by the table with one elbow resting on the red table cover, and my father was getting out a bottle of rhubarb wine from the corner cupboard. Mr. Jessop's well worn pork pie hat lay squat against the empty white vase in the centre of the table. Sticking up in the hat, like a tired sail in a cockle boat, was a large buff coloured envelope. It was easy to cotton on to what they were hatching.

'Hullo Albert,' said Mr. Jessop. 'How's life in the army?'

'Oh, it's all right, Mr. Jessop,' I said, sitting down on one of the small wooden backed chairs at the end of the room. 'One day's very like the next.'

'It strikes me,' said Mr. Jessop, picking up a glass of rhubarb wine that my father had set down before him, 'that you are wasting your time in the Army when you could be doing a lot more good driving your tractor on the farm and producing food.'

'Yes,' said my father. 'No good having guns without bread.'

'I don't see much forecast in being in the Army in peacetime and then sliding out when there is a war on,' I said.

'You're being piddle minded,' said my father, 'the army's gone to your head. Have a glass of rhubarb Albert.'

'No thanks Dad,' I said.

Mr. Jessop picked up the buff envelope and said, 'I've got a form here for you to sign Albert. All farm workers are in a reserved occupation and, if you sign this at the bottom it will get you out of the army.'

'Albert,' said my father, 'this may be the last chance you have of getting out.'

'No,' I said, 'I think I'll stay in.'

'You know Albert,' said Mr. Jessop, handing round his cigarette case, 'your father bet me five shillings that you wouldn't sign.'

'I reckon then that Dad's won five bob,' I said, giving Mr. Jessop a light.

'He's not likely to change his mind,' said my father, 'he's a contrary customer when he gets his mind stickled into some hot brained notion.'

Mr. Jessop picked up the buff envelope and put it in his inside pocket and said, 'I can see you're set on staying in Albert so I'll wish you luck. We shall miss you on the farm, and I can only say one thing and that's that there'll always be a job here for you as tractor driver when you come back.'

'Thank you very much Mr. Jessop,' I said. 'Let's hope that time won't be too far ahead, and thanks for the partridges, they made a nice change from the army cookhouse rations.'

When Mr. Jessop had gone my mother busied herself raking the fire and straightening the kitchen. 'I don't know,' she said, 'I had three boys at home and now I've got none.' My eldest brother, Reg, had got a job with a mobile road tarring gang in Lincolnshire, and Weaver was tea boy to the steam ploughs in the north of the County. Weaver slept either in lodgings or in the van during the week.

As my mother lit the brass hanging lamp over the table I could see that her eyes were wet.

'Mum,' I said, 'the war won't last long. They say that half of Hitler's tanks are made of cardboard.'

*   *   *   *

Towards the end of October, during the second month of the war, there appeared on the order board, outside the Battery Office, information which led to a ferment of speculation and put the Regiment in a pucker of fidgety fever. All ranks in the

Regiment were to be given five days home leave. A to L Tuesday to Sunday, and M to Y Monday to Saturday. This brought out the first hint of long journeys to come.

'It stands out a mile,' said Lance Bombardier Underwood, 'that this is embarkation leave, and we shall soon be on our way.'

'The sooner we go, the better,' said Siggy Buckenham. 'I'm browned off with this fugging place.'

Captain Adams and Sergeant Pettigrove were posted to an artillery training regiment at Aldershot.

The rumours started to fly, and, puff and broadside sprouted and grew. A guessing skurry was on in the pubs of Middlesham. The 'Grapes' thought that we were off to Singapore, but the 'Black Lion' had heard that it was South Africa. Someone had seen some snow boots in the stores. Gunner Gibson, one of the cooks, set us all afloat when he said that he knew for sure that we were being sent to the United States on a recruiting drive. 'You're a bloody tree of knowledge,' said Kevin, 'the Yanks aren't in the sodding war yet.'

Two large coloured posters were pasted on to the doors of the Drill Hall: 'CARELESS TALK COSTS LIVES' and 'BE LIKE DAD AND KEEP MUM'.

There was plenty of careless talk humming round Middlesham but if there had been an enemy spy around he would have his work cut out to make head nor tail of it.

*   *   *   *

Over on the western front in Europe there had been no real fighting. Just infantry patrols and a few air raids. The Germans were staying put behind their fortifications on the Siegfreid Line, and the French and British armies had dug in and had taken up positions in and behind the great French concrete and steel, Maginot Line. The papers said that no modern army could penetrate the Maginot Line. We didn't think that we would be needed there.

My Matchless was still unofficially garaged in the little tin shed behind the gun park. I kept a bit quiet about it as the Colonel or the RSM wouldn't be too pleased about it if they knew. Petrol was already on ration and I had a couple of gallons in a can in one of the lockers of my Quad. Sergeant Reeve knew that it was there and had said, 'See you get it out Albert if there is a vehicle inspection, the Colonel like to poke his nose under seats and inside lockers.'

On the Tuesday of my first day of leave I pushed the Matchless quietly out of the shed and set off for the short journey home, and puttered up to my parents' cottage at about half past ten. The old cottage with its weather beaten thatched roof, and its black tarred weather boarding, seemed born of the earth. The pale wood smoke from the chimney was curling upwards through the elms. The dirt and gravel path leading up to the cottage had been trod by many a hobnailed boot and by more good ploughmen than bad. It had been a pathway of the baker of the warm cottage loaves and the ragpicker, it had felt the light step of the children, it had been the line of way for the patient tradesmen for long long years.

Half the roses were still at full and the climber over the water butt had lengthened by five feet. Two of Dad's thick flannel shirts, pegged out on the line, bobbed and rippled like a fluttering crucifixion. Three disused bee skips, like overgrown toadstools, stood framed against the dark blackthorn hedge.

As I stood there holding my bike and looking up, bringing the cottage in to me, a shiver ran down my spine. This old overlay of a cottage had been my home and my anchorage for eighteen years and as I stood there my mind drove me to ponder, 'After this leave I may never see my home again.'

My mother came round the corner of the house by the chicken run to meet me. She carried a small wattle basket full of late apples.

'Hullo Albert,' she said. 'Just picked a few Bramleys for a pie.' My mother knew that I was gone on her apple pies and, when I was home, she always made sure that there was a big jar of brown sugar on the table. I had a sweet tooth and all along relished the syrupy taste of soft brown sugar, and I've seen the time when my mother had said, 'What would you like for tea Albert?', and I have replied, 'Bread, butter and brown sugar please Mum.'

My mother said. 'Dad will be home for beaver at twelve, what are you going to do this afternoon?'

'I'm taking Julie into Ipswich,' I said, 'we're going to the pictures.'

'See you don't get her into trouble,' said my mother, she's a nice girl.'

'Oh Christ Mum,' I said, 'I shan't do anything to make you have to take half a pound of rat poison or jump in the barnwork.'

'I know what you soldiers are,' said my mother.

*   *   *   *

My father came in for beaver wearing a pair of soiled cord working trousers, a collarless striped shirt and hob nailed boots. He hung his cap on the nail on the back door and tipped some cold water from the white enamel jug into the tin basin and washed his hands. He dried his hands on the torn roller towel that hung on the wall, then threw the dirty water outside the door.

'What have you been doing this morning, John?' said my mother, who was cleaning the multicoloured shred rug with a dustpan and brush.

'Ploughing the tater land in the fourteen acres,' said my father, 'can't do nothing with it, it's coming up like liver. Unless there's a hard frost we'll never get it down for wheat.'

'Albert's home,' said my mother.

'I see his bike's in the yard, where is he?'

'He's upstairs looking out a clean shirt for going to Ipswich.'

'Albert,' shouted my mother, 'Dad's home.'

When I came downstairs my father was unknotting the big red handkerchief that he always wore round his neck.

'Hullo, Dad,' I said, 'had a good morning?'

'Only half tidy. One of the whippletrees broke and I reckon Watchman's just about to lose a shoe. Anyway Albert, Happy Birthday, I've got a little present for you upstairs.' My mother said 'Dad's been worrying about your birthday present for over two weeks, and he bussed into Ipswich on Saturday afternoon after he drew his wages.'

'Perhaps it's a pair of sunglasses,' I said, 'I may need some where we are going. There had been rumours this morning that a few hundred topees had been delivered to the stores.'

I heard my father open and shut the drawers in the bedroom and when he came down the creaking wooden stairs he held in his two hands something wrapped in a piece of worn blanket, tied round with string. He laid it on the kitchen table, untied the knot and carefully unrolled the piece of blanket. Inside there was a small leather case which he handed to me. It was a seventeen jewelled silver Omega wrist watch, which must have cost my father several weeks' pay. It was the best present I'd had in my life.

'Thanks Dad,' I said, lifting the watch out of its case and laying it on my wrist, 'that's smashing, its got a second hand and all, and its made in Switzerland.'

'Look on the back,' said my father.

I turned the watch over and, engraved in small neat letters were the words 'A. Cooper. West Suffolk Yeomanry.'

'I got it done special,' said my father.

★ ★ ★ ★

I picked Julie up at half past two. She was wearing a cream silk blouse and a grey divided skirt underneath a light coloured belted mack. A red and white spotted scarf was loosely tied round her neck. Her long golden hair was hanging loose, and her shoulders were dripping bunches of curls. I'd never seen her look so gorgeous. Christ she was lovely. She was bright eyed and precious. I was right gone on her and no mistake.

'Hullo Albert' she said, giving me a little peck on the cheek. 'Dont I get a proper kiss?' I said.

'Later' she said 'Mum's looking'.

'You're looking lovely Julie darling' I said, holding her hand. 'Thanks Albert' she said 'and you're looking really handsome. I'd rather have you than Clark Gable and you smell nice too'. 'That's the Brylcreem,' I said. 'Get sat on the pillion.'

Julie said 'What shall we do in Ipswich until the pictures open?' The bike was still on its rest and I had hold of the handle bars while Julie climbed on. I thought I might as well step right in.

'The first thing we're going to do Julie' I said, not believing it was me speaking, 'is to buy you a ring'.

There was a long silence and my heart was racing. 'Well, say something,' I said. But Julie said nothing and I looked round at her sitting on the pillion. Slowly, ever so slowly, a tear ran down her cheek, followed by another and another, and then through her tears she gave me that lovely ready smile that I knew so well, and I knew that it was alright.

Oh Albert' she said 'I'd love to be engaged'.

'It certainly doesn't look like it' I said, getting out my handkerchief and gently dabbing away her tears, 'crying like that'.

'Oh, dear Albert' she said, catching hold of my arm, 'I was crying because I love you so and you are going away'.

'I'll soon be back' I said, tucking the handkerchief in my top pocket. I kissed her on the forehead and said 'Don't cry, your Mum may be looking'.

'Mum thinks you're the cats whiskers' she said smiling. My heart was bursting with love for her. I'd never been so happy and that's the truth.

We bought the ring in a small jewellers in Westgate Street. It wasn't a very big diamond but it sparkled like a firefly when Julie held it up to the light.

'You'll either have to draw the blinds or wear smoked glasses to look at that' I said. Julie gave her gentle laugh, which I loved.

As we left the jewellers, with Julie's arm through mine and a new ring on her finger, my mind was hazed with brimmed up happiness and yet, deep inside was that uneasy wherretting like a paper pellet fibbling at the roots of my need, about the future of the war and about leaving Julie.

Walking slowly out of the smoke filled cinema into the large car park, smoking a cigarette like George Raft and with Julie by my side, I had that feeling of longing that our happiness could move on this floodtide for ever.

The clear October night sky was peppered with stars, and a light ground mist gently glazed the lights of the traffic and the dimmed street lights of the town. The blackout curtains were tightly drawn as I rode my throbbing machine through Queen Street and St. Matthew Street out on to the Norwich road. The night air was cool and Julie clung tightly with her arms round my waist, and with her head resting on my shoulder. The bright headlight split the rolling darkness and, with the blanket of stars like purple starfish, a seeming two rooftops away, we could have been flying through space miles above the earth.

★   ★   ★   ★

The five days of embarkation leave slipped by like a windy afternoon. Julie became quiet and tearful. My mother was stroppy with Dad.

On the Friday I had dinner and tea with Julie and Mr. and Mrs. Porter. Mrs. Porter got out her best cups and made a fuss. According to Mr. Porter, Julie was spending all day looking at her ring.

Mr. Jessop brought up another brace of partridges.

Miss Bonner, my teacher of earlier times at the village school, in her stout weekday shoes, and still wearing her old brown felt hat, came to say goodbye and brought me three linen handkerchiefs.

'I hope Albert' she said 'that you are still reading'.

'Most weeks Miss Bonner' I said 'I try to get a book out of the Church library'. I reckon Miss Bonner wouldn't have minded how long I was away, as long as I read a book every week.

Sam Hogget and Charlie both called in. Sam said that I could leave my motor bike in his garden shed for the duration and that he would jack it up and look after it.

I began to feel warm and well up the ladder with all the attention I was getting. I seemed to have made a mark in the village.

My brother Reg came down from Lincoln on the Saturday, and Weaver showed up on the Sunday. Reg had received his call up papers and was due to report at the Training regiment at Oswestry in a month's time.

The deep dyed thought of parting from Julie ran in my head and brought an uneasy brooding lump to my innermost marrow, but there was also that way down latent excitement of going to new places and into possible danger. Miss Bonner had long ago shown us on the giant multi-coloured map of the world that hung on the wall beside the tall school book cupboard, the vast pink areas blazing the British Empire. From the age of five, in the infants' class, we sang, with innocent fervour, 'Land of Hope and Glory', and when we came to the lines 'God to make thee mighty' and 'Make thee mightier yet' Miss Bonner thumped the piano and her eyes took on a glazed look. To tell you the truth, we all got a bit carried away and, little as we were, everyone of us, with Miss Bonner to lead us, would have stormed the barricades.

So when they said that Hitler had to be beaten, I knew the reason why. Hitler wanted our Empire on which the sun never sets, and he had boasted that the German Reich would last a thousand years.

I had to be back at ten o'clock, so all Sunday afternoon and evening I spent with Julie. Mr. and Mrs. Porter went out and said that they would'nt be back till 9 o'clock, so we had the house to ourselves. Mrs. Porter had left some sandwiches and a plate of cakes, and Julie was going to make the tea. We both stood at the stove waiting for the kettle. I had my arm round her waist, it was warm and peaceful and my love for Julie was stronger than anything I had ever known. Every moment was precious and my love was bubbling over like a running sea.

Julie pushed the kettle off the hot plate and gently pulled me on to the sofa and the yielding cushions. She wore little makeup and her eyes were sparkling. Her hair was falling about her face and we folded into each others' arms. I looked into her glowing blue eyes and her lovely innocent face. Her arms were round my neck and joy surged through me. 'Albert you're wonderfully good to me' she said softly. We were a closeness drunk with warmth and tenderness, beholden and safe, joining hearts wrapped and bound with love. Clutching her tightly I kissed the soft strands of her hair, and her breath was soft against my chest.

The fringed curtains moved, touched gently by the night breeze as she lay curled in my arms in gathered loveliness. She moved her lovely long legs and pulled me closer to her. Her cheek against mine was burning hot, and I could hear her heart thudding as loudly as my own.

'Oh Albert,' she said. 'I do so want you to be happy.'

Her chestnut hair was hanging loose, the moist shine was in her eyes, and the light from the dull oil lamp caught the splashes of gold. Time stood still as blessed moments hung in the air. We would so certainly marry one day, and I could not believe I would never return, that we agreed to wait for lovemaking real and pure.

As we hugged and caressed each other in these precious moments, my heart was wild with joy, yet there was a sad aching emptiness at the thought of parting from this cherished adorable lovely girl. Her eyes darkened like liquid fire as her hands tightened on my shoulder, and we were united in happiness.

'Can you hear my heart beating?' she murmured.

Time was passing, my heart was on fire and I could hardly hide my tears. 'I'll be true to you Albert,' she said, 'I'll be true to you.'

Quietly and tenderly, she pulled me to her golden softness in the warm radiance of love, and I covered her face with soft clinging kisses.

CHAPTER TEN

Journey from the Homeland

'RIGHT, PICK UP your kit bags and follow me,' shouted Battery Sergeant Major Watts. It was just before midnight and a large convoy of R.A.S.C. three tonners was drawn up in a long line on the tar sealed road outside the Drill Hall.

The whole of K Battery personnel were grouped in twenties in full drill order in the half lit hall. It was a cold dark night but the heavy khaki great coats were hot and uncomfortable under the tight buckled webbing. My back pack was stuffed and weighed down with clothes, metal and leather. Over my right shoulder was slung the Mark II gas mask. My heavy tin hat, with chin strap looped through the epaulet straps on my left shoulder, rested where Julie's head had been as we rode the Matchless home from Ipswich three nights before.

My haversack was crammed full of small heavy items and a few precious personal belongings, including a photograph of Julie, and also one of Mum and Dad at the door of the cottage. The postcard size photograph of Julie was taken by a seaside photographer during a trip on a hot bright Sunday just before harvest. We had journeyed up to Aldeburgh and Julie had been photographed sitting on the sea wall, with her hair and scarf just flicking up in the soft easterly sea breeze. She was looking neat and bonny, and was bubbling bright eyed with happiness.

To add to our burden we each carried a hulky drag of a Lee-Enfield rifle. 'Never leave it,' they said. There was no bigger crime than to lose it. My memory floated back to the occasion when Sergeant Pettigrove had been taking a squad for rifle drill.

'The rifle,' said Sergeant Pettigrove, with the authority of years of repetition, 'is the soldier's best friend.'

'I thought, Sergeant,' said Roderick Lee, with flippant insolence, 'that a dog was a man's best friend.'

'I said a soldier's best friend,' said Sergeant Pettigrove, blackening, 'and to show us that you are both a soldier and a man just run at the double with your rifle three times round the gun park.' That put the stoppers on Roderick and no mistake.

Laden with pack, haversack, kitbag and rifle, we staggered after BSM Watts towards the dark forms of the canvas-covered, waiting three tonners. The lorry tail boards were down and we were again counted off in twenties like pens of market sheep.

'You know what?' said Malcolm Burgess, shuffling along beside Siggy Buckenham.

'No,' said Siggy, bending under the weight of his equipment.

'My arse itches,' said Malcolm.

'I can't see that you'll be able to scratch it for at least two days,' said Siggy, heaving his kitbag into the back of a three tonner.

It had been a hustling and tiring day. We sat uncomfortably on our kitbags in the back of the jolting three tonner. The convoy rumbled through the streets of the old Roman town of Colchester. Siggy said, 'Let's stop and pick up a few oysters.'

Philip Underwood, who seemed to know everything, said, 'The oyster season is from September to May so perhaps the cooks will put a dozen for each of us on tomorrow's menu.'

'The cooks woudn't know a bloody oyster if they saw one,' said Bombadier Benson.

An hour later the lorries clattered into Chelmsford, the County town of Essex. At this early hour the blacked out town was quiet as the grave. The three great factories of Hoffmans Ballbearings, Marconi and Crompton Parkinson were hushed after the late evening shift. The route took us round London by the North Circular Road. The pace was slow like single file, clockwork elephants progressing in low reduction.

I tried to snatch some sleep and had just managed to doze off when the convoy came to a halt in a quiet rural lay-by a few miles short of Basingstoke. We were stiff and cold, and were still suffering from the affects of our Cholera and Yellow Fever injections, but our spirits were still reasonably high at the prospect of adventure and a real change from the dreary routine of army life at Middlesham.

We clambered down from the high backed lorries and stretched our aching limbs. Two small blue tea vans, with let down sides, stood about twenty feet apart in the lay-by, and four cheerful members of the Women's Voluntary Service, in uniform, each holding large steaming tea pots, filled our coarse discoloured enamel mugs with strong sweetened tea.

The RASC drivers had told us that our destination was Southampton. A very young looking sergeant from the RASC told us not to pee against his lorry wheels. Lance Bombadier Philip Underwood said, 'No one in the Royal Army Service Corps is going to tell a soldier of the Royal Horse Artillery when he can piss.'

The sergeant, who obviously didn't think it was worth his while to bring Philip to book, said, 'You are ill mannered and disgusting Bombadier, and a bad example to the rest of your riff raff.'

When the sergeant had gone Kevin said, 'You're an arrogant bastard Philip.'

Philip, who was doing up his fly buttons said, 'I can't help that. That young sergeant is over educated and under employed, he's got a cushy number, and he doesn't want to meddle with the fighting troops.'

'And a fat lot of fighting you've done,' said Kevin.

As we climbed back on board our waiting transport, Philip said, 'Southampton Docks is the port for sailing to America. The Queen Mary sails from Southampton.'

'I'm dead impressed,' said Kevin, who was sitting with his back against the spare wheel which was bolted to the front of the lorry buck. 'But several cross channel steamers go from there as well.'

As we drew into Southampton docks, tired and cold, the first splitters of dawn began to lighten the hueless, ash coloured sky. There was no rain and the land back at the farm would be fit for drilling the winter wheat, and the land lying under stubble would be in good order for turning over.

'What's Greenwich, Kevin?' I said.

'According to Ransomes horn and Jacksons whistle,' said Kevin, looking at his wristwatch, 'it's a few minutes past seven.'

My father would by now have left his warm cottage and walked to the stables over the misty meadow of damp grass. Watchman and Prince would be harnessed. Their tails would be plaited up to keep them out of the way of the reins and traces, and to protect them from the mud. The two horses had always worked abreast, with Prince on the land side and Watchman as furrow horse. At five minutes to seven my father would have blown out the stable lamp, and at dead on seven o'clock the stable door would be opened and he would lead out his two strong obedient giants for a full day's ploughing. The bravest rook would soon be by his feet and, a hair's breadth behind, the following gulls, like fluttering handkerchiefs, with their strident shrieks and beating cascading wings. My father couldn't ask for anything more.

It was a cold cheerless November morning with a washy coloured sky and a strong north easterly wind as we lined up on the quay for breakfast. The long patient queue of soldiery which the Army had been trying to lick into shape by discipline, training and fear, meekly held out their mess tins at the battery cookhouse truck for two sausages, two slices of bread and a mug of warm tea. Not much glamour, not much flaming excitement, I was glad Julie couldn't see me.

The rough white waves splashed up against the quay. Sergeant Harold Reeve said that it could be choppy in the Channel. Up by the head of our column of lorries, rising and falling in the swell, there lay a squat grey cross channel ferry steamer, 'The Lady of Man'. The thick black dripping hawsers stretched and flopped as the ship edged and rocked in the slithering gun metal sea. With little sleep and churning stomachs, the adventure of foreign travel was wearing thin.

'You know,' said Malcolm Burgess, 'I very much doubt if anyone knows we are here.'

'Where's the band?' said Kevin.

'Where's Gracie Fields to sing "Wish me luck as you wave me goodbye"?' said Vincent Parsons.

After waiting for an hour and a half we straggled by fits and starts like a very tired creeping wreathy serpent up the steep restless gangway of the 'Lady of Man'. The smell was of engine oil and shellfish. The screaming of the gulls weighed against the low moaning of the wind.

The Colonel had opened the sealed orders, and a full battery muster parade on the deck for officers and N.C.O.'s gave news that the regiment was destined for Palestine and we would be routed via Cherbourg and Marseilles.

'Where's Marseilles?' said Siggy.

'I've always fancied a bit of Arab crumpet,' said Vincent.

Philip Underwood was arranging his pack, haversack and greatcoat in a corner in the ship's lounge.

'You'll be lucky,' said Philip, 'If the Arabs catch you interfering with their women they'll separate you from your goulies. And what is more,' went on Philip, 'the surgical operation is performed without anaesthetic with a two handled sword.'

*　　　*　　　*　　　*

The 'Lady of Man' was in mid channel and the crossing was rough and waspish, but the NAFFI bar kept open all day. Beer was cheap and gin was threepence a go. The choppy sea and the rolling motion of the ship pulled the check strings on our desire for food, and we weren't sorry when the 'Lady of Man', telegraph bells ringing, nosed her way into Cherbourg Harbour in the late afternoon. The weather had worsened and a drifting mist hung above the angry green sea. It started to rain mournfully as the 'Lady of Man' crept into its berth.

The French pilot was involved in a noisy exchange of words with the dockers, in navy jerseys, who were tying up the ship. A solitary miserable looking British military policemen could be seen on the quayside with his hands behind his back.

'I wonder,' said Malcolm, 'what that flatfoot M.P. reckons he's doing down there.'

'He's there to see you don't bloody well slide back on the next boat,' said Vincent.

Our blue canvas kit bags, on which had been stencilled in white paint 'NOT WANTED ON VOYAGE', had been loaded into the hold and were now being swung over the ship's side in large nets. A little French tug bustled by, ploughing the water, and sounded three shrill whooping blasts on its fog horn.

'I don't know,' said Lieutenant Kershaw, 'whether that was a salute or a raspberry.'

As we shuffled across the wet slippery wharf road towards a waiting military train of the French Railways, there was no way of knowing that this vital Normandy port of Cherbourg was to be the focus of the Allied invasion of Europe four years later. Everything was drab and dirty under the grey ashen sky with its heavy dark clouds. The intermittent rain was cast over like a wet harvest day as the downpour dripped sadly through the leaky station roof.

Someone shouted 'Grub up on platform four'. The rush was like a couple of hundred chickens after a handful of cracked maize, and two long queues were quickly formed in front of a large French Army field kitchen. On the simmering stoves stood two gigantic black iron cooking pots of stew. Behind each huge cooking pot stood two, unhappy looking but well fed, shavetails from the French Army Catering Corps. They were dressed in dirty white caps and overalls, and they all had a well chewed droopy cigarette dangling from their lips. In their hands they wielded a large wooden ladle.

'The Froggies must have stolen these pots from darkest Africa,' said Kevin, 'they'd take a fully grown missionary.'

'Very cordon bleu,' murmured Lance Bombardier Underwood.

'Albert reckons they're full of horse meat,' said Siggy, drumming his knife and fork on his mess tin.

'How do you know that Albert?' said Kevin.

'Saw four horse shoes in the dustbin,' I said.

The sea air on the Channel crossing had made us hungry and the hot stew and the fresh french bread filled a gap, and the black unsweetened coffee from huge black dixies seeped into our entrails and gratified the inner man. One of the small passing pleasures of army life after a full hot meal, was the lighting up of a cigarette and drawing in that first palmy lungful of smoke. In times of boredom and frustration, and sometimes in moments of fear, the genial nicotine slaked the edge of a soldier's discontent.

We cast our eyes round the dreary station and surveyed the long grey military train that was to transport us to Marseilles.

'Take a squint at those two freight trucks in front of the brake van, and read what's stenciled on the side,' said Bombardier Wilson. Bombardier Wilson was a lean and studious looking signaller who, like Philip Underwood, had been to the Grammar. There, staring at us in bold black letters, were the words 'QUARANT HOMMES OU HUIT CHEVAUX'.

'I reckon that's French,' said Siggy.

'Clever boy,' said Bombardier Wilson, 'translated it means "Forty men or eight horses".'

Lieutenant Kershaw came along. We hadn't seen him during the channel crossing as he had been closeted with the other officers in the Captain's cabin. Lieutenant Kershaw was a good sport and Philip was always full of innocent impertinence, and he said, 'We wondered if the two trucks are for officers only sir.'

Lieutenant Kershaw smiled and said 'I hope not Bombadier Underwood, they would appear to be relics of the last war and in fact will carry your kitbags and heavy baggage.'

'My father was over in France in the last war,' volunteered Malcolm.

At that moment Battery Sergeant Major Watts strutted up all of a bustle, and said, 'I didn't know you lot had any fathers. Get a move on and get yourselves over to Platform two.'

Six to a compartment, and sitting on wooden slatted seats, provided further experience of submitting to any discomfort the Army and the war might bring. 'A Troop's' Number One gun subsection were all together in one small compartment. Harold Reeve, Philip Underwood and Malcolm Burgess sat on one side, and Siggy Buckenham, Kevin Porter and myself sat with our backs to the engine. We had all soldiered together in England and had become a fairly well knit gun subsection. Sergeant Harold Reeve was a born leader and his whole presence inspired confidence. We would all do anything for him and felt ourselves lucky to be on his gun.

The slow tortuous night journey to the South of France was punctuated by seemingly unnecessary stops and starts. Throughout the long night, between short snatches of sleep, we woke to the banging of doors, the sound of screaming whistles and the hissing of steam. Every time the train moved forward, or came to a stop, shuntering buffers crashed and rent into each other.

'These wooden seats are enough to give you the piles,' said Kevin.

'Stick a greatcoat under your bum,' said Malcolm, 'and you'll think you've been transferred to First Class.'

As it wasn't a corridor train, it became necessary to pump ship out of the window. Malcolm Burgess stood there with the window down doing his best.

'Hurry up Malcolm,' said Philip, 'before we all catch pneumonia, and mind you don't scrape John Thomas on the ground.'

'Not much fear of that,' said Malcolm, 'it's so cold, I want a bent pin to find it.'

*   *   *   *

At Marseilles, in a biting easterly wind, we boarded His Majesty's Troopship 'The Dilwara', and K Battery were herded down to E deck in the overheated noisy bowels of the ship.

'If we go much further,' said Philip, as we lurched down one gangway after another, laden with equipment, 'we shall have to have an anti aircraft gun to fire at the torpedo when it passes through the ship.'

On each of the crammed decks there was no more than six feet six inches between the floor and the bulkhead. They moved in two more regiments of artillery into D and E deck. I doubt whether E deck could have squeezed in one more stunted underfed soldier.

A pale looking fat petty officer waddled up and tried to show us how to sling our hammocks. No one listened to him. We were tired and in ill humour. 'Breaker' Day, a tall gangling part time docker from Manningtree, who drove one of the B Echelon vehicles, said, 'Christ help us if there are any more like him in the Navy.'

After a couple of hours of stowing and unpacking, Troop Sergeant Major Sandy Evans shouted, 'Eyes front for the M.O.'

The Regimental Medical Officer was a short bulky fair haired man with short arms and podgy hands. He wore a badly fitting uniform and baggy trousers. He carried the honorary rank of Captain and he tried to look stern, to compensate for his lack of height. He stood against one of the long, heavily scoured, mess tables and removed his cap.

'Listen men,' he said, 'some of you may get shore leave while you are in Marseilles.' The sweat was beading out on his forehead. 'If you go ashore, and you run into some whores in the bars who offer copulation, my advice to you is – don't have it.' He paused while a titter ran through and the smirks wore off. 'If you must have it,' he continued, 'for God's sake take precautions. See you eat your toffee with the paper on. And, finally,' he said, 'report to me at once if, during the next few days, you feel that you are urinating tintacks.' The M.O. mopped his brow and said, 'That will be all Sergeant Major,' and he hurried off to his next 'surgery'.

'Sounds clear enough,' said Siggy, hanging his haversack on one of the long hooks on the bulkhead.

'Anyone got any toffee papers?' enquired Vincent Parsons drily.

We tried to sleep in the swaying canvas hammocks, which were as tightly placed as a litter of piglets at the teat. The next morning, after the hammocks had been rolled and stowed, BSM Watts informed us that this was going to be a great day for us as we were to be inspected by none other than His Royal Highness the Duke of Gloucester. We were to ensure, said BSM Watts sternly, that the deck and our kit was spotless and tidy, and we were on no account to leave lying around the ship any 'nefarious objects.'

Knowall, Bombardier Benson, informed us that Prince Henry of Gloucester, the King's brother, had one of the highest titles of nobility in the peerage of England.

'I'm glad then,' said Gunner Stan Palmer, who was doing duty as mess waiter, 'that I've scrubbed the bottoms of the mess tables.'

'And what is more,' said Bombardier Benson importantly, airing even more of his great knowledge, 'Prince Henry married Lady Alice Montagu-Douglas-Scott.'

'That's a mouthful,' said Gunner Palmer, with more than a hint of disrespect, 'I've no doubt that her Ladyship has stayed behind to scrub the floors in the castle.'

Kevin, who was a bit quicker than some, intoned 'Lady Montagu hyphen Douglas-Scott swabbed the ramparts with a mop.'

'Could do better,' said Bombardier Benson.

It was nearly 11 o'clock when the Duke and his entourage arrived on E deck. He must have been behind schedule because the Duke, in General's uniform and full of medals, strode at a very fast pace straight through E deck looking neither left nor right. The Brigadier and the two Colonels at his heels, like worried spaniels, showed signs of breaking into a pained, unhappy trot.

No one could blame the Duke for disengaging himself from E deck with urgent willingness, as there was a high degree of smelling armpits and carbolic soap, and fresh air only reached E deck by sheer accident.

In the late afternoon of the second day, the burdened 'Dilwara', ballasted with patient soldiery, steamed out of Marseilles harbour to the three mile limit where we were joined by three more ships and an aircraft carrier, which stood off a mile to starboard. Three destroyers, like busy mother hens, busied themselves round the convoy.

'I don't know why we have to have an escort,' said Darkie Hunter, who was a member of the Regimental Survey Party, anxiously, 'I understood that there were no enemy submarines in the Med.'

'There weren't supposed to be any enemy submarines in Scapa Flow either,' said Philip Underwood, 'but a U Boat got in past the submarine nets and sunk the "Royal Oak". It must be a lot easier for a sub to get into the Med through the Straights of Gib. than it would be to get into Scapa Flow.'

'Shut up Philip,' said Kevin. 'You make me nervous.'

A couple of slow ponderous Fairy Swordfish, with torpedoes slung, flew tardily over the convoy at about five thousand feet. They were heading east.

'I reckon,' said Philip, 'that they are after a German pocket battleship.'

'Oh Christ,' said Kevin, 'don't for fuggsake say that there is a German pocket battleship in the Med. It could sink our whole sodding convoy.'

'You've got your rifle haven't you?' said Philip, 'and we could always create a precedent and be the first troopship to ram an enemy battleship.'

'One thing,' said Kevin, optimistically, 'being on E deck means that we won't have so far to sink to the bottom.'

*   *   *   *

The Army would refer to the Regiment as being 'in transit'. All I can say is that being transported in the lower decks of an overcrowded troopship in wartime was an experience that could bend a sensitive soul.

The cramped eating and sleeping quarters were diabolical. We slept where we ate and we ate where we slept. The constant inspections of kit and mess decks were tedious and unnecessary. The compulsory daily boat drill mainly consisted of running up and down companion ladders and colliding with each other in the gangways. Nowhere was comfortable, no area was private and there was no quiet niche or secluded corner. The smell of bodies, like a stale unused food cupboard, collided with the damp pungent odour rising from the hot spicy curry of the dark skinned Lascar seamen down in the galley below. The long heavy wooden mess tables, bolted to the floor against pitch and roll, were scrubbed and scoured. The pots and pans and dixies gleamed with rag and the mess waiter's elbow grease.

*   *   *   *

'Eyes down – look in.'

'Clickerdy click, sixty six.'

'Key of the door, twenty one.'

The old sweats and sailors of earlier troopships ran the Housey Housey and kept the change. There was the incessant flat drone of the caller as he dipped his hot hand into the dirty black canvas bag of metal discs to the complaining cries of the players 'Shake it up, shake it up.'

'Doctors orders, number nine.'

'All the sevens, seventy seven.'

'Shake 'em up, shake 'em up.'

I reckon that if Miss Bonner could have seen me, head down over a Housey Housey card like a sick donkey, she would have well founded reason to suspect that she had wasted a lot of her time on my schooling.

The nights were hot and stuffy as the convoy moved slowly through the placid Mediterranean towards the east. We were the covered wagons, and the destroyers were the scouts and outriders galloping alongside and, like the pioneers of the west, we were moving into an obscure and mysterious unknown.

Shortly after daybreak on the sixth day out from Marseilles, the constant clamour and drumming of the ship's engines which, night and day, had shivered and vibrated through E deck, suddenly ceased and we found ourselves rocking gently on the Mediterranean swell.

'Christ, it's peaceful,' said Kevin, who had already been to the overcrowded ablutions and was rolling up his hammock, 'I reckon we've arrived.'

Sergeant Harold Reeve, who was an early riser, had come down from the Sergeants' quarters and had called across and said, 'If "A Troop" number one gun wants to see the ship being tied up and to behold the Promised Land, they had better come up on deck with me.'

The rolled up hammocks were tightly tied for the last time, and we followed Harold Reeve up on to B deck where we were joined by Lieutenant Kershaw.

'Enjoyed the cruise Bombardier Cooper!' he said.

'Not much Sir,' I said, 'down there it's like being in an overheated cattle crush.'

'Just as well we're not in a tank regiment,' he said. 'To climb in and out of a tank is a shoe horn and tin opener job.'

We stood leaning on the rails looking out over the side of the ship. It was still early but the morning sun was well up and we gazed in mild wonder at our first sight of Palestine, the Land of Jesus Christ and wild wheat, where Arab and Jew were spun together in bitter hatred.

Below the ship, in the bowl of the hills which ran up from the sea, lay the town of Haifa, seemingly drenched in unmatched square blocks of whitewashed boxes. Lieutenant Kershaw pointed to the high tree covered slopes to the north east.

'That will be Mount Carmel,' he said.

'What are all those gasometers doing down there?' asked Malcolm Burgess, pointing to the clusters of enormous round storage tanks which gleamed against the shaded buttress of the mountain.

'They are not gasometers,' said Lieutenant Kershaw, 'They are oil storage installations and they supply most of the oil for our Navy and Air Force that operate in the Mediterranean, as well as our land based Middle East Army.'

'Fuggin roll on,' exclaimed Malcolm, 'I reckon an enemy bomb on those tanks would set the whole bloody lot alight.'

'No need to fear that happening Gunner Burgess,' said Lieutenant Kershaw, 'our Air Force will ensure that no enemy aircraft approaches the installations.'

'Where does all that oil come from sir?'

'Well, as far as I know, some of it comes from Iraq and some comes from the Persian Gulf.'

'Strike a light,' said Philip Underwood, 'the Persian Gulf must be a thousand miles from Haifa.'

'Yes, it is,' said Lieutenant Kershaw, 'and the oil is pumped from one side of the desert to the other along a massive pipeline which is patrolled by the Camel Corps.'

'It must require a big pump to pump the oil a thousand miles,' observed Kevin.

'It's not one pump, Gunner Porter,' said Lieutenant Kershaw, 'it's a series of pumping stations strung across the desert. I should think there could be as many as ten big pumping stations between here and the Gulf.'

'Very educational,' said Siggy.

'Nothing like seeing it for yourself,' said Lieutenant Kershaw. Down on the quayside, the surly looking Arab dockworkers, in dirty long sleeved caftans and grey looking galabiehs were tying up the ship.

CHAPTER ELEVEN

Palestine – Land of the Bible

THE FIRST WARTIME camp of the 51st (West Suffolk Yeomanry) Regiment R.H.A. in Palestine, was at Ghedera.

Ghedera lies about twenty miles to the south east of Tel Aviv and Jaffa, and forty miles west of Jerusalem.

On arrival at the tented camp, three hard wooden bed boards, three short palliase biscuits and a mosquito net, were drawn from the stores.

The countryside around the camp was dry and parched. Scraggy sheep and goats grazed the poor quality brittle pastureland. Compared to this burned up tract of tableland, the rural areas of Suffolk were indeed blessed with milk and honey. The further countryside around Ghedera, however, was spread with orchards and orange groves which were irrigated from deep artesian wells.

Because of the war, export shipments of oranges and citrus fruit from Palestine had been halted, and great pyramids of ripe oranges and grapefruit, over ten feet high, were left to rot by the roadside.

Outside the wire fence at the back of the camp there lived a mottly rabble of Arab contract workers. They dwelt in shabby black tents and were employed on various duties round the camp. On the Battery order board the Arab camp followers were always referred to as 'WOGS' denoting that they were Workers on Government Service.

Behind the WOGS tents, tied to a wire boundary fence, was an amorous cluster of about a dozen donkeys. They were of various colours and sizes and they created a hell of a row, I can tell you. They were bawling most of the day and half the night. It was worse than Charlie's pigs at feeding time.

'I wonder what those sodding donkeys are making that bloody row for,' moaned Stan Palmer from number three gun.

'Lust, dear boy,' said Lance Bombardier Philip Underwood.

'Well,' said Stan Palmer, 'I don't make all that row every time I have sinful thoughts and get the urge to partake of forbidden fruit.'

'No, but you haven't got anything to shout about,' said Philip, 'I don't expect you've ever seen a donkey rampant, and don't forget that to a she donkey that racket is like honeyed words of love.'

'I reckon the sun is already having its affect on you Philip,' said Stan Palmer, as he picked up a wooden mallet and went outside to tap down the tent pegs and tighten the guy ropes.

★   ★   ★   ★

During the following months our quads and guns clattered noisily through the modern white painted Jewish settlements and through the older mud walled Arab villages. In day long exercises the regiment took up gun positions and O.P.'s all over Palestine. Divisional battle schemes, some of them lasting several days, were set out in the desert country bounded by the Dead Sea, Beer Sheba and the Wilderness of Judea. We took our guns down as far south as Aqaba, where the gulf shapes down to the Red Sea. From here the regiment moved into Trans Jordan and up to the ancient red sandstone city of Petra.

'You know,' said Harold Reeve, as we gazed up at the high sun drenched red temple of Petra, in the desert mountains, 'it would cost a civilian a fortune to come and see all this.'

'That's right,' said Philip 'we are getting all of this bounteous holiday free through the generosity and benevolence of King George. As he spoke a very dignified, proud looking, Bedouin Arab, high plumed in spotless white galabieh and burnous, rode by on a very small donkey. Trotting hotfoot some three paces behind, in black shawl and yashmak, was his wife.

'Sayeeda,' we all said as the man rode by.

'Sayeeda,' said the Arab, 'Alamda lula mabsut.'

'And may Allah be praised,' said Philip.

'You know what,' ventured Kevin, 'they certainly know how to treat their women.'

'You wouldn't like me to treat your sister like that Kevin,' I said.

'They tell me,' said Philip, 'that the only time they let their women walk in front of the donkey is when they think they're near a minefield.'

*   *   *   *

I won't forget driving down into the old city of Jericho in the Jordan valley when Arab children brought us bananas straight off the trees. They were certainly on the green side but we parted with our ackers. I just wished Julie could have been there to have seen this green oasis of Jericho, surrounded by the scraggy desert, and with the bananas growing and all.

It was near Jericho that Pinky Willis, a low level operator and a driver in B Echelon, was ordered by the Regimental Sergeant Major to drive his 15 cwt. truck to the waggon lines.

'Which way shall I go sir?' he enquired.

'The quickest bloody way of course, you idle man,' shouted the R.S.M., and straightaway Pinky drove his lorry right through a field of melons. The melons were squelching and popping like hand grenades. The R.S.M. did his nut, he really did, and Pinky, who always seemed to drive his truck in bottom gear with maximum revs, didn't hear the R.S.M. shouting, neither did he see the highly charged Arab farmer, in wrathful unavailing fury, jumping up and down and waving his arms in the air.

Meanwhile, two thousand miles away, Germany had invaded Holland, Belgium and Luxemburg, and Winston Churchill had become Prime Minister.

By the end of May the Dutch and Belgium Armies had capitulated, and by the 4th of June the evacuation of the British Armies from Dunkirk was completed.

On 10th June 1940 Italy declared war on Britain and France. The war was moving nearer towards us in the Middle East.

*　　　*　　　*　　　*

The Regimental guard and fire picket, some thirty strong, were lined up in two ranks outside the Battery Office. It was mid afternoon and the sky was pale with heat. We squinted our eyes in the bright sun. The regimental flag drooped dismally on its thin white pole like a moping shroud. Harold Reeve was sergeant in charge of the guard, and I was senior bombadier.

The siesta period had been fully taken up with polishing and cleaning and, to escape from the swarms of flies, most of the cleaning had been done under mosquito nets. Boots were shining, webbing was blancoed and khaki drill slacks and shirts were straight back from the dhobi. Our highly polished topee chin straps gleamed in the afternoon sun.

Guard and picket mounting took an hour and a half by the time the guard sergeant, the Regimental Sergeant Major and the Orderly Officer had carried out their inspections.

We stood at ease in the breathless heat. Rifles had been pulled through with wads of two by two, and the butts smelled of an affusion of linseed oil. Harold Reeve had carried out the first inspection, and we had sloped and ordered arms a couple of times, when the R.S.M. appeared out of his tent.

'Here comes Dracula,' whispered Pinky Willis.

R.S.M. Lynch was a bit of a puzzle really. He had a thin hollow face and often looked sort of tormented, as if possessed of some inner imprisoned demon. He talked out of the side of his mouth and he spoke with that artificial clipped accent that is used by some jockeys and hunt servants that come into contact with the 'gentry'. Lynch had had over fifteen years service in the Regular Army and he was a power crazed bastard. Even the sergeants didn't like him.

Harold Reeve brought the guard to attention, and R.S.M. Lynch found fault with everything. He stalked and hovered behind the front rank like a caged tiger, and tapped three men on the back with his cane in rapid succession.

'Haircut! Haircut! Haircut!' he roared. He confronted Pinky. The R.S.M. and Pinky didn't get on, and you could sense that Pinky was set for a bollocking.

'Gunner Willis,' he bellowed, 'when did you shave?'

'This morning sir.'

'Then stand closah to the razah. Report to me tomorrow morning at six o'clock in full kit and properly shaved.'

We knew that Lynch was a bully, and we were sorry for Pinky. What we didn't know at the time was that within 12 months Regimental Sergeant Major Lynch would have died in a Cairo Hospital with a tumour on the brain, and that Pinky Willis would have been blown to bits by a bomb from a Messerschmitt 110 some fifteen miles south of Fort Capuzzo in the Western Desert.

The guard was marched down to the gun and vehicle park which was in a eucalyptus grove, and the small guard tent was nearby. Warm cocoa would be brought round from the cookhouse at about nine o'clock, and we could look forward to another hot sub tropical night with jackalls howling round the camp and the persistent chirping of the cicadas under the mantle of stars which glittered remotely under a luminous sky.

We were warned that, at any time, murderous Arab assailants might creep into the guard tent and slit our throats, but all we heard that night were the bells of a camel train plodding along, with an effortless soft shoe shuffle on the duty track to the east of the camp. Harold Reeve, as guard commander, sat at the bare wooden table in the guard room tent. A smokey lantern gave a dull yellow light.

The Orderly Officer came round at about eleven o'clock and we heard the army rigmarole as he approached the gunpark in the semi darkness. The sentry barks 'Who goes there?'

'Orderly Officer.'

'Advance and be recognised.'

The sentry shouts 'Turn out the guard' and everyone springs off their bedboards and lines up with their rifles, in the soft clammy darkness.

'Everything all right sergeant?'

'Yes sir. A lot of mozzies about tonight.'

'Got plenty of insect repellant?'

'Yes sir.'

'Right, fall out the guard and I'll sign the book.'

'I have often thought,' said Harold Reeve, when the Orderly Officer had gone, 'that in a camp such as this, our sentries would have more capability of hindering intruders if they wore dark coloured overalls and gym shoes, and carried a decent sized cudgel, instead of this stomping around in heavy boots, wearing white blancoed webbing and carrying a damned great rifle which, in the dark, would have more chance of killing one of our own comrades than of mowing down the enemy.'

'Even a Field Marshall should be able to understand that,' I said, laying my rifle on the table and sitting down on the hard form beside Harold. 'You know they said that lions were led by donkeys in the last war.'

'I haven't heard that one,' said Harold, 'but I always blame the politicians more than the Generals. All the politicians thought about during the 1930's was disarmament, and appeasement, now France has fallen and that bastard Hitler with the swastika and jackboots are in all the capitals of Europe.' Harold hated the Germans, I had never seen him so emotional and waxed up.

'Now that Winston Churchill is Prime Minister perhaps things will change for the better,' I said.

At two o'clock in the morning Harold gave me a light shake to wake me up, saw the two new sentries on shift and then he handed over to me while he got a few hours rest. I sat at the table, the lantern by my side. The tent smelt of smoke and kerosene. The off duty members of the guard were sleeping soundly on the hard bedboards. They all had their boots on and were in full kit. The remains of the watery cocoa, which had now gone cold in the lidless dixie, stood on the ground just inside the tent flap where the cookhouse orderly had left it five hours earlier. A crumpled copy of yesterday's 'Palestine Post', full of propaganda, lay on the corner of the table. For reading I had brought 'The Birds of Palestine'.

At about half past five in the morning Gunners Wilkinson and Hobbs came rushing into the guard tent. Gunner Hobbs said, 'How many jeeps are we supposed to have out there Bom?'

'Three,' I said.

'Well there are only two there now,' said Gunner Hobbs.

'Don't be stupid,' I said, 'there were three there an hour and a half ago, I checked them.'

'Straight up Bom,' said Gunner Hobbs, 'there's only two there now.'

I grabbed my torch and rushed over to the other side of the gun park, past the eight twenty-five pounders and their quads, and there was no doubt about it, a jeep was missing. I rushed back, woke up Harold Reeve and the rest of the guard and got on the blower to B.H.Q. In about ten minutes the orderly officer and the duty driver turned up in an 8 cwt. and we examined the area all round the gun park with torches, but there was no sign at all of the missing jeep. Although there was soft sand all round the gun park, there was not a fresh track or wheel mark to be seen.

'The bloody thing can't fly,' said Harold.

At seven o'clock the Palestine Police arrived with a couple of alsatians and a mine detector. The Colonel was reported to be considering putting the whole of the guard under arrest and there were threats of punishment to Harold Reeve and myself. I spoke to a corporal of the Palestine Police who I found came from Colchester. He said that they had a very good idea of what had probably happened.

'I reckon,' he said, 'that the thieving bastards have pushed it into a hole.' The Palestine Police corporal proved to be right. The mine detector went beserk at a spot some three hundred yards outside the perimeter of the gun park and there they found the jeep well buried and covered up so carefully that it was impossible to see that the sand had been disturbed. Gunner Wilkinson said that it looked as if the final levelling had been done with a shite hawk's feather. The corporal said that the Arabs would have waited until we moved camp before digging up the jeep. He thought that it must have required at least a dozen men to get the pit dug during the night, and the jeep moved and buried so quickly.

Kevin Porter returned to the tent one night after a visit to Jerusalem. 'Do you know,' said Kevin, 'right down in the nethermost depths of the Holy Sepulchre there was a Greek wog holding out a plate for us to put money in.'

'That's nothing,' said Philip Underwood. 'When I went to the Mosque of Omar in Jerusalem we had to take our shoes off before they would allow us in and then, when we came out, we had to pay two akkers to get them back.'

'That's a laugh,' said Siggy Buckenham, 'you working for Freeman, Hardy & Willis and all.'

★   ★   ★   ★

My big moment in Palestine came in late July. I was in the canteen writing a letter to Julie when I felt a tap on my shoulder. I turned round, and standing above me was a distinguished looking grey haired person in civvies. He was hatless and was wearing a very well cut light tropical suit. The Colonel was standing behind him and I noticed two redcaps standing in the doorway. I tried to stand up, but the civilian put his hand on my shoulder and said, 'Don't get up Bombadier, what's your name?'

'Cooper sir,' I said, and he said, 'No, what's your name?' and I said, 'Lance Bombadier Cooper sir.' 'No,' he said, 'what's your first name?' and I said, 'Oh, Albert sir.'

'Well, Albert,' he said, 'how are you enjoying life in the Middle East?'

'Oh, very much sir,' I said, and then I thought I'd give him a bit of bullshit so I said, 'but I wish we could be sent somewhere where there was a bit of fighting and we saw a bit of action.'

'You may not have long to wait,' said the civilian and, as he made his way out through the door, I heard him say to the Colonel, 'Morale seems good Colonel.'

The Regimental Sergeant Major, who had been lurking in the background, came over to me and said, 'Do you know who that was Bombadier?'. I said, 'No sir.'

'That,' said the R.S.M., 'was Mister Anthony Eden, the Foreign Secretary.'

★ ★ ★ ★

'Accuracy,' said Sergeant Major Hatcher, in a loud garish voice, 'is the foundation of good gunnery.' Lean jawed Sergeant Major Hatcher was the I.G. (the Instructor in Gunnery). He was a rat faced little man with eyes that were never still. His leathery face was grooved from foreign stations. He walked with a slight limp due to his foot having been run over by a 3.7 screw gun on the barrack square in Bombay. He wore his peaked cap as straight as a plumbline and he knew the Manual of Artillery Training Vol. II forwards and backwards. He knew the amendments, and he knew the amendments to the amendments, and he could quote from the pamphlets on the Principles of Fire Discipline and the Procedure for transmitting Artillery Fire Orders. He would expand on the Rules and Systems of Counter Bombardment, the Silent Registration of Targets and the Adjustment of the mean Point of Impact. He had read and memorised the salient points of Ballistics and Ammunition.

Sergeant Major Hatcher had joined the army from Barnardo's and had done twenty-six years' straight service in the Royal Artillery. He was on loan from the Artillery Training School in Haifa. He taught the Officers and he taught the N.C.O.'s. He was master of his job.

It was a scorcher of an afternoon in midsummer and Hatcher was giving it to the Battery N.C.O.'s. We sat in the white fire of the sun on the hot sand in a semi circle outside the Battery Office, our white topees pulled down over our eyes. Sergeant Major Hatcher stood behind a table in the shade of the veranda.

'Now pay attention,' he said, 'and you might learn something.' He licked his cracked lips and sharply tapped his cane on the table.

'Guns, howitzers and mortars,' he said, 'all have the following properties: (a) They give projectiles specified initial velocity and direction of motion, and (b) they do so by the rapid burning of a propellant charge in a chamber, producing gas under pressure which forces the projectile to move along the barrel.' He rattled off without a pause.

'Each shell has a driving band. The driving band is made of copper and imparts spin to the projectile.'

'The shell is made to burst on impact by means of a percussion fuse, and the velocity of the projectile as it strikes the point of impact is known as the "striking velocity".'

Sergeant Major Hatcher had lectured to Field, Medium, Heavy and Anti Tank regiments, and junior subalterns had been intently heedful of his words before going on firing ranges, from Salisbury Plain to Hong Kong.

'The charge that you will ram in behind the projectile is made of cordite. Cordite is a "double base" propellant based on nitro cellulose and nitro glycerine. It usually consists of 65% nitro cellulose and 29% nitro glycerine.'

A clinging, panting lizard with rolling eyes, seemed glued to the Battery Office wall, which was drawing the sun's flame.

'Sir,' called out Philip Underwood.

'What is it, Bombardier?'

'65% and 29% doesn't make 100% sir. What is the remaining 6%?'

Hatcher's sun weathered face, like dried seaweed, stretched with tension as his thin lips hardened, and he said stonily, in a voice that drew blood with every word. 'Report to my office fifteen minutes before parade tomorrow morning and I'll tell you.' That shut the rest of us up for sure. Philip wasn't the first artful cleversides of a junior N.C.O. that had crossed his path, you can be sure of that.

'You will wish to know,' went on Sergeant Major Hatcher, 'about the fragmentation of high explosive shells. The best size of fragment for attack on men is found to be about $\frac{1}{20}$th of an ounce and you will also be interested to know that, with the modern shell, fragment velocities are in the region of three thousand feet per second.'

'I would imagine,' said Lance Bombardier Wilson, with his hand to his mouth, 'that a $\frac{1}{20}$th ounce fragment of steel, travelling at three thousand feet per second, would make quite a dent in your topee.'

* * * *

It was early September 1940 and the news from England was grim. German planes were unloading their bombs over England's ports and cities, and we heard of Londoners camping out in Epping Forest. A German attempt to invade England across the Channel was very much on the cards.

We were worried and disturbed that our homeland might be invaded and the thought of German soldiers on English soil preyed on our minds.

For the first time since leaving England, almost a year earlier, our G1098 (which is the official name given to the full scale of stores and equipment which should be held by an artillery regiment), was up to establishment. We were fully equipped with brand new guns and lorries, and there was a full complement of wireless sets and other signal equipment. The ammunition lorries and limbers were fully loaded, and everything pointed to an early move.

On the 4th September a Battery muster parade was called in the Regimental canteen. There was a lot of raking around of rumours as we sat on the forms and tables and on the floor. A matter of leading importance was obviously blowing in the wind. We were to be addressed by the Battery Commander, Major Coleman.

We were all brought to attention by the BSM as Major Coleman strode in followed by Lance Bombardier Wilson who was carrying a large rolled up map.

'Please sit down,' said Major Coleman.

Lance Bombadier Wilson unrolled the map and hung it on the wall behind the B.C. The map clearly showed the north coast of Egypt and Libya.

'Looks like a river trip down the Nile to inspect the dancing bints at Aswam and Luxor,' whispered Kevin.

Major Coleman banged the table with his cane.

'Pay attention,' he said.

We were hot with expectation and had the feeling that in this war we had been marking time. We were eager for new contingencies and new horizons.

'As you will know,' said Major Coleman, 'a few weeks ago the Italian army advanced into Egypt.' He pointed with his cane to the frontier between Egypt and Libya.

'Since then the Italian army has moved eastwards some eighty miles. The enemy have captured the village and sea resort of Sidi Barani.' He again pointed to the map.

'The Italians have now dug in along a line south of Sidi Barani and are now preparing for another assault into Egypt. The clear intention of the enemy is to capture the Suez Canal and ultimately to control the Middle East oilfields and the Persian Gulf. It is important that that should not be allowed to happen.'

'There are estimated to be three hundred thousand Italian troops deployed in Egypt and Libya but they should pose no problem.'

'Our own forward troops are defending a line and patrolling an area some fifty miles east of Sidi Barani between the Libyan Plateau in the south, and Mersa Matruh on the coast. In the course of the next few days the Regiment will be taking up positions close behind Mersa Matruh. The Regiment will be ready to move at 0700 hours on 6th September, that is in about thirty six hours from now. The journey will take four days, and route maps will be distributed.'

'Are there any questions?' There were no questions.

During the last few months, living under canvas and with plenty of exercise and work in the hot sun, we were brown and suntanned and fit. Everything pointed to our going to see some real action at last. We were fully trained and ready to be blooded, and for most of us it couldn't come too soon.

*   *   *   *

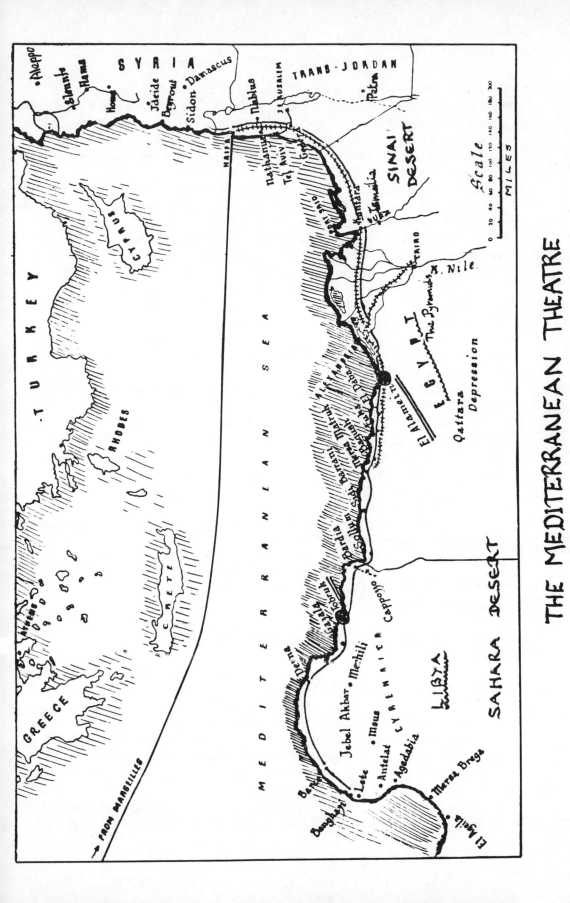

THE MEDITERRANEAN THEATRE

At crack of dawn on 6th September 1940, like a giant awakening, the leading trucks of the convoy pulled away from Ghedera Camp and slowly headed west onto the coast road of Palestine. They were followed by the guns with breech and muzzle covers securely fastened, the three tonners of B. Echelon carrying food, water, ammunition and stores, and the Light Aid Detachment with their mechanics and fitters.

All lorries and guns had been painted and camouflaged to blend with the desert sand. Twenty rounds of .303 rifle ammunition a man, and hard rations of bully beef and dry biscuits had been issued. Petrol tanks and water bottles were full, bedrolls had been loaded, tin hats were stowed and spare socks and shirts were packed. Shovels and sand channels were strapped to the quads. But with all the filling, packing, wadding and fixing, these were only trimmings and trappings compared to the heartcore of the Regiment – the guns, powerful, lethal and ready.

All day long, under the scorching sky, we drove south along the hot black ribbon of the tar sealed road towards Egypt.

The whole population of the Arab town of Gaza seemed to be lining the streets as our two mile long convoy rumbled through leaving the road to Beer Sheba to the left, and continuing on the coast road to El Arish. During the late evening the convoy pulled off the road to bivouac on the northern edge of the great Sinai Desert.

Some of the best moments of the war were when, after a long day's march, and after the day's work was done, we would lay out our groundsheets and blankets and lie down under the dark mantle of the star brindled sky. We would have a quiet smoke and talk.

'You know,' said Philip Underwood, 'Lawrence of Arabia operated round this area during the last war.'

'That's very interesting,' said Malcolm Burgess, smoothing out his ground sheet, 'but Lawrence is a very unusual name for an Arab.'

'He wasn't an Arab, stupid,' said Philip. 'He was an Englishman who was sent out here to work up the Arabs to fight the Turks.'

'That's right,' called across Bombardier Benson, the battery clerk who had settled down in the back of the 15 cwt. truck of the survey party, 'and they say that he could ride a camel for a week without getting saddle sore.'

'He used to operate from Aqaba,' said Philip, 'down below the Negev Desert where we went for our Divisional Scheme, and he would come up across the desert with bands of Bedouin Arabs and blow up bridges and wreck trains in Palestine.'

'Whose trains were they?' said Malcolm.

'Well Turkish trains, of course,' said Philip, 'they were full of Turkish troops.'

'I reckon those old Arabs were after something,' said Kevin.

'They certainly weren't farting about for nothing,' replied Philip, 'they were after loot. They used to blow up a railway line and shoot as many Turkish soldiers as they could and then they looted the train.'

'Did the Arabs have rifles then?' said Kevin.

'I'll say they did,' said Philip, 'but they also had two or three Lewis guns with them as well, and there would be one or two British N.C.O.'s to keep things on the move. Later on the Turks put a price of £15,000 on Lawrence's head, but the old Arabs didn't betray him.' Philip was a bit of a knowall but he had learned a lot of things at the Grammar that we didn't know, and there was no doubt that Philip was happy to be leading off and to have us listening.

'And you know who else came round this way?' said Philip.

'Who was that?' I asked.

Philip lit up another cigarette, lay back on his blankets and slowly inhaled the first deep draw of smoke.

'The Children of Israel,' he said.

'Oh yes,' I said, 'and what were the Children of Israel doing up here in this God forsaken spot?'

'You blind yourself to the Good Book,' said Philip. 'You should know, if you went to a Church of England school, that old Moses led the twelve tribes of Israel out of Egypt, across the Sinai Desert, to where we've just come from, and they had their tabernacle with them and all.'

'If you ask me,' called across Bombadier Benson, 'when they reached here they ought to have left their sheep and goats and their bloody tabernacle behind and kept on going east till they got to the Persian Gulf and all the sodding oil.'

As we settled down for the night in this Sinai outpost the moon rose above the desert skyline, and silhouetted against a reddening sky was a solitary palm tree and the outlines of the two sentries doing the early shift.

As I drifted off to sleep, I imagined I could smell my father's stables at home. The smell of the horses and the harness and the leather, and I had the odd feeling that I was looking down on my own body and saying from the backstreets of my mind 'Albert Kitchener Cooper, is this real? Can you really come to an understanding and comprehend that you are in the Sinai Desert and in this expanse of unlimited space and wilderness, thousands of miles from home?'

⋆   ⋆   ⋆   ⋆

The following morning saw our convoy stretching its length as it spanned this arid borderland strip, and crawling like a funeral procession of injured beetles towards the Suez Canal. As we set in towards the ferry crossing at Kantara with the morning sun behind us, a huge sluggish cargo ship appeared to move ponderously across the open desert. The ship's black shape towered high above the spreading flatness. Two funnels stood raw against the bright blue background like fat cigars reaching for the sky.

At Kantara, one by one the hot dusty guns and vehicles were carefully loaded on to the flat decked ferry and conveyed across the narrow waterway. After five tedious hours our military caravan had been safely transferred to the west bank of the Canal, and preparations were made to journey across the Land of the dead Pharaohs and the Land of King Farouk, that puffy devious Egyptian monarch who, reasoning that Hitler was winning the war, was becoming hostile to the British and to the British Empire.

Making course for thirty miles due south of Kantara, with the road running close to the Canal west bank, we drove into the staging camp near the bustling canal city of Ismalia, and the following morning we headed out into the vast Nile Delta.

From the burning glare of the whiteness of the Sinai, our sore eyes were rested on the lush green countryside and, by the late afternoon, a point had been reached nearly half way across the wide teeming Nile Delta to the north east of Cairo. On both sides of the road, in the tight patchwork of low lying fields in this rich fertile basin, the seething crops and vegetation was full of rich promise and steamy growth.

'They say,' said Harold Reeve, 'that they grow three crops a year here in this quaggy mud.'

'By the look of the crops,' said Kevin expanding his agricultural knowledge, 'if you stick a walking stick in, it would grow.'

Seated in the roadside eating houses of the grey mud brick villages, in their white robes and burnouses, were male dwellers of the Delta. These peasant farmers, all sons of Islam, smoked their hubble bubbles and drank their bitter coffee as loud Arab music blared forth. Nearby, their skinny tethered horses stood with lowered, unhappy heads and laid back ears.

Blindfolded ill used camels plodded mechanically, treading the tight circle of the creaking wooden cogged turntables that lifted the Nile water into the irrigation channels. Sheep and goat herdsmen were drawing up water in leather buckets, and sloshing it into long wooden troughs, while sad eyed donkeys, resigned to the throw of toil and burden, drag weighted and back loaded, were straining against the primitive wooden ploughs to the harsh shouts of the goading fellaheen.

Old worn out lorries, the drivers continuously leaning on the horn to thrust and warn the listless and drony peasants and animals off the road, dangerously overloaded with cotton, potatoes onions and sugar cane, were moving towards Cairo.

★   ★   ★   ★

Desert veterans will remember the army staging posts and transit camps from Palestine up to the western battlefields. Asluj, Kantara, Ismalia, Mena and Barhig where the road weary soldiery could stretch their stiff legs, where they could be fed and watered, and where they could spend the night.

The last of these staging posts was at Barhig, some twenty miles to the south west of Alexandria and, on the following day, in the bright coloured glow of the evening sunset, the long dusty column drew in to the Barhig stockade after fourteen tedious hours on the road. This would be our last opportunity to hear the gurgling bubble of running water for many months to come, and some good comrades, now in the prime of life, would never turn on a tap again.

In a few weeks time we were to be followed along this desert route by the men of the famous 6th Australian Division and two years later, along this same road, the men and the fighting vehicles of Montgomery's Eighth Army travelled up for the great battles of Alam Halfa and Alamein.

CHAPTER TWELVE

The Bagush Box and the First Blood

THE FOLLOWING DAY, a day of cracking sun and brittle heat, young men from Suffolk who, just over a year ago, had been farm men, factory workers, mechanics and engineers but were now fully trained for war, continued to progress westwards along the dusty featureless North African coastal road. Six of us were packed into the quad, and the sun beating down on the steel body and the waves of heat pushing into us from the noisy engine brought warm trickles of beaded sweat coursing slowly down our faces, necks, backs and arms, like small lost Cheviot lambs gingerly feeling their way down the mountainside.

Strict orders were given that one man from each vehicle should act as aircraft spotter, and keep a sharp lookout for enemy planes. The milometer on my quad, which had been set at zero as we pulled out of our camp in Palestine, now registered six hundred and fifty miles.

We had now moved into the war zone, and I was filled with a strange excitement. For mile after mile the black ribbon of road shimmered in the vivid sunlight, and the bright dazzling glare of the white sand seemed to have a hypnotic effect as it danced and pencilled in the lenses of my sand goggles.

We wended past the tiny settlement of El Alamein, which is the narrowest point between the sea and the great Qatara Depression, that strange vast basin of soft sand and salt marshes. Here it was, two years later, that the mighty and frenzied battle of Alamein was savagely fought and won, a place where two great armies were locked in battle and where thousands were to die in this desert waste.

Like a buzzard to the lure, the regiment was drawing near to its destination in the fortified area known as The Bagush Box, and during the hottest hours of the afternoon the vehicles and guns were diverted to the dry flat desert to the north of the road.

The date was the 10th September 1940.

Ahead of us the GPO and his ack were knocking markers into the dry earth to indicate the position of each gun and, as we approached, the GPO pointed with fully stretched arm the direction of the zero line.

Harold Reeve and the other gun sergeants leapt out of their moving vehicles and ran to their markers, indicating to the quad drivers where they were to drop the gun. Harold Reeve stood by the marker with his arm raised above his head, and when the gun was on its marker he sharply snapped his arm down to his side and I jammed on the quad brakes. Before the quad had come to a complete halt the gun crew had flung open the doors and leaped out and were quickly manhandling the gun and limber into position.

71

The four troop guns were laid on their zero lines, heavy boxes of stores and ammunition were quickly unloaded and, within three minutes the lorries had been sent back to the wagon lines, some two hundred yards behind the guns. The O.P.'s were set up and the signallers ran out their lines to the troop positions and through to Battery Headquarters and to Regimental H.Q.

The occupation of this, our first Battery gunsite in an active war zone, was carried through with no more fuss than if we had been on an exercise in Alton Park, near Ipswich, the residence and estate of our Commanding Officer, Lieutenant Colonel Buchannan-Spooner.

The Bagush Box was a barren desolate area and no mistake. Not even a drought wizened tree or a piece of camel scrub grew. If we were destined to live here on this flat open stretch of sand we should be like top rabbits with no place to hide from the lurcher.

The wind whisked and scurried like fighting birds and the sky was the colour of woodsmoke. The blustering flurries of sand beat against the guns and the lorry windscreens. In spite of the wind, flies were everywhere, clinging to our faces and our shirtless bodies. The water in our bottles was warm and tasted like rusty metal. There was no sound of gunfire or bombing, just the whining of the desert wind.

In the powdery sandstorm, breathing became more difficult and we tied rags, handkerchiefs and scarves round our faces. We should have been glad of an Arab shawl.

The cooks made some tea, and the whirling sand cascaded into the open dixies.

Lieutenant Kershaw informed us that the enemy was many miles away and we wouldn't be brought into action unless the Italian Army, which had already advanced some sixty miles into Egypt from the Libyan frontier, attacked and endeavoured to bypass the first of the three fortified boxes at Mersa Matruh.

Our own Bagush Box was six square miles in area with the sea as its northern boundary, and a high escarpment to the south. The Brigade of infantry manning the Bagush perimeter consisted of three famous regular regiments, the 2nd Queens Regiment, the 2nd Leicesters and the 1st Argyle and Sutherland Highlanders.

To the south, between the road and the distant escarpment, lying low in the dry wadis, were the tanks, armoured cars and guns of the British 7th Armoured Division.

*   *   *   *

On that blistering afternoon the orders were for every man jack that could be spared should dig gun pits and slit trenches. Digging gun pits three or four feet deep is hard work. A bulldozer would have been handy I can tell you. Several tons of soil and sand had to be moved and sandbags, which were filled and tied, were neatly built up round the rim. Kevin, who was filling sandbags, said 'If anyone says again that it's better to lose sweat than blood I'll crown him with my fugging shovel.'

Siggy Buckenham was lifting the filled sandbags up on to the gunpit rim, and Philip was building them neatly round the top. 'See you lay them two headers and a stretcher Philip,' said Siggy.

'Get knotted,' rejoined Philip.

'Want another hod of mortar, Philip?' called Kevin.

'If you've got Portland cement, hydrated lime and clean sand,' said Philip.

'Sorry, Philip,' said Kevin, who was holding out a sandbag for Malcolm to fill, 'I'm two ingredients short, but I've got plenty of sand.'

'Joking apart, let me tell you that rubbish wouldn't be accepted for the beach by the Southend-on-Sea Borough Council,' said Philip, 'let alone by a first class building site like this.'

There was plenty of moaning going on one way and another but soldiers are supposed to have what Mrs. Buchannan-Spooner called 'a special brand of humour'. I must say that although the sweat was pouring off us we had a laugh or two.

By midnight the guns were all dug in and the large sacking and net camouflage covers were pulled over the whole of the gunpit. The wind had dropped and cocoa came round. We laid our groundsheets and blankets round the gunpit. There was no water for a wash.

'You know what I'd like now?' said Siggy.

'A nice feather bed,' suggested Kevin, undoing his bedroll.

'No,' said Siggy, 'an onion sandwich.'

'An onion sandwich?' said Kevin.

'Yes,' said Siggy, 'a nice chopped onion sandwich with olive oil, vinegar and brown sugar.'

'You know what you'll get?' said Philip, untying his boot laces.

'What's that?' enquired Siggy.

'A soldier's supper,' said Philip.

'And what might that be?' said Siggy.

'A piss and a turn in,' said Philip.

'I've just had the first course,' declared Siggy.

Philip lit a cigarette under his blanket, and then he said, 'I wonder what that Itie plane was doing buggering about over here this afternoon.'

Philip was referring to a C.R.42 Italian reconnaissance plane that had flown lazily over our positions at a very great height. It was well out of Bofors range and the little silver plane looked harmless enough glinting in the sun, and after it drifted over us it turned north and flew out to sea.

'It was probably just having a shufti and taking a few photographs,' said Harold Reeve.

It was a dark and moonless night and we had just got off to sleep when we were awakened by the loud unmistakable irregular drone of a diesel engined Italian war plane. It was approaching from the north west, and we heard it circle round twice in the darkness and then it came in to fly right across the Brigade area.

We waited for a stick of bombs, but there was nothing.

Kevin said, 'You awake, Albert?'

'Yes,' I said.

'Hear those plops just now?'

'Sounded like cow pats delivered from a great height,' I said.

'Can't have been bombs,' said Kevin, 'otherwise they'd have gone off.' We were so tired that we turned over and sunk into an uneasy slumber.

In the early morning, just before first light, Siggy Buckenham announced that he was going to see a man about a dog. He pulled on his boots and scrambled out of his blankets, and staggered off into the dimness of the half shadow away from where Number One subsection was sleeping beside the gun.

We were all half awake as Darkie Maclure and Roderick Lee, who were both on sentry duty, had given us a shake and said that 'Stand to' would be in ten minutes. 'Stand to' was a ritual throughout the Desert Campaign. At first light everyone was expected to be fully alert with rifles ready at hand, and the breech and muzzle covers were taken off the guns. Dawn was reckoned to be a favourite time for an enemy attack.

It was a chilly morning and the thought of having to get out of bed and to stand about in the cold semi darkness made what Kevin called 'the blankets hang'.

Suddenly there was a loud explosion, followed by the sizzling hiss of airborne metal.

'Christ, what was that?' said Philip Underwood.

Darkie Maclure shouted,' Anyone know First Aid?' With that, Harold Reeve leaped out of his blankets and grabbed his haversack which contained the field dressings and the First Aid box and, without waiting to pull on his boots, he rushed out into the half light and shouted, 'Albert and Philip follow me, Malcolm go and get Mr. Kershaw, and Kevin get the Duty Signaller at the Command Post to raise the M.O.'

Siggy was lying in a crumpled heap some thirty yards from the gunpit. He could well have been a pile of deranged and lacerated old clothes, he was quietly moaning when Harold, Philip and I reached him.

'I've had it,' said Siggy in a muffled whisper, which was only just audible.

'No you haven't,' said Harold. 'We'll soon patch you up.'

'My leg hurts like hell,' murmured Siggy. As he spoke he sank into the soft cushion of unconsciousness.

Although the full light of dawn was still on its way, we could already see how badly Siggy had been wounded. A steady stream of blood was running down his leg. Siggy's right arm had been completely blow off and his right eye was a mass of blood.

Harold Reeve steadied us all. No panic at all.

'Albert,' he said quietly, 'hold one of these field dressings on his eye, and Philip press this towelling firmly on the leg wound, while I put a tourniquet on his arm.'

Harold, who in civilian life was foreman of a gang of steel erectors and was used to giving orders, was as unruffled as if he had been putting a plumbline to a stanchion on a half built general purpose farm building in Suffolk. We all considered that Harold should have been Regimental Sergeant Major, and Philip had always maintained that if he had been to a public school and had the grammar, he would have been a full Colonel.

Lieutenant Kershaw came across and said, 'Well done Sergeant Reeve, the M.O. and the field ambulance will be here shortly. What happened?

'I don't know, sir,' said Harold, 'but it looks very much as if Gunner Buckenham picked up something and it exploded.'

'Could be something to do with those plops we heard during the night when that plane flew over,' said Philip.

'You are probably right,' said Lieutenant Kershaw, 'they may have been dropping grenades, but Buckenham has seen grenades before and I wouldn't have expected him to pick one up.'

The M.O. arrived with an overcoat over his pyjamas and pumped a syringe of morphine into Siggy's arm. I was still trying to talk to Siggy but there was no response and his face and skin had gone as pale as ashes.

The morning sun streamed out in bright splendour as the 'blood wagon' appeared from the direction of the road. Two orderlies carefully lifted the unconscious Siggy on to a stretcher and he was driven away to base hospital, and away from the war, and away from the still waters of fear.

'What do you think?' enquired Lieutenant Kershaw of the M.O. when the ambulance had gone.

'I should think he has a fifty fifty chance of surviving but, at best, he will lose an eye and the lower part of his forearm, and there is a probability that the leg will have to come off.'

Suddenly, yesterday, when Siggy was filling sandbags and wishing he could have an onion sandwich, seemed a very long while ago, and the whole dark catastrophe seemed trapped in measureless time.

'Whose his next of kin?' asked Lieutenant Kershaw.

'His mother sir,' said Harold Reeve. 'His father died six weeks before we left England and, as he was the only son he was given two weeks compassionate leave, but he rejoined the Regiment. He was very keen to come abroad with us.'

'Bloody hell,' said Lieutenant Kershaw.

At that moment Ken Buroughs, a bombardier on Number Two gun, came running up and said, 'There is a strange looking object lying on the ground about forty yards in front of our gun sir. It looks like a thermos flask.'

'Right, stay here while I go and have a look at it,' said Lieutenant Kershaw.

We watched him walk up to the object and kneel down to examine it. He then quickly returned to the guns and said, 'Sergeant Major, see that no one is allowed within eighty yards of that thing out there. It is almost certainly a bomb. It looks exactly like a thermos flask, but I can't hear it ticking. I think it may blow up if it is moved.'

'The bastards,' said Ken Burroughs.

Malcolm Burgess said, 'These Ities will do anything rather than fight,' and Peter Wilson said, 'I thought that Italy was supposed to be a civilised country.'

A quick search was made of the area and three more bombs were found, two disguised as thermos flasks and one as a fountain pen. Although the fountain pen bomb was smaller than the others, it contained enough explosive to blow off a hand or to blind you for life. All were set to explode if moved.

The Royal Engineers soon dealt with the bombs by two men dragging an iron bar over them with very long ropes, but we were sick at Siggy's terrible wounds.

It was 11th September, and Siggy was our first battle casualty, and as Philip and I were washing Siggy's blood from our hands Harold Reeve came up to us and said, 'Well done lads, I've got a little nip of rum for you over on the gun position.'

Philip said, 'You know Albert, Siggy's blood felt really hot.'

*   *   *   *

Letters and parcels for the Middle East Forces had been arriving fairly regularly when we were first stationed at Ghedera in Palestine. When Italy came into the war the deliveries of both airmail and sea mail dried up completely. Imperial Airways and the Dutch airline KLM, who had previously brought our welcome morale boosting airmail letters, seemed to have been grounded. No letters or parcels had arrived for nearly twelve weeks. The war news was that the German bombing assault on the U.K. was as frenzied as ever, and we were worried about the lack of direct news from home.

The day after Siggy's accident Bombardier Benson, the Battery Clerk, drove up to the Troop Command Post in his eight hundredweight truck, climbed out of the door and shouted 'Mail up.' We ran from the guns over to the mail truck and gathered like starving famine stricken victims round a mission truck with a consigmment of Gumbo.

'I reckon,' said Vincent Parsons, 'that this little lot has come round the Cape.'

'It stands to reason,' said Lance Bombardier Wilson, keeping a keen ear open for his name to be called, 'there's bugger all coming through the Med.'

Julie wrote four pages every week, and Mum wrote once a fortnight, so there were nearly twenty letters for me, including one from my dear old Dad.

There were four letters addressed to Siggy from his widowed mother, who would still be unaware that her only son's short life was hanging in the balance. If Siggy lived, and the telegram that would eventually be sent spoke of wounds, there was no way that she could speak to his surgeon or his nurses. From far away in the hamlet of Kersey, the prettiest village in rural Suffolk, she would be floating on a sea of bewilderment and uncertainty.

Julie wrote in one of her letters that she had left Joslins, the chemists in Middlesham, and had been directed into an aircraft factory in Ipswich. Julie said that she had been trained to operate a lathe and she thought that she was turning out parts for Hurricane fighters. She described the part she was making as a 'sort of cranky bit' but she didn't know what it was for! That gave me a laugh that did, with Julie making a cranky bit for an aeroplane and not knowing what it was for!

Julie's last letter, written in her small neat handwriting, said;

'My dear darling Albert,
     You have now been away for nearly one long year. I am terribly lonely without you and my heart aches and aches. I wept buckets when you left, but Mum said that I was to pull myself together and that you would soon be safely home.
     Nearly everyone I meet asks me how you are, and I have to tell them

that I haven't heard from you for eight weeks and that we haven't heard from Kevin either. Are you and Kevin still on the same gun? I cycle over to see your mother and father whenever I can to see if they have any news of you.

You father really spoils me and last Sunday he took me over to the stables to see his horses. We hadn't got any sugar lumps to spare for them so we took them some windfalls and a few crusts of bread, as bread isn't on the ration.

Watchman is lovely, but he is getting a lot of grey hairs in his black coat, but Prince looks as young as ever and his coat is glossy and shines like polished ebony. I shouldn't think that any two horses are better looked after.

The war is not going too well here, what with the fall of France and Dunkirk and now the bombing, but Winston Churchill is keeping our spirits up and says that the tide will turn.

Dad is doing well on his smallholding. He got permission from the War Agricultural Executive Committee to grow an acre of canary seed. You won't believe this, but the seed came to a thousand pounds. They say that Jack Pitwood, who farms three hundred acres near Needham Market, applied for permission to grow canary seed and was turned down, so Jack thought he'd be clever and sowed two acres to canary seed in the middle of a forty acre field of wheat. As the wheat is taller than the canary seed, and the canary seed is harvested first, he thought he'd be all right. So he would have been if we hadn't had the grandfather of a thunder storm, followed by an inch and a half of rain in just over half an hour, which flattened the wheat and left the canary seed standing as proud as you like in the middle. It could all be seen from the main road and, although Jack Pitwood put the disc harrows in sharpish to rip it up, someone from the Ministry of Agriculture had seen it and Jack was fined five hundred pounds, so that will teach him a lesson.'

I read Julie's letters over and over again.

According Jim Spragg, our waggon line officer Second Lieutenant the Honorable Charles Hester-Hewitt, received a letter from his mother, Lady Honor Hester-Hewitt,

'Circumstances are irksome and one is beset with unending problems and difficulties.

Wilkins has just been called up and Corker has gone to munitions, which leaves us with just one gardener. It is very trying and for the last two days I have been watering, weeding and dead heading for most of the afternoon.

The Rolls has been put away in the coach house for the duration as there is no petrol. The little man from the garage has placed wooden blocks under the axles. He says it will save the tyres. He has also drained the radiator and removed the batteries. He has charged me a pound for less than two hours work, which is exorbitant.

Your father was offered a hush hush job in the War Office by Bugsey Palethorpe. They were at Eton together and Bugsey is now a Brigadier in Supply. Your father has the use of a staff car, together with an ATS driver. She is such a pretty girl and she is frightfully helpful with the shopping.

We must all do our bit and I have organized a knitting circle for comforts for the troops, and I do Red Cross every Thursday afternoon, so there is a great deal to interest one.

Your cousin Melissa, who is now quite a beautiful girl, has told me that she won't become engaged to Rupert Finwallis. Rupert's mother is a striking woman but unfortunately, his father is a Liberal M.P. and Rupert is rather dull, but I have told Melissa not to be a goose, as Rupert is the eldest son he will come into the Cumberhill Park Estate and the Hall has over thirty rooms and is quite beautiful.

The Churchyard, which Wilkins used to keep tidy for nothing, in his spare time, is absolutely frightful and is a tangle of high grass, ragwort and thistles.

The Rural Dean attended our last Parochial Church Council. He's such a nice man and I have signed covenants for the Distressed Gentlefolks and for The Sons of The Clergy.

Last Sunday in church the rector prayed for your safe return. I understand that your men adore you.

Your affectionate,

Mother.'

The gun sergeant on number three gun was Don White. When war was declared Don was driving a ten ton Foden lorry for a firm of corn and seed merchants in Wickham Market. Most of his time was spent in collecting loads of sacked corn from the farmers' grain stores and delivering milling wheat to the flour mills in Bury, plus high grade barley to the various Norfolk and Suffolk maltings.

Most of his loads were in sacks weighing eighteen stone, and he would think nothing of taking every sack of his ten ton load off an elevator and carrying it across his back to build his load in the back of his lorry. It is not surprising, therefore, that Don, whose dark curly hair was tinged with grey, had a tremendous pair of shoulders on him and he was possessed of enormous muscular strength.

Sergeant Donald White received a letter from his wife Alice.

'Dear Don' she wrote,

'I am sorry to have to tell you this, but I have been seeing a lot of Jack Budd lately and, as you know, Gwen walked out on him last year. I have now moved in with Jack, and the children are very fond of him.'

Clutching the open letter in his hand, and with his broad shoulders shaking with rage and grief, Don White's strong suntanned face turned ashen with bitterness and disbelief. His eyes were blazing and his knuckles shone white. He slumped on to an empty ammunition box and, with clenched teeth, he muttered over and over again, 'I'll break his neck, I'll kill the bastard.' He pulled an empty sandbag towards him and spread it over his knees and proceeded to tear the letter slowly and deliberately into tiny pieces. Carefully, like a stalking cat in slow time, he gathered together the shredded pieces of paper and held them in his open hands while he spat on them. He then rolled them round with the spittle into a tight ball. Jumping to his feet he hurled the wet ball of paper, with all his might, into the ground in front of his feet and slowly ground the odious, hated pellet into the sandy earth with the heel of his boot. He was tense and drawn and the tears were streaming down his face.

*   *   *   *

The Colonel received a letter from his father-in-law, Lieutenant General Beresford-Drake, K.C.B., C.B.E., D.S.O., D.L., who, although in his seventies, was a Home Guard Divisional Commander.

'We read in the press of the great exploits of the Western Desert Force and we understand you have been in action. It is our earnest hope that you will soon hit the wops for six right out of North Africa.

Dunkirk was a bit of a setback, but our morale at home is sky high. Your brother Jeremy is trying, with considerable success I may say, to keep the pack going and they are managing to hunt two days a week. You will be interested to know that the pack is now known as a fox control unit. This helps in all sorts of ways and enables the authorities to make us an allocation of meal to feed the hounds. However, the farmers are being very good and continue to send in the odd casualty. Last week a dairy farmer from the Tuddenham area let us have a three year old Friesian which had got on its back in a ditch. There's no earth stopping, of course, and the poultry fund stands at just over £200. Although the number of hounds has been reduced to nineteen couples, they have had some capital days sport and last Wednesday they made a point of two and half miles and then killed in the open.

Some of the chaps come out from the camp and we find them horses. The adjutant has been out four times. He was complaining the other day of lack of scent. It was a dull misty morning and Jeremy told him that there is always scent when the hedges stand out black and clear, but if there is a blue haze you might as well go home.

Jeremy was telling me last week that they had a sailor out. He was Commander of a corvette which was berthed at Harwich. As you know, we always reckon that the Navy doesn't know one end of a horse from the other but this fellow apparently took a very good line and on one occasion they found in Bealings Wood and ran Charley along by the railway up to Henry Batchelor's Christmas Tree covert straight up to the spinney at

Norton Manor and into Fred Partridges' kale. Charley was flushed out of there and they lost him when he doubled back by the river. Jeremy says that they went a fast gallop for twenty five minutes and that only the huntsmen and this sailor chap were up with hounds.

Your mother and I are walking two puppies this year. So you see we are not letting Hitler get us down.'

CHAPTER THIRTEEN
Toughening of the Sinews

THE DAYS AND weeks in the hot dusty enclave of sand and rock in the Bagush Box passed wearily and uncomfortably by. Without being aware of the change, we weren't tender any longer and our bodies had toughened up like a knead of clay hardening in the dry.

Not a man in the regiment escaped the rack of dysentery, and few were spared the painful desert sores on our arms, legs and bodies. Every small cut or abrasion turned septic. Small spots became a rotting suppurating canker, infested and polluted, and harrassed by tenacious flies.

We accepted and tolerated the sandstorms which forced and drove and swelled, two or three days every week, like a wild rudderless stampede. Occasionally the choking dust storms would last for three whole days. However, steadily everyone was becoming hardened to living in the desert. We were like animals of burden gradually being loaded with more and more. It is true that we chafed and grumbled at our unpleasant, hapless circumstances, and we cursed the desert and the army and 'they'. 'They' who couldn't organize a tea party, 'they' who had forgotten that we were up in the desert, 'they' who didn't know their arses from their elbows.

But we were brown and suntanned and, after the gnawing twinges of dysentery had passed and the irritating puss ridden desert ulcers had cleared up, most of us felt fit and ready, and were impatient for action.

*　　*　　*　　*

It was early November and the teeming crowding swarms of summer flies were thinning out although many, resolute to live and molest, dug and clung and hovered like hissing malevolent pigmy engines. It was announced that the Regiment was to have an intake of twenty reinforcements. They arrived at RHQ in the back of a three tonner. They had been called up with the second draft of the Militia and had been trained at Oswestry, and had suffered a long and tedious sea voyage round the Cape. They were freshly shaved and dressed in newly laundered kit with blancoed webbing. Their skins were pale and they looked apprehensive and somewhat bewildered at our harsh and unsavoury living conditions and at our uncouth, sun beaten and weather hardened gunners.

Two members of the new draft were allocated to A troop. They were Gunners

Ernie and Charlie Briggs, two brothers from Bethnal Green who had asked to be posted to the same unit so they could stay together. They had both been trained at Oswestry as artillery signalmen.

In civilian life the two brothers had assisted their father on his shellfish stall at Billingsgate and, according to Charlie, they drew a lot of their supplies from the cockle sheds of Southend-on-Sea and Leigh. Charlie also told us that his father wore a bowler hat and a knotted scarf on Sundays and could carry 12 stone of fish on his head. Charlie said that they would often get up at three in the morning and walk the two miles to Billingsgate. 'Where's Billingsgate?' asked Malcolm Burgess. 'On the River a foo yards from Lunnon Bridge and abart 'arf a mile from the Tar of Lunnon,' said Charlie.

The brothers Briggs in fact were two London cockneys like you read about in the 'Daily Mail' after an air raid. They were cheerful and good hearted, and had plenty to say about things in general. Ernie and Charlie had plenty to say about football. They were both rabid Arsenal fans and they wouldn't hear a knocking word against the Arsenal Club or against any member of the team that wore the red and white jersey.

'One fing abart the Ars'nil plyers,' said Charlie, one day as he sat on the bonnet of the signal truck cleaning his nails with a pen knife, 'they're all real gentlemen, they're the cleanest sarde in football and, if you wanna see the best team in the World, just trot along to the Manor Grarnd at 'Ighbury, the best bit o' turf in Norf Lunnon.'

It so happened that among the new draft was a worried looking ginger haired lad from the Stoke potteries called Willie Oxendale. Willie said, 'I grant you that the Arsenal are a good team, but they haven't got any player there to touch Stanley Matthews.'

'One man doesn't mike a team,' said Charlie.

'No,' said Willie, 'but one man can win matches. Stanley is the best ball player in the World and he will make a goal from nothing. I once saw Stanley beat three men down the wing and he then lifted the ball across from near the corner flag and laid it 'on the head of the centre forward, who only had to nod it in. I also saw Stanley, when we were playing Preston North End at home, do a double body swerve, and the Preston right half fell over backwards and he hadn't even touched the ball. Talk about laugh.'

'But look at the number of Internationals we've got at Arsnil,' said Ernie, 'Moss, Male, Hapgood, Copping, Drake and Cliff Bastin. Christ, wot a team, wot a line up.'

'An' you've forgotten Alex James,' said Charlie.

'No I 'avent,' said Ernie, 'you can't forget the best centre 'arf in England.'

'All I can remember about Alex James,' said Philip, 'is that his shorts came half way down to his ankles.'

'Do you know,' went on Ernie Briggs, 'in 1934 my farver took me an' Charlie to 'Ighbury to watch England ply Itily and, you'd never believe it, there were seven plyers from the Gunners in the England team. I was nearly firteen at the time and Charlie was fourteen. I remember that because it was Charlie's birfday and Dad took me an' 'im to 'Ighbury for Charlie's birfday treat, and afterwards we had fish 'n chips. We done it proper.'

'Yes, I remember,' said Charlie, 'because when we got back we got a bollockin' from Mum.'

'Cor, wot a match,' said Ernie.

'Fifty farsand people,' said Charlie.

'An' anuvver fing,' went on Ernie, 'that bastard of a crackpot Mussolini had promised before the match that, if Itily won, the plyers would be exempt from military service.'

'So I expect some of that bastard team are over there,' said Charlie, waving his hand in the direction of Mersa Matruh, 'because England won 3-2. Christ, I wish I was at 'Ighbury now instead of this muckheap of a desert wiv no pictures, no fish 'n chips and no boozers.'

'Bloody hell,' said Philip, 'you want to get some service in, you haven't been out here five minutes. You want to get your sodding knees brown. We've been away from England for twelve months. It's like doing bloody time.'

★   ★   ★   ★

Throughout the month of November the silvery high flying Italian reconnaissance planes continued to fly over the Bagush Box. The only exceptions were when the sandstorms were at their zenith and vast clouds of fine dust like heavy yellow smoke were syphoned into the higher altitudes on the warm rising currents of air.

Occasionally, a lone enemy bomber, keeping safely out of range of the light ack ack, would drop a stick of bombs or booby traps in the area. Little damage was done.

At least once a week the Regiment took part in exercises with units of the 7th Armoured Division. These large scale troop movements took place in the area between the sea and the vast Libyan Plateau to the south. On two occasions the regiment moved along the edge of the great cliffs to the north of the Qatara Depression, that vast flat sea of sand and salt marshes, and we were able to gaze over the hundreds of square miles of treacherous quick sands which stretched endlessly to the distant horizon.

The 7th Armoured Division was a desert-trained armoured group with the fast, lightly armoured Crusader, Valentine and Honey tanks, a regiment of armoured cars and three regiments of artillery. Their divisional sign, which was painted on all their vehicles was the long tailed kangaroo desert rat.

We were training to go for long periods without water. From the time the exercise started in the early morning until late evening, water bottles were securely imprisoned in the quad lockers. Returning from these divisional training schemes to our own defensive box saw many vehicle radiators boiling and everyone tormented by lack of water, covered in thick layers of soft powdery brown dust.

Guns were taken out on to the firing ranges for calibration, but not a shot had we fired in anger. We were beginning to fear that the war would be over before we did any fighting.

News filtered through from base hospital that Siggy Buckenham, who had been wounded by the thermos flask bomb, had survived five operations and was now convalescing in Palestine. The surgeons had removed a leg and an arm, and Siggy had lost the sight of his right eye.

'Poor Siggy,' said Kevin, when we heard the news, 'I expect that, after due consideration, Siggy will be awarded what they call a 100% disability pension.'

'No amount of money can compensate for being messed up like that,' said Philip.

'Bloody hell,' said Kevin, 'Siggy should have stayed at home with his poor old widowed mother.'

Our bodies had changed and matured and strengthened under the pain and the discomfort of hard living. There was compression on our arteries like a tanner spent bark being pressed for fuel. The surplus fat had long since gone and the outer layers of softness had been peeled off. We were stiffening in the sinew. Our determination could remain firm for longer under unaccustomed forces. We were hardening and braced against stress. We became furnished with endurance.

During the last few days of November and the first week in December there was a considerable increase in the military activity in the desert. Scores of lumbering sand camouflaged three tonner transports crept into the forward areas, heavy with ammunition, petrol and other supplies. Two busy groups of newly arrived light tanks kicked up clouds of dust to the south of the coast road.

Suddenly, all leave was cancelled.

★   ★   ★   ★

Just before dawn on the morning of 9th December, as we lay in the well of our gun pits, a low continuous distant rumble could be heard to the west.

'Sounds like a big air raid somewhere,' said Kevin.

'That's not an air raid,' said Harold Reeve, 'that's an artillery barrage.'

'Theirs or Ours?' ventured Kevin.

'Let's hope it's ours,' said Harold.

As we flung off our dusty sand covered blankets, and reached for our boots and rifles for the dawn 'stand to', we didn't fully realise that the long Desert War, which was to be stained on our memories for the rest of our lives, had begun.

That memorable December morning the desert worthy British Seventh Armoured Division, with its tanks, armoured cars and guns, had advanced forty miles westwards and had surrounded the Italian stronghold of Sidi Barani, cut off the line of retreat and had taken prisoner thousands of Italian soldiers.

The surprise British attack was the result of a bold plan by General O'Connor and over the next forty-eight hours victory was complete and all the strong points around Sidi Barani were in British hands. The news was that the victorious army was continuing to move westwards and advancing on the Libyan frontier.

On the afternoon of the Sidi Barani attack the West Suffolk Yeomanry, moulded into shape and hewn for battle, received orders from G.H.Q. to proceed with its full complement of guns to a rendezvous a few thousand yards south east of an Italian stronghold of which we had hardly heard, called Bardia.

The Bardia bastion lay some five hundred and fifty miles into the Western Desert from Cairo and is situated on the Libyan coast a few miles over the Egyptian-Libyan frontier. Bardia was an Italian fortress heavily defended by thirty five thousand blackshirt troops armed to the teeth with modern weapons.

All vehicles were checked and loaded and, as a precaution against giving away our positions in the desert, all vehicle windows and windscreens were covered with oil and sand so that the glass would not reflect in the dazzling glint of the desert sun. Narrow slits were cleared in the windscreens for the drivers.

The next morning our long convoy, with vehicles keeping a distance of one hundred and fifty yards apart in case of air attack, journeyed further and further westwards. A thrill of tingling excitement ran through our bones. There was always that faint chance that a sudden attack by Italian fighter planes could at any time rip into us with machine gun and cannon fire.

During the afternoon we came suddenly and unexpectedly upon the scene and carnage of the battle of Sidi Barani. This was the first time our eyes had witnessed the havoc of battle and, in spite of long and extensive training for war, we were caught by surprise and were unprepared for the devastation and for the harsh, crude scenes of violent death. Every house and shack had been levelled to swathing piles of smouldering rubble. Smashed and overturned lorries, scarred from shot and shell, littered the vast battle area. Hundreds of discarded rifles, stacks of live shells and charges and unopened boxes of grenades lay scattered around like the confetti of an arms breaker's yard. The whole area was deeply pock marked with blackened shell craters, like scooped out gourds for giant metal forged poached eggs.

Many Italian soldiers lay dead in contorted shapes, faces to the sky, or in obscene green bundles grouped around their trenches and weapon pits. Two grim faced British burial parties, assisted by Italian prisoners, were carrying out the gruesome business of loading the dead on to trucks for burial.

Harold Reeve said, 'A farmer once told me that you never see a dead donkey, but just look over there.'

By the corner of a demolished mud walled shack lay the swollen carcasses of two fly covered dead donkeys. Already they were bloated with putrefaction, and one of them had passed a huge dollop of dung as it died, and it lay swag bellied in the stink and dross of its self made midden.

A solitary Italian steamroller was neatly parked by the side of the dusty track. It appeared to be in good condition and untouched by the battle. We had always been given to understand that the Italians were experts at road making, and we could imagine that this yellow painted steamroller had seen commendable service in the Fatherland before being requisitioned for the fascist Army in North Africa.

'Christ alive,' shouted Kevin, pointing to the left of the road, 'look at that fugging gun position.'

In a shallow wadi, not forty yards from the road, was the shattering sight of a troop of four wrecked Italian 105 m.m. guns which had been overrun and destroyed by British tanks and artillery. Here was the demolished residue of an enemy fighting force. At least a dozen gunners had died at their posts, riddled with bullets, mangled and mutilated by the shrapnel. Some of the dead gunners were sprawled over their guns, and others lay in grotesque positions in their agony of death on the edge of the gun site. They had been slaughtered as they fought for that bloated Dictator, Mussolini, and his fascist Blackshirts. Here on the battlefield of Sidi Barani, with its uneasy smell of war and death, lay the tattered candle ends of total destruction.

Philip, who was nineteen, said 'Half of them don't look more than school kids.'

'Don't start feeling sorry for them Philip', said Harold, 'you aren't exactly ready to draw the old age pension yourself.'

'If we get on a gunsite and get shot up like those poor sods,' said Philip, 'we won't get an old age pension at all.'

★   ★   ★   ★

Soon after nightfall the weary drivers, wrenching on a fistful of levers, stuck their gear shifts in bottom and, with no headlights and masked side lights, cautiously nursed their vehicles round the dangerous hairpin bends of the steep rock face of the escarpment of Halfaya Pass (known throughout the Western Desert Force as 'Hellfire Pass').

Halfaya Pass was the tenuous connecting road link from the Egyptian coastal town of Solum up to the Libyan Plateau and, after an hour's tortuous climb up into the unknown darkness, the regiment found that it had hoisted itself into hostile country. We were now in Libya and within range of the enemy's guns.

After three more uncomfortable cheerless hours of slothful sustained night driving, the drivers, who had been fixedly concentrating on following the small pin point of the single rearlight of the vehicle in front, were directed on to the gun positions which had been reconnoitred and surveyed earlier on in the day. Our position, that night in the black unfriendly Libyan Desert, was on the perimeter of the Bardia fortress some ten miles west of the old Italian strongpoint of Fort Capuzzo.

Masked torches guided us to the gun positions. There was no shouting, no revving of engines, and a minimum of low voiced instructions, and it was past midnight before the guns had been set up on their zero lines.

The night seemed strangely quiet. A British plane was dropping flares over in the direction of the Bardia harbour and a couple of green Very lights were fired from a pistol some five hundred yards to the north.

We pulled out our groundsheets and blankets and settled down for the night. Lying there beside the guns, in a patch of barren desert two thousand miles from home, there was a feeling of intense relief that we were going to see some action at last.

★   ★   ★   ★

Gunner Roland Sandford-Smith was the driver of the troop cookhouse truck. They say some people are accident prone, but Roly Sandford-Smith was untidy prone and he sometimes looked like a maukin that had scrambled out of bed backwards. He had an ample backside and big feet, and he wore outsize boots which were known as 'Roly's dewbeaters'. Battery Sergeant Major Watts, who had been a regular soldier, didn't like gunners who were fat and untidy. Neither did the B.S.M. like soldiers in the ranks with double barrelled names like Sandford-Smith, so he called him 'Smiff'.

Roly relished his provender and certainly carried too much belly timber, but he had a heart of gold and when his mother sent him parcels, he shared out everything. Roly wore horned rimmed glasses and looked like an owlish jellyfish. He wasn't stupid, he just looked that way.

Roly's grandfather was Jack Smith, who owned a drapery store in Sudbury. Jack Smith married Doris Sandford, who was a pushy opinionated schoolteacher from Castle Heddingham. Doris was high souled, purse proud and gave herself airs, and reckoned she was on a shade higher social scale than Jack Smith. When their son was born he was christened Thomas Henry Sandford Smith and it wasn't long before Doris saw that a hyphen crept in, and a generation later, when Roly was born, the Sandford-Smiths were very highly respected, and Thomas Henry Sandford-Smith was Church Warden and Deputy Chairman of the Parish Council, and his wife Maureen was secretary of the local W.I. and Treasurer of the Potters End Flower Club. Roly was their only child and they thought the world of him.

Everyone in this sterile wilderness outside the Bardia perimter had been told to dig bed holes to sleep in. Bedholes were usually dug about six feet long, two feet six inches wide and eighteen inches deep, as protection against bombing and shelling. That night Roly took his shovel out of the back of the cookhouse truck and decided that if he dug his bedhole too close to the truck, and the vehicle was set on fire or blown over in a blast, he might end up right underneath it. Roly decided, therefore, to dig his bedhole some ten yards away from his vehicle.

When he had done this, Roly laid out his groundsheet carefully in the bottom of the trench, wrapped a dirty towel round his haversack for a pillow, and made a rough bed with a couple of blankets and his overcoat. He then stood off to leeward in the cold night air for a pee, took off his boots, and, otherwise fully clothed, climbed down into his bed. He took out his packet of Victory V army issue cigarettes, lit one up and replaced the packet in one of his boots, and placed his boots beside his pillow. Boots were usually placed near our pillows for two reasons. One was that if we were called to 'action stations' during the night we wouldn't have to grope about in the dark for our boots, and secondly if a sand storm blew up in the night it would cover everything in the bedhole with several inches of dust and then, finding anything at all in the deep sand was worse than the treasure hunt at the village fete.

During the night two infantry Bren carriers, one following in the tracks of the other, were feeling their way through the Troop area. It was practically pitch dark and the first carrier ran right over Roly's bedhole, and the second one had followed before anyone realised that they had run over a sleeping soldier. Roly must have been killed instantly and two men were detailed to dig him out.

Some of us spent an uneasy night dealing with the aftermath of Roly's death, and few men in the troop had more than two hours sleep.

In the morning Roly's gasmask was swinging to and fro from the metal hook on the tailboard of his truck, and his untidy pack was lying half open on the driver's seat spilling out his mess tins, his hussif and a bundle of letters from home. His tinted sand goggles hung over the steering wheel and sagged down like a sloth from his tree, and his chipped enamel mug, covered in dust, had been planted upside down over the gear lever like a clown's top hat.

CHAPTER FOURTEEN

The Blooding of the Guns

BEFORE THE FIRST streaks of that bitterly cold African dawn hatched into first light the Troop were 'standing to' on the guns. Breech and muzzle covers were removed and packed away into their canvas holders and, for the first time, the guns of the West Suffolk Yeomanry were pointed in real anger at the invisible enemy.

Roly's body, now wrapped in a coarse army blanket, still lay beside his truck in awful stillness.

Half an hour earlier, Lieutenant Kershaw, coat collar turned up, tin helmeted, and with prismatic binoculars hanging round his neck, had gathered together his crew to venture forward to the Observation Post area. Lance Bombadier Henry Leathers was his driver, Gunner Ernie Briggs the signaller, and Lance Bombadier Ralph Bowman the specialist ack. The fifteen hundredweight unarmoured truck was laden with equipment. Two rifles were strapped on to the inside of the side runners, and a radio set with a six foot aerial, was affixed to the floor. A spare field telephone and a full day's rations were stored in ammunition boxes. Spades, shovels and sand channels were tied in and Ralph Bowman packed in maps and compasses and note books.

They were going forward to take up position from where they could observe the enemy.

We huddled round the gun, jaded from loss of sleep and raw from a desert winter's night. Our limbs were cold and stiff. It was too wintry to wash or shave. Our clothes had not been off for two whole days and our bodies felt tacky and curdled.

'I wish we could light a little fire and make a cuppa char,' said Malcolm.

'Unless you want a load on top of you, you won't light a fire until it's really light,' said Harold, looking at the sky.

'I slept in my overcoat and balaclava last night,' said Malcolm, 'and still I was as cold as a fugging frog.'

'It might start to warm up soon,' said Harold, 'and I don't mean the weather.'

'I'll tell you what,' said Philip, 'I feel sorry for those base wallahs down in Cairo that won't be getting out of bed for a couple of hours.'

It was still a glimmering pale pre dawn, and there was no sound of shot or shell.

'All quiet on the western front,' said Malcolm, giving forth a leisurely fertile yawn.

'I dare say this will turn out to be a quiet rest day,' declared Kevin, optimistically.

Just after a quarter past six, orders came down from the O.P. to the Command Post.

'Troop G F target.'

2nd Lieutenant Hester-Hewitt was Gun Position Officer and shouted: 'Take posts.'

Harold picked up his rammer and ran to the trail of the gun. Philip quickly took his seat as gun layer by the firing lever, with his eyes on the dial sight.

I was number two and knelt down on the offside of the gun barrel to open and close the breech.

Malcolm and Kevin stood by the stack of shells and charges.

'Load.'

The four gun sergeants raised their hands in acknowledgement. All four guns of the troop were involved.

Kevin drove a shell into the breech with his fist, and it was rammed home by Harold Reeve.

'Charge three.'

Malcolm picks up a charge case containing the correct number of bags of gun cotton and rams it in behind the shell, and I slam the breech shut and kneel down behind the offside gunwheel.

'Zero 336 degrees,' shouts the GPO.

Philip sets the angle on the micrometer head and the dial sight is checked by Harold.

'Five eight hundred.'

The range is set on the gun by elevating the gun barrel using the elevating handle. The setting is very precise.

'Angle of sight 15 minutes elevation.'

This indicated that the target is 15 minutes higher elevation than the gun position. Harold raises his arm to indicate that we are ready.

'Right ranging.'

Number one gun of A Troop is to fire the ranging shot. Our gun will be the first gun to fire on the enemy in Bardia.

'Fire.'

Philip pulls the firing lever and, with a blinding orange flash and a piercing cracking explosion which bladed through our unprotected eardrums and into our brain, the shell thundered off into the Bardia defences. The twenty-five pounder kicked and jumped like a giant iron stallion. Three more ranging shots were fired by No. 1 gun and then there was a call to the whole troop for two rounds gunfire and eight shells which had, in all probability, been transported thousands of miles from England, thrashed into the enemy lines.

The response by the enemy to our two rounds of gunfire was quick and considerable. Almost before our second round of gunfire had reached the target, the Italian gunners had opened up, and about a score of shells landed on top of a low crest some four hundred yards in front of our guns. Great plumes of smoke gushed from the exploding shells.

Next four medium sixty pounders, which had drawn in some three hundred yards behind us, opened up with five rounds gunfire, with the enemy guns as their target. This, in turn, resulted in a sharp reprisal as about thirty enemy shells whistled over our heads and burst a quarter of a mile behind us. In the meantime, our sister Batteries, P Battery and Q Battery, has opened fire.

The engagement had turned into a sharp artillery duel and the whole area was becoming very noisy. Considering that we had only been in actual and substantial action for about a quarter of an hour, it had proved to be a lively start to the day, and several tons of hardware had been exchanged in our sector. To emphasize that this was not just an exercise at Middlesham, a three ton R.A.S.C. lorry, loaded with petrol and which had been parked between our guns and those of the medium regiment behind us, had been hit with the shelling and was blazing fiercely in a pall of fire and smoke.

The noise and activity then quietened down considerably and the 'stand easy' order from the O.P. enabled us to relax and tidy up the gun pit. The sun came out and we began to feel its warmth, and the cookhouse sent round a dixie of hot tea.

The troop had fired some eighty twenty-five pound shells into the enemy defences, and we had learned what it was like to be on the receiving end of a battery of Italian 105 millimetre guns, and in a few short minutes we had learned to feel a tinge of respect for the speedy reaction of the Italian gunners. In fact, if the first enemy salvos in response to our opening rounds had been increased in range by four hundred yards or so, we could have been looking for our slit trenches.

Most important of all, we no longer suffered the disgrace and shame of being virgin soldiers. We could never be the same again and, now that we had seen the real sparks fly, our morale had improved no end.

Although during training we had been almost grafted on to the gun and had been enlightened and instructed in gun drill till the cows came home, none of our many instructors had given any indication of what to expect when under enemy shellfire, because no one knew. Did an exploding 105 milimetre shell kill a man at twenty yards, at two hundred yards, or five hundred yards? No one really seemed to know.

Already, however, we felt different, almost as if we were achieving some measure of fulfilment, and the upshot of it was that instead of being lame and impotent blunderers lurching through the war, we were now being hammer hardened and buttressed against the dark blindness of the unknown. It was also very much on the cards that our mental self counsel was being compressed and stiffened.

During the morning five rounds gunfire were loosed off at an enemy working party, and Lieutenant Kershaw was able to spot ambulances in the target area afterwards. Salvos of shells continued to fall around the ridge in front of us, and a few more rounds of enemy long range stuff whistled over our heads and crashed behind us, but we had lost most of our fear and apprehension in the benighted anxiety of the unknown.

After mid-day the proceedings in general, along the whole of the front, appeared to stagnate, and we tentatively lay down beside our guns in the warming sunshine.

Several infantry troop carriers and support lorries arrived in the area, but for over an hour and a half not a shot was fired on either side.

The Italian gunners, like ourselves, had probably been instructed not to waste ammunition, knowing that their sea transports between the Libyan port of Tripoli and the Italian mainland had to run the gauntlet of submarines of the British Navy, bombers and torpedo carrying aircraft of the Royal Air Force and the Fleet Air Arm.

As the Mediterranean was now a closed area for our British convoys and reinforcements, our own further supplies of ammunition would have to be shipped eight thousand miles round the Cape.

★   ★   ★   ★

At dead on two o'clock in the afternoon a distant noise was heard of purring engines. It was a protracted beating drone like a snarling muffled drum, and it was getting louder.

'What's that?' said Kevin.

'Sounds like aircraft,' said Harold, suddenly alert and shading his eyes.

'They're aircraft all right,' said Malcolm, pointing at the sky towards Bardia, 'There's scores of the buggers.'

Turning our eyes to the north we could make out forty twin-engined bombers escorted by about half that number of fighters. The bombers were formed into three tightly packed waves, and none of us had seen so many planes in the air at one time. They were crossing the fortress of Bardia itself at about ten thousand feet, and were heading straight towards us in the gun pits. It was a chilling and awe inspiring sight, and a tiny shudder of apprehension ran through.

'Blenheims,' said somebody.

'If they're Blenheims,' said Kevin, 'why aren't the fuggin Itie ack ack in Bardia opening up?'

Ten seconds later the single Bofors gun attached to our battery launched its attack with its clips of five, and fired into the advancing horde of bombers.

'Take cover,' shouted Troop Sergeant Major Evans from the command post. We all dived into the shallow slit trenches behind the guns.

Malcolm said 'We're going to be bang in the bullseye of this lot, I reckon that Musso has sent the whole of his bloody airforce.'

I remember thinking to myself 'Albert, in one minute you'll be dead.' I had never been so certain that I'd be killed. None of us had any idea of what a bombing raid in the open desert, and with only shallow slit trenches for protection, would be like. For all we knew, the concussion from a thousand pound bomb, bursting fifty yards away, would smash us to smithereens, even though we were in slit trenches.

'Keep your heads down lads,' said Harold Reeve, cool as ever in the van of the approaching hostile aerial flotilla. 'No need to look up.'

It was all very well for Harold to tell us not to look up, but my eyes were irresistably drawn to that great black bomber formation. It was like a swarm of ugly black, egg laden dragon flies, swollen and obese. From my slit trench I just couldn't help watching intently the fat under bellies split as the bomb bays gradually opened. Each plane released a stick of eight bombs simultaneously and, looking up, it was like a Devil's black snowstorm.

The little black eggs quickly increased in size as they hurled themselves on to this God forsaken blighted wasteland on the Libyan Desert. Once the bombs were on their way we buried our noses in the bottom of the slit trench, which somehow felt cold like dead marble. Then the high pitched scream of falling bombs and the crashing climax of the indescribable discharge of the explosions which rent and tore at the ear drums. Simultaneously the shattering, violent earth vibrations merged in huge shock waves, which convulsed through our unstable trenches.

Inches above our heads the shrieking flying metal coursed with vicious velocity together with the deadly flung slashes of rock and sand.

Half a second later the burning hot blast flashed and scorched with unleashed driving heat. It sucks the wind out of you, I can tell you. And then suddenly, as if by magic the hellish raining of the shock waves and singing steel seemed to be over.

I was surprised to find that, apart from lungfulls of dust and ringing ears, I was undemolished and complete in all my parts. There was a feeling of up to the brim relief.

Still choking from the rough twangy devil dust, we clawed our way out of the slit trenches and peered around.

Nothing could be seen through the clouds of smoke for nearly two minutes and then all went strangely quiet, except for the urgent screams of a wounded man, and the distant drone of the receding bombers which grew fainter and passed into nothingness.

It was clear that at least five bombs had dropped within fifty yards of our gun. Harold Reeve was standing up to check that his gun detachment was O.K.

'Gunner Porter and Gunner Burgess O.K.?' shouted Harold, peering through the smoke.

'Both O.K. Sergeant,' shouted Kevin, who was indulging in a fit of coughing.

'Bombardier Underwood and Bombardier Cooper O.K.?'

'Yes, Sergeant,' I shouted. Philip and myself had sheltered in the same slit trench.

The whole area around the guns still reeked of high explosive, and some thirty yards from our trench there was a bomb crater in which you could hide a car. Vicious prongs of sound were still buzzing in our ears.

Second Lieutenant Hester-Hewitt, in the Command Post, picked up the megaphone and shouted,

'Number One Gun O.K.?'

'Number One Gun O.K., sir,' shouted Harold Reeve.

'Number Two Gun O.K.?

'Number Two Gun O.K., sir,' shouted Sergeant Neville Steele.

'Number Three Gun O.K.?

There was no reply.

'Number Three Gun O.K.?' repeated the Second Lieutenant.

'Two men wounded, first aid required, sir.'

'Right Sergeant White, the M.O. will be sent for. Number One Gun assist Number Three Gun.'

'Through on One, sir.'

'Number Four Gun O.K.?'

'Men O.K., sir, but dial sight smashed.'

'Gun artificer to Number Four Gun.'

We often considered Second Lieutenant Hester-Hewitt feeble and short winded, and his thoughts sometimes seemed tied together with a rope of sand, but Hester-Hewitt was doing well and his mother, Lady Honor, who had to dispense with two of her gardeners, would be proud of him.

The Troop position soon cleared of dust and smoke, and Harold Reeve, Philip Underwood and myself found ourself once again fixing field dressing on wounded men.

Curly Mortimer, the layer on Don White's gun was unconscious, and was giving out all the signals that his short life was on the point of surrender. He had a terrible head wound and his face was the colour of sheeted alabaster. I held Curly's limp wrist, but could feel no life. His bloodless hand, that only minutes before had pulled the plug on his gun for a 'Brave New World', was already waxing cold.

Well we did out best. You know what they tell you at First Aid. Do not move the patient, don't pour hot liquid down his throat, keep the airway clear and keep him warm and all that. But what the hell were we supposed to do about Curly with a deep four inch gash across the top of his head, and what looked like bits of his brains hanging out?

I remembered that there was something about concussion and compression, and about head wounds and brain damage, but nothing about sticking brains back. Most of our First Aid instruction was to patch up a school kid that had been knocked off his bike, and not someone that had been slashed across the head by a bit of jagged steel from a two thousand pound bomb.

Wilfred Musgrove was the number four on Don White's gun. His father owned a couple of cattle lorries at Westerfield. Wilfred was losing a lot of blood, but it was mostly coming from a wound in his arm. So we concentrated on Wilfred. He was conscious but there was blood everywhere. As Harold Reeve tied a clean field dressing round Wilfred's gashed arm I said, 'Wilfred you lucky sod, you'll soon be helping your father cart cattle and horses all over Suffolk.'

Wilfred said, as he sat with his back resting on the trail, 'you known Albert, my arm feels as if it will burst, do you think they'll save it?'

'Wilfred,' I said, 'this is only a flesh wound, and you'll be as right as rain.'

The M.O. arrived with his syringes and his morphia.

*   *   *   *

That night, as we sat round the guns smoking and scratching around for cigarettes, Geoff Griffiths, a specialist from Battery Headquarters, strolled over to see his friend Philip Underwood. Visitors from BHQ were always welcome on the Troop positions because they always heard the latest rumours before we did down on the guns.

'What's the griff about our neck of the war, Geoff,' said Philip.

'Well,' said Geoff. 'It said on BBC news last night that the British guns had smashed Bardia's iron ring.'

'That means bugger all,' said Philip.

'Precisely,' said Geoff, 'but you did ask me.'

Geoff threw a cigarette over to Philip and, cupping his hands against the night wind, gave Philip a light and then lit his own.

'I'd give something for a packet of Players,' said Geoff, 'these fugging army issue Victory cigarettes come from India, and they burn your bloody lungs out.'

'I thought they came from King Farouk's stables,' declared Malcolm.

'Well,' said Geoff. 'I saw some information on file in the Command Post and they estimate that there are forty five thousand Italian troops in Bardia, and they have four hundred guns. When the Australian infantry join us in a few days time we shall have between fifteen and twenty thousand troops, and we have half the number of guns that they have in Bardia. But they reckon,' went on Geoff Griffiths, 'that we have some new tanks called "I" tanks, and the Eitie tank shells will just bounce off them.'

'More propaganda,' said Malcolm.

'No, that's the truth,' said Geoff, 'and the other thing is that the British soldier is worth three Ities.'

'The British soldier,' said Harold Reeve, 'is worth six of those bastard Dagoes, and the sooner we lay down our barrage and get into Bardia the better.'

Over to the left a machine gun chattered and half a dozen Very lights were fired one after another. An enemy plane was dropping flares a long way behind us and the rumble of heavy transport could be heard in the east.

It was a quiet night really.

*　　　*　　　*　　　*

It was surprising to us, as denizens and backwoodsmen of Suffolk, to discover how cold it was in the North African desert a few days before Christmas 1940. There were times when the chill blast of the Bardia mistral gusted night and day. The swirling cold added to our general discomfort and the frustration of the unvaried hard rations. It was rare for us to have a hot meal of any kind, and the water being supplied was worse than dreggy bilge water.

Before retreating, the Italians had thrown dead goats and bags of salt into all the wells round Solum from where most of our tainted water supplies were drawn. By the time our water people had added excessive quantities of chlorine and other chemicals to make it 'safe' it stank like a rook's nest.

'I'd rather drink water from the bottom layer of the village duck pond,' grumbled Kevin.

'I reckon,' said Philip, screwing up his face at the foul and bitter taste of his mug of lumpy tea, 'the water cart has found King Farouk's racing camels' piss pot.'

It was late morning on Christmas Day. There had been a more than lively exchange of gunfire during the morning and on Christmas Eve, an enemy battery of heavy guns had tossed several shells around us during the early part of the night.

We were sitting round the end of the gunpit. There had been insufficient water for us to wash or shave for five days, and with our woolly headwarmers, our long bushy hair and scraggy beards, we began to resemble shaggy coated wog goats.

As we slowly munched our quarter tin of Fray Bentos bully beef and the hard square biscuits, Harold said, 'I remember, Malcolm, when you were put on fire picket in Palestine, that you said it was high time we got into action instead of hanging round the camp to put out non existent fires. Your wish has now been granted so I hope you are a happy man.' Harold wasn't above sarcasm.

'I may have said that in a weak moment,' said Malcolm, 'but I didn't say that I wanted Bully and biscuits for my Christmas dinner.'

'I don't know what you are complaining for,' said Philip, digging a broken Italian bayonet into the four pound tin of margarine and spreading his biscuit, 'you're having a wonderful Christmas. Last night you had a free display of coloured Christmas party lights. The pretty green, yellow and red Very lights and star shells should bring you great Christmas joy. Those two Vickers machine guns threw up a very pretty line in tracer bullets, and the R.A.F. parachute flares, dropped over Bardia during the night, must have made you feel Christmassy. As for fireworks and bangers that little packet that we had here last night, and the sprinkle we had this morning, plus that battery of three point seven ack ack letting off just after midnight should make this your best Christmas ever and, what is more, you're being fed and clothed and paid for it.'

'Pipe down, Philip,' said Malcolm, wiping his mouth with the back of his hand, 'I bet this is the best fugging Christmas dinner you've ever had.'

We all laughed and Kevin, who had just thrown half of his mug of lumpy tea away, said, 'I shouldn't be surprised if we don't get an issue of fags and beer today.'

'The Generals,' said Ernie Briggs, 'fink that if we've got fags an' beer we don't need nuffink else.'

'What pesters me,' said Kevin, 'is why we get issued with beer, and the officers get issued with whisky and gin.'

'You couldn't be trusted with alcoholic spirits,' said Malcolm, 'you're uneducated and you would just make a pig of yourself.'

*   *   *   *

This was our second Christmas away from home and that night, lying there among the dark ammuniton cases by the camouflaged gun, with the winter night peppered with stars, I was homesick and, to tell you the truth, I was lovesick and couldn't help it. I just couldn't get Julie out of my mind. The flame of my love burned as brightly as ever.

As the full desert moon rose into the purple sky, flooding the eerie flatness with light, I thought of one warm gentle afternoon when I took Julie for a walk down to Chalk Wood. We strolled through Church meadow, which was coming for second cut hay, under the shaded brow of the tall hedge on the churchyard side of Sheepcote Pasture. The hedge was seething with chattering sparrows and the sun lay all along the faces of the leaves. Brightly coloured Peacocks and Red Admirals and fritillaries in pale jewel colours, were skimming and hovering over the cow mumble, and starlings were bustling up the dust in the dried up pond holes. We wandered in lingering time, hand in hand down through the shafts of sunlight on the unkempt bridleway to the edge of the wood. On this rare glory of a hot summer's day the burnished buttercups and paigles were in golden bloom right across the meadow. Hurdles for the sheep fold stood in the gateway. Julie pointed out the horse goggle tree with its wild plumes pulling the little branches towards the earth. A much used rabbit run spilt carelessly down the side of the dried up dyke through the butchers broom and the cuckoo pint and the field scabias and the red campions.

I remember Julie squeezing my hand as a brood of pheasants ran in front of us between the horse track and the ruts in the wagon lane. A trilling skylark spun up from its nest among the birdsfoot and trefoil into the breathless blue high air like a skybound ball of music.

I turned over in my rough shakedown sleeping berth on its trestle of sand shielded against the wind and widespread to the open sky. I drew the shrouding blankets round me, but I was restless and could not sleep.

*   *   *   *

THE AUSTRALIANS

They marched as if they'd stand their ground and make head against a hostile adversary.

Some two hundred men of the 16th Australian Infantry Brigade, as the advance guard of the famous 6th Australian Division, marched through our gun positions. The men of the 6th Australian Division had all enlisted as volunteers under the banners of liberty against the far distant fascist contravention. It was a far cry and a giant's span to their great pulsing cities, their one horse towns and beer swilling shearers, the red roofs, gum trees and farms the size of Yorkshire. They were eight thousand miles from Cootamundra and the Murrumbidgee, and half a world away from their women and kids and their great new country of wide spaces and its intafusion of people.

Watching them with their brim pinned bush hats, rifles slung and wearing brown leather jerkins to keep out the cold, it was easy of belief, in this dying year of 1940, that they were tough, leathery and self reliant.

There was no sign of uncertainty as the dust swirled about their feet as they stirred the slaked ease of the earth. Their easy studied indifference showed wistful relish to leave the beaten track and an inclination to tasting resistance to the pattern of conformity.

It was clear that many of them had a cheerful disregard for their sergeant major and short patience with authority. One square faced infantry man was giving a colourful back answer to the CSM as they passed behind our guns, and the Sergeant Major shouted, 'Wait till I get you, Private Baker, I'll knock your bastard teeth out.'

To have these keen eyed Aussies with us in the field at Bardia slaked the edges with a kind of happiness, and their presence was a subconscious poultice to the rawness of desert life.

Our gathering confidence took further impetus when, the following day, nine squat, steelbound British tanks churned and squealed their dusty way into a nearby lager just before nightfall. These tanks were the highly secret 'I' tanks which became known as 'Matildas'.

Six of the tanks were Mark Is which weighed eleven tons and mounted one .303 machine gun, and the remainder were Mark II's which weighed twenty six tons and carried a crew of four. They were armed with one two pounder gun and one Besa machine gun. The armour thickness on the front was in excess of three inches and it was confidently said that no gun the Italians possessed would penetrate the front armour of these 'I' tanks.

I'd never seen Harold Reeve so edgy. Harold hated the Germans and he despised the Italians. His father had been killed at Verdun during the last war and he could not hide his impatience for the battle for Bardia and the artillery barrage to begin. Harold was half in love with his gun and he wanted to test its metal in a major barrage.

Before a major battle the days pass slowly, but preparations were now ready to play our part in demolishing Mussolini's dream of dominating the Mediterranean and of rebuilding the former Roman Empire.

Almost every day at about noon the Regia Aeronautica appeared at a very great height and dropped clutches of bombs on the first visible target, but now that we were well dug in and our vehicles well dispersed they worried us no longer.

During the night of New Year's Day many tons of ammunition were quietly ferried up to our forward battle positions and camouflaged under vast nets. It is a well established practice, the night before a major battle, that the guns are moved up under cover of darkness to a completely new gun site. To remain on the same site, with aerial photographs providing the previous day's position for the enemy, would be to invite deadly shelling from the enemy's heavy artillery.

On the night of 2nd January 1941 the regiment moved its twenty-four guns up into the forward battle positions for the main assault on Bardia. It was a cold dark night and a keen wind blew from the north. By 0400 hours on the early morning of 3rd January all guns were in position, and all was set for the impending battle.

*   *   *   *

'Renown awaits the Commander who first in this war restores Artillery to its prime importance upon the battlefield, from which it has been ousted by heavily armoured tanks.'

Winston Churchill, as Minister of Defence,

CHAPTER FIFTEEN

Bardia Surrenders

AT 0515 HOURS the guns, to which we were anchored, were fully manned as the countdown to zero hour began. The Regiment was programmed to fire a three hour creeping barrage on fixed lines. The Survey Parties of Brigade had planned every detail of this comprehensive fire programme.

The gunners' first main objective was to reduce two of the heavily fortified concrete strong points which were emplaced in zigzag formation behind the anti tank ditch and the double apron wire fences. These enemy strong points were bristling with anti tank guns, machine guns and mortars. Behind these heavy fortifications of concrete and steel the enemy had placed a formidable weight of artillery.

At dead on 0530 hours orders rang out over the desert to 'Fire', and one hundred and forty British guns in one synchronised roar in a concert of concentrated thunder such as these arid reaches of the Libyan desert had never known before. Violent stabs of flame lit the darkness, and in this crashing crescendo of thundering white fire the guns were bucking and dancing like living things. It roused the blood.

Sergeant Harold Reeve was in his element as he shouted and checked the fire orders imperative. In the moments leading up to the barrage those of us on the guns were in an irrational vacuum, a no mans land of the mind. Our time was stretched. This was war and we had been taut and braced as a drum skin, but now we relaxed into the rhythm of work and gun drill and comradeship. There was no thought of home, or even of victory. This was full time commitment and our minds were focused and concerned. No one that hasn't seen war in close measure can ever know the feel and the flavour and the racket and the smell.

Under Sergeant Reeve we were a tight inward operating unit of a gun crew, drilled, resolute and determined to do its Country's promise and to be candidates for the Regiment's charter and history. There was no rejection of our circumstance, we had kicked down the ladder and there would be no turning back. Our ties and links, and our reference to our comrades gave us no discretion. The surging gunfire was becoming welded into our existence and we were part and substance of the hard reality of this dramatic and spectacular artillery creation. Our thoughts were pulled together by consequence of these stark moments and the urgent deeds at hand.

The shells were now leaving each of the guns at four a minute, and were ripping into the enemy forward line to blast gaps in the minefields and barbed wire. It was a fearsome display of firepower, and in this world of continuous explosions there was that strange portentious bond between the gunners and their gun.

At six o'clock there was a brief pause in the barrage while the Australian infantry from the 16th Brigade began to move forward. It was a dingy, cold, steel grey dawn, but already streaks of sallow yellowness were making fight to force themselves through the dim dawn curtain.

As the barrage resumed, the engineers, following closely behind our curtain of fire, cleared two lanes through the minefields and threw two bridges over the tank trap.

Under Harold Reeve, our gun had already fired, in the first hour, almost five tons of high explosive shells. Our muscles were aching and our eyes were sore with dust and smoke. We were wearing no protectors and our ears were ringing with the impulsive intensity of the guns' roar in their frightful zenith as we fired round after round into the obscure half tone of the morning.

Suddenly a louder and more urgent series of explosions rent the air. The fetid odour of cordite and the screaming thang of flying metal was clear intimation that the enemy batteries were seeking our quarter of the earth and trying to pin point the tiny piece of sterile territory where we had stamped our feet and scratched our mark, but there was scant concern for the enemy counter battery fire. The pace had been full tilt and our tired arms felt like undirected traffic. Our bodies were wincing, and our boots were heavy.

At daybreak, like skeins of wild geese, three waves of red, white and blue ringed Blenheim bombers, escorted by eight Gloster Gladiator fighters, flew in from the southern sky. They passed high over our lines and penetrated the Bardia airspace.

Grey smoke coloured puff balls of enemy ack ack, like exploding balls of wool, burst and shattered among the tight formations as they raided deep into the sphere and dominion of established enemy territory. They bombed the area to the north of the bridgehead. The dense columns of thick black smoke which shot high into the air, followed by the earth shaking bombursts, was as a surged mushroom pall which hung heavily over the pivot of the battle.

It was like a moving picture and the appearance of friendly aircraft did much for our fixity of purpose and somehow, for us, subsidised the battle. As our thoughts skidded and plunged into the next round of gunfire, to have our highly trained Australian compatriots engaging the enemy over the battle arena, subscribed to reinforce our will and nourish our resolution.

Our line of bombardment changed direction against the backdrop of the burning sky. The pummelled and battered centre of attack had now made the area open to occupation by the infantry, and the guns had new targets. Firstly, there were the fortified strongpoints on the flanks of the main attack to be neutralised, and secondly, counter bombardment was urgently required against the enemy artillery that had been pasting and savaging our regimental area. The enemy gunners were doing more than just committing themselves to an exchange of fire, and it was necessary to join issue before their stinging response to our bombardment put havoc and disaster among us as we rode the whirlwind.

At long last, after the wild plunge and fury of two solid hours of hammering and throbbing gunfire, the orders came through to 'Stand Easy'.

Harold counted the empty ammunition boxes. 'Three hundred and fourteen,' he said. 'That'll give the bastards something to think about.'

The gun sat there in its circle of sandbags, still set on its firing line, like a greyhound bitch on the leash and watchfull for the hare. It still simmered from its harsh power, and Kevin half filled a canvas bucket from the radiator of a smashed and doomed infantry carrier and poured it over the barrel, and it geysered clouds of steam.

A nervous looking procession of seven field ambulances slowly edged their way up to the forward Field Dressing Station to collect the wounded.

The enemy were still sending over high bursting shrapnel and we kept our tin hats firmly on. Harold said, 'We want to get our guns forward so we can blast those bloody shrapnel guns.'

There was time for a swig of metal tasting water from our water bottles, and time for a cigarette.

The Regia Aeronautica was making its second visit of the day, but they dropped their bombs between us and the bridgehead.

A little Daimler Dingo scout car was dead unlucky. It seemed to catch a shell right underneath its front axle. The car reared like a frightened hunter before toppling over on its side and bursting into flames. There was no hope for the crew. One moment a sergeant, a driver and a wireless operator, all tuned in to life, and within thirty seconds no proper cremation, no laying out, no passing through the village church lych gate with proud loved ones, but a devastating crash and a quick steel bound pyre. Not enough to bring them to ashes, but enough to leave them burnt and blackened and unrecognisable, where even blood relatives could not tell.

Our own faces were grey with smoke and battle dust but we were now getting our second wind.

An ammunition lorry arrived, but there was no time to unload as it was back to the guns.

This is how it was. Something happening all the time.

★   ★   ★   ★

THE MAN IN THE LYSANDER

We could all see him in the Lazy Lizzie on that first morning at Bardia. In that clapped out looking crate with short stubby wings. He may have been spotting for medium artillery, or he may have been getting a situation report for the Generals. He flew in that short take-off recci plane officially called the Westland Lysander, so dear to the desert troops. Beneath him seethed the cauldron of the battle.

The Lizzie was so slow that she sometimes seemed to hover like a kestrel with its eye on the quarry and ready to swoop for the kill. The enemy flack was exploding round the plane like balls of dandelion fluff.

Who was this man? Who was this pilot? Was he of the R.A.F.? Was he an artillery officer that had learned to fly, or an airforce man that had learned to be a gunner O.P.? Was he a wild colonial boy from Australia, or a white Rhodesian farmer who had flown all his life and now was far from his maize and his tobacco?

He flew backwards and forwards over the front line for twenty minutes, and then pulled away from the flak and headed east. A CR 42 fighter would have made mincemeat of him. Who he was and what he was doing we never knew.

As we entered the second phase of our barrage I felt far from the contented grunting of the farrowing sows and from the Fordson and the pigeon pie and from the quiet peace of Suffolk mares with Spring foals cropping the clover.

By eight o'clock the first committed waves of the Australian Infantry Brigade, and most of the British manned 'I' tanks, were well inside the Bardia perimeter. The urgent chatter of the machine guns and the dull crump of the mortars indicated a sharp engagement taking place just over the crest.

It was not until nearly mid-day, after six hours of battle, that orders came down from Brigade and 2nd Lieutenant Hester-Hewitt picked up his megaphone and shouted 'Prepare to move.'

'And about time too,' said Harold. 'The Royal Horse Artillery was intended as a mobile unit and was never devised to sit about all day in a gunpit.' While Harold and the subsection were quickly hitching the gun to the robust steel clamping hook behind the ammunition limber, I ran over to my quad and brought it down to the gun.

In the meantime, B Troop, who had had three men killed and two wounded during the morning, were trying, with their three remaining guns, to make the enemy gunners keep their heads down while A Troop moved forward.

It was just after noon, with the roar of the morning barrages still ringing in our ears, that our Troop column of guns drove through the two minefields and the double apron wire fence and on to the hastily contructed tank trap bridge. The Italian gunners had the range of the bridge, and salvo after salvo was crashing into the area. It was hairy all right as we sat up there, three feet from the ground in thin skinned vehicles. We were probably under observation by the enemy and, at one stage, due to a hold up in front, we sat on the bridge under heavy shelling for over three minutes without moving. At any moment we could have been blown to bits. It was an interlude to remember, but we were getting firepower forward; and I had to concentrate on driving forward the moment the bridge was clear. My left hand gripped the gear lever and my foot rested on the clutch and I kept the revs spinning. It was no time to stall the engine. Two more exploding salvos bracketed the bridge and then, thankfully, we were on the move again, deeper into Bardia.

Two Australian dead lay face downwards side by side in a crumpled heap in the minefield. Were they infantry that had strayed off the cleared lanes? Were they killed on a recent night patrol, or were they engineers who were slaughtered and deprived of life as they bayonet prodded for mines during that early morning?

An Australian sergeant and three of his men, with rifles and bayonets still clenched in their hands, still, and bereft of life, lay sprawled on the open ground, machine gunned to eternity, a few yards short of the concreted strongpoint they were storming. Then a squat, disabled Matilda tank, with one track shot off and hanging in the idlers. It had become a sitting target as it lay sideways on to the

Fascist anti tank gunners who had pumped in relays of armour piercing shells to annihilate tank and crew. Then an 'I' tank and crew, burned and twisted and locked in life's surrender in this field of blood.

All around us eddied a swirling mass of thick black smoke and dust. A half track lay smouldering in the field of fire in front of a wrecked enemy anti tank gun.

And then we came to the enemy dead. There were dozens of them, and one fortified pill box contained a mass of bodies contorted in ugly anguished misproportion. Here we were able to witness the devastating effect of our artillery barrage. There was hardly a square yard in this swathe of destruction that had not been pitted and blackened by a twenty-five pounder shell. Two enemy M 10 tanks were still burning to the right of the track, and for the first time we recognised the foul, pungent odour and stench of burning flesh. Another cleverly sighted anti tank gun had received a direct hit from the barrage, and the two dead members of the crew lay headless beside it.

Number One Gun of A Troop was the first gun through the gap and into the bridgehead, this pleased Harold no end. By now all the enemy shells were whistling over our heads. In a piteous state of distress and shock a group of badly wounded men, some of them covered in blood, lay in the shelter of a gun emplacement. They were being aided by a short, harrassed looking Italian medical orderly who was moving from one to another with a water bottle. A dead, red tongued Alsatian dog, used as the eyes and ears of the pill box, lay in its mortal fixity, across the sandbagged parapet, with its lifeless glassy eyes.

A group of about thirty unarmed Italian soldiers ran towards us waving white flags and handkerchiefs. Many were wounded and already had bandages round their heads and limbs. They were an unshaven, shell shocked, and demoralised ragbag I can tell you. We were too busy to take them prisoner.

Kevin said, 'They are flouncing out of their holes like rats out of a bushel. You know, Albert, we are seeing more here in a few minutes than we see at the Suffolk Show in twenty years.' Kevin was really saying something then because a visit to the Show, which was run annually by the Suffolk Agricultural Society, had always been the highlight of our year.

What were we to make of this strange violent world of mirages, suspense, uncertainty and danger? We could almost believe that we were on a high spinning light navigating the very crest of insight and experience.

Who and what were we in this crucial dimension, and how was I, recalling on the tablets of my memory, the uneven brick floors of my father's cottage and my young untroubled existence, steer and regulate my emergence into maturity and manhood?

The chapter of passage we were witnessing was near unbelievable and these torn killing corridors were pulling at the very sleeve of the unknown.

In these wild, fluttering moments in Bardia, with fiery emotion at its zenith, I had a mind for a 'whipper in' to collect and compose my scattered thoughts and emotions.

As the guns were dropped into action and the G.P.O. relayed the urgent fire orders, Harold said, 'This is what we were trained for — now let's get stuck into those bloody Itie shrapnel guns.'

During a brief lull in the attack, a long straggling column of Italian prisoners, which had surrendered to the Australian infantry, shuffled past. Two bored looking Aussies with rifles slung walked in front, and two brought up the rear. The Itie prisoners looked like a mob of draggle tailed weathers being driven unwillingly to the sheep dip. As they trudged, snail like, behind our guns one of the Aussie guards shouted over to us, 'What shall we do with these bastards?'

'Better order a couple of tons of spaghetti,' said Philip, helpfully.

When darkness finally came the whole battlefield settled down to a period of almost unnatural stillness as, with eyelids heavy with the fullness of battle, we lay down beside our guns. We had been two days and nights without sleep and as we pulled out our bedrolls I said, 'I think that I could sleep standing up, just like my Dad's carthorses.' Malcolm said, 'I think I could sleep till the boat sails in to take us back to Blighty.'

Harold said, 'We may be called upon at any time to take posts, so there's no need to take your boots off.'

'I haven't got the strength to undo the fugging laces,' said Philip.

*   *   *   *

By noon on the following day, with the exception of the odd gun which seemed to fire absent mindedly, all enemy resistance had ceased and the whole of Bardia was in our hands. Mussolini had lost five divisions consisting of forty thousand men, and vast quantities of guns, tanks and other equipment. We were elated at having won a clear battle victory, and we felt distinctly flushed and chirrupy.

The remainder of that battle gained day was spent, like that of all soldiers of fortune, foraging for loot and plunder. Inside the Italian concrete and steel fortifications, which had been abandoned in an unseeming haste, we found large quantities of food, clothes and stores. There were chocolate bars and bottles of Chianti everywhere. We discovered a dozen bottles of brandy in an Italian officers' supply truck, and thousands of small, loosely rolled cigars, fashioned and filled from strong Balkan tobacco. There were watches, binoculars and beautifully made sleeping bags. We filled sandbags with tins of pineapple and peaches, and packed haversacks with canned meat, excellent cheeses and tins of condensed milk. There were crates of tuna fish and packets of dried vegetables. We crammed the loot into the quad lockers, even though we knew that most of it would probably have to be jettisoned when we loaded up with spare petrol and ammunition.

That night a fire was lit and gallons of brandy, wine and liqueurs were drunk from mugs and mess tins or straight from the bottle. Charlie Briggs poured some bottles of Chianti and brandy into a two gallon brew can and then added a bottle of a thick green liqueur. Charlie said that it should make a dead camel kick. The Charlie Briggs special cocktail was potent and no mistake.

At first we felt merry and gloriously elevated, then befuddled and top heavy.

By half past ten no one was sober, many were plastered and blind to the world.

In the morning most of us felt distinctly the worse for wear, and Philip suggested that an Italian NCO and ten men could have taken the whole of the British Army prisoners during the night.

The Colonel couldn't wait to write to his father-in-law, Lieutenant General Beresford-Drake, and tell him about the victory at Bardia. He wrote:

> 'I am enormously proud to be in command of this Regiment and we have had an excellent party at Bardia. We let off a vast quantity of shells and we gave the Wops a tremendous hammering and, by lunch time on the second day, stumps were drawn.
>
> The chaps have got their tails absolutely sky high.'

*   *   *   *

I'll warrant that there can have been no army in history that felt more confident of winning the next battle than did the victorious Desert Army after the Battle of Bardia.

The Seventh Armoured Division, with its tanks and armoured cars, had already thrust on ahead and cut the coast road which runs westwards from Tobruk to the capital city of Cyrenaica, Benghazi.

The reduction of the garrison at Tobruk was to be our next objective. Tobruk lay some sixty miles to the west of Bardia and, with our battle hardened artillery and the 6th Australian Division, there was that sharp, solid, inward feeling that nothing could stop us.

There was to be very little rest and relaxation and on the following morning of the 5th January 1941 the regiment pulled away from Bardia and headed south into the desert, and then westwards towards Tobruk. The regiment, with its cumbersome vehicles, travelled across the wide open spaces of wartime Libya in what was known as 'Desert formation'. Each troop leader headed a group of guns and vehicles spread in a diamond formation with two guns on each side of the diamond. The soft skinned vehicles of the signallers, the ammunition lorries and the cookhouse trucks travelled in the middle of the diamond. All vehicles endeavoured to keep two hundred yards apart to discourage the enemy reconnaisance planes from calling up an air strike. It was correctly reasoned that a very scattered target was wasteful of bombs. As a consequence of this, most attacks on moving desert convoys were by enemy fighters with machine guns and cannon.

The first intimation that there were enemy planes in the vicinity, to those of us inside the cab, was the furious tatoo, by the aircraft spotter, on the roof of the vehicle. Brakes would be slammed on, doors flung open and everyone would grab their rifles, dive out on to the ground, and hope to get off a few rounds as the planes zoomed in to attack.

On this turgid pressing journey over sand and scrub towards Tobruk, the persistant choking dust was sucked into our vehicles. The going was rough and bumpy as the quads billowed and plunged, and the rate of travel was no more than ten miles an hour. That's how it was in this desert immensity of dunes and flat expanses. Changing gear up and down through patches of soft sand. Don't rush it, change down, give her a little throttle and let her pull herself through. There is a sizeable hard rock ahead. Don't let it get under the axles and damage the prop shaft or rip out the crown wheel and pinion on the differential. The sun is sinking in the west, glinting straight in the driver's eyes. Another cloud of devil dust sweeps into the cab. Lips are cracked and hair is full of fine dust particles.

I take off my clammy boots and drive in my bare feet and crouch tensely over the hot engine. The overworked engine is churning and the noise drums round the inside of the metal cab of the quad. Keep the wheels turning, keep your correct distance, nurse the engine. Lucky if we get eight miles to the gallon, we are mostly in bottom gear. It would be very agreeable to drive on a smooth tar sealed road.

There is ammunition in the lockers and more is stacked in heavy green boxes on the floor of the cab. We are fully loaded. The steering wheel is wet and sticky. I am not wearing a shirt and the sweat is running down my back on to the back of the seat. I try moving up to second gear but the quad bucks around worse than ever and tries to stall. Then back again to first and then down into low reduction.

My position on the extreme right of the diamond formation must be maintained. I slide open the driver's window to let in some fresh air but all that comes in is a billowing cloud of dust. Which is worse? To keep all doors and windows tightly shut and keep out no more than ninety per cent of the dust, as it will seep through the badly fitting doors and windows, or open up the windscreen and windows and get lashed by the cooler but more abrasive sand and grit? My mouth is as dry as a ball of wool and fine grit has worked in between my teeth. I spit on the floor.

The engine is boiling. It's only just on the boil but precious water will be required to top it up. The oil must be getting thin in the heat of the engine. Can I smell burning rubber? There is a low sand dune ahead, not more than fifty yards across. Shall I avoid it by taking a long swing round to the right, or shall I take a chance and drive through the middle? I decide to drive straight through. I ram the gear lever into bottom and thrust forward the low reduction lever which reduces the gearing by half and engages the four wheel drive. It is an unhappy choice. The decision to try and force my quad through the sand dune is a bad one. The quad grinds to a halt and we are stuck in the soft sand. It is pointless to churn away, it will only sink in worse. The gunners all pile out of the quad and put their shoulders to the gun wheels. I slowly let out the clutch. We are just moving, Harold shouts to everyone to 'heave'. It is no good and we become stuck again, worse than ever.

The Troop Commander sees our predicament and halts the column. The gunners unhitch the gun and limber and without the weight of the gun I am able to drive forward thirty yards. I let out the winch which is slung under the back of the quad. The gunners hitch the great metal hook on the winch cable into the thick steel ring on the trail of the gun. Harold stands out on my right and raises his arm.

I push forward the winch lever and slowly let out the clutch. The great cable underneath the quad slowly turns and the wire rope tightens. Slowly the gun and limber are winched towards the quad, Harold brings down his arm. The gun is now up tight against the quad and Harold gives me the signal to drive forward another thirty yards and to release the winch cable. We had carried out this procedure many times during the past year. It was the only way to get a couple of tons of gun and limber and ammunition through the deep sand.

At last we were through. Everyone had known exactly what to do and we had only held up the convoy for six minutes.

We heard a long loud rumble in the distance. It could have been bombs, it could have been guns, or perhaps the sappers were blowing something up. You never knew.

CHAPTER SIXTEEN

The First Battle of Tobruk

SADLY THE NUMBERS of dead and wounded in the Battery mounted. In all, the Regiment had lost seventeen men killed and wounded at Bardia and another four had been killed by two Savoi fighters that had swooped down machine-gunning the convoy on its journey up to Tobruk. Reinforcements from the Royal Artillery Base at Almaza, on the outskirts of Cairo, were on their way.

The Troop gun positions outside Tobruk were in a very exposed position and the guns squatted on a flat desolate surface of rock and sand. There was no hill or crest in front of the guns, as recommended in the Artillery Manual, to shield the gun flashes from the enemy. With binoculars it was possible to discern the crows nests and observation towers used by the enemy and it wouldn't have been surprising if our guns and lorries were in view of the enemy O.P.'s.

It was a repeat of the steady build up that we experienced leading up to the Bardia battle. 'Stand to' before the first light, breech and muzzzle covers off and rifles at the ready, the resolute cursing and swearing in the cold dawn. The morning sun sticks its great yellow disc over the distant eastern horizon like the wheel of a fire god. Fires are lit, tea is brewed and breakfast is taken. There may be a call from the O.P. for a few rounds to pot at a moving vehicle or to scatter an enemy working party. After breakfast a walk into the desert with a shovel and army form blank in our pocket.

The sun climbs higher and throws out some warmth and there are hopes for the new day. Rumours abound. When are we going to attack?

A couple of bewildered looking reinforcements are dumped unceremoniously outside the entrance to the Command Post. Their webbing is white and their boots are still showing signs of polish. They are pale and suet faced from the English winter. They somehow look young against the weather hardened desert soldiers. There is a bang about a mile away and they look worried. 'What is that?' one of them says. We are unable to tell them. A bofors gun opens up at a high flying reconnaissance plane. Nothing to worry about, but these lads have just come from a bombed England and ask if there is an air raid shelter. We tell them that a little bit of thunder in the ear and banging is just the pride of the morning.

They were talking among themselves about a programme on the wireless at home called 'ITMA', with a comedian called Tommy Handley, and the one that had been trained as a signaller had actually seen Vera Lynn at an Army concert at Aldershot.

The fair haired one that is going on the guns looks as if he couldn't pull a spratt off a gridiron but in four weeks' time, living in the desert as a responsible member of a gun sub section, and with the sun making the blood run better through his body, he'll be a different man, I know that much.

*   *   *   *

The rocky Tobruk sea coast was two miles away from the guns, and when activity on the front was at a low ebb one man from each gun, one signaller and one driver from each troop were allowed to leave the gun position and go down to the sea for a swim. The duty swim truck was an Italian Lancia diesel lorry that we had captured at Bardia, and this was probably the first time that any of us had swum in the sea stark naked and, contrasting with our brown legs and bodies, our sun starved white bottoms bobbed up and down in the Mediterranean like a family of rabbits bolting for cover.

During the second week of impatiently waiting for the attack to begin, I went with the swimming party down to the beach and we met up with about thirty Australians from the 6th Infantry Division, who were also down for a swim. Many of them were from the 16th Infantry Brigade, and all of them seemed to have been in the forefront of the attack on Bardia. When they realised that we had put down that curtain of fire, behind which they had so successfully advanced into Bardia, they made much of us and there was instant cordial friendship. Out came the much prized Log Cabin tobacco, tins of Australian peaches and bottles of Australian beer.

'Gee,' said one chirpy round faced digger, called Barney, who had been in the thick of the Bardia battle, 'that artillery barrage was a honey, and I've only got one complaint.'

'What's that?' I said.

'Well,' he said, 'I had my rifle sights lined up on a bastard Itie, and I was just going to pull the trigger, when you bastards had to go and blow him up.'

All the Aussies were blackened by the sun and looked fit and mettlesome and full of voluntary energy. As gunners, we experienced rays of gladdened comfort and confidence to have this leather tough body of volunteers in front of us in the weapon pits. We tried on their bush hats and they made us some tea.

The biggest and toughest looking of them all was Captain Fraser. Someone had told us that to be an officer in the Australian army you had to be fitter and a better fighter than any of the men. Captain Frazer was six foot four and he must have weighed fifteen stone, and the hairs on his chest were like a doormat. The men called him Frank.

Frank Frazer helped his men make a dixie of tea for us and afterwards one of the others said, 'Frank, it's your turn to wash out the bastard billycan.'

Frank said, 'Stuff you Blue, it can't be my turn agin.'

*   *   *   *

Frank soon found out that I worked on a farm in England and he said, 'How big's the property you work on then Cobber?'

'Just under five hundred acres,' I said.

'Jesus,' said Frank, 'that's only a paddock. You surely can't make a living out of five hundred acres, what do you do in your spare time?'

'I don't have any spare time,' I said, 'and nine other men work on our farm.'

'My word,' said Frank. 'Well I'll tell you something,' Frank pulled his pack of cigarette papers out of his trouser pocket, 'me and my brother work three thousand acres between us.'

'Bloody hell,' I said, 'a three thousand acre farm in Suffolk would employ over forty men.'

'Where's your farm then, Frank?' I said.

'Our property is near a place called Leeton in New South Wales,' said Frank. 'It's about three hundred miles in from Sydney.'

'What do you grow on three thousand acres, stuck up there in the outback? I said.

Frank shook some loose tobacco on his opened cigarette paper.

'Leeton isn't outback,' said Frank. 'We've got the snow fed Murrumbidgee running close by and we can take out water and irrigate our rice.'

'Rice?' I said. 'I thought they only grew rice in India and China.'

'No,' said Frank, 'some of you Pommey bastards want to take a trip down under and see how we do things in Australia. First of all we level the paddock with a grader, so that we can flood irrigate the rice from the river. Then we let the paddock dry out and harvest the rice with a header. And if you want some dinkum duck shooting Albert, you should show up when the rice fields are flooded.'

'And I'll tell you something else,' said another Australian they called Jack. 'Up where Frank farms there's the biggest bastard snakes you ever did see.'

'They ain't as big as all that,' said Frank, 'the browns and the blacks ain't no more than six feet long. Anyway,' went on Frank, 'we haven't got any of those bastard tiger snakes round Leeton.'

'What else do you grow?' I said.

'Well,' said Frank, 'we've got 600 acres of wheat and four and a half thousand Merinos.'

The sheep are the biggest trouble and it ain't no use getting a Jackeroo in to help with the lambing because the bastard Merinos are so wild. They hardly ever have more than one and I've seen the bastards drop a lamb, turn round and look at it and then bugger off into the bush and leave the lamb for the first bastard dingo that comes around.'

'I'll tell you what,' said Frank, 'when we've won this war for King George, you want to come out to Leeton, and I'll show you a thing or two. It's not far from Wagga Wagga and there's a big airstrip there.'

'Here's my address,' and he wrote it on the back of my packet of Victory V's issue of cigarettes.

'What I can't understand,' I said, 'is how you can leave your farm in Leeton and come out here.'

'Well,' said Frank, 'me and my brother were running the station by ourselves and we tossed up to see who would join the army and who would stay behind, and I won. My wife, Mavis, and Rod's sheila, Jan, can run the sheep and can do most jobs. Mavis can ride a horse better 'n' any man, so the station won't come to any harm.'

In the meantime, half a dozen of the Diggers had moved up to a little creek a hundred yards along the shore, and they were throwing grenades into the water and this was sending several dead fish, bellies up, to the surface.

'Steady on you bastards,' shouted Frank, 'we might want them grenades in a few days time.'

'When do you reckon we'll be going into Tobruk?' I said.

It won't be more than a few days from now,' replied Frank, 'and we've got it all worked out. When you gunners have jacked in a two hour barrage, we are going to walk up to the wire and tell the Itie bastards to throw us over a pair of wire cutters and then we are going to cut the wire. Then we'll get hold of about twenty wops and get them to fill in the tank trap, and I can tell you it's a bloody great tank trap, bigger than the one at Bardia.'

'How do you know?' I asked.

'I saw it two nights ago when we were out on patrol,' replied Frank.

Troop Sergeant Major Evans was getting us all together for the return to our gun position.

'You know,' said Frank, 'my old man was killed in Gallipoli and my old Ma never did get over it.'

'I'm sorry,' I said, shaking his hand. 'So long, Frank.'

'So long sport, see yer in Bengazi.'

'Too true,' I said.

By the time we had returned to our gun position, sitting in the well of the open topped Italian Lancia lorry, in spite of a swim and a good wash down in the sea, we were covered in a thick layer of grimy dust and sand.

★   ★   ★   ★

By the 19th January all ammunition needed for the main barrage had been ferried to the forward battle positions. Gun pits had been prepared and covered with camouflage netting. All the initial targets for the opening barrage had been surveyed in by the specialists, and during the hours of darkness the guns were quietly drawn up and set on their zero lines like eager crocodiles with eyes on their prey.

There was little sleep for anyone. It was Bardia all over again.

For this barrage I was to be the gunlayer on Harold Reeve's gun. Philip Underwood had a poisoned finger and was slightly under the weather.

The specialist G.P.O. ack was Lance Bombadier Simon Wilson, an insurance salesman from Hadleigh, and just after midnight he set up his director, which is a micrometer on a three-legged stand, some forty yards behind the guns, and called out the angle to each gun. On the director itself there was a small pinpoint light. I used this light as my aiming point, and by rotating the micrometer head on my gun dial sight while looking through the eye piece, I set the gun on the zero line called by the G.P.O. Ack. Although I had layed the gun many times before, this was to be my first barrage as a gunlayer and I felt just a bit proud to be doing it.

With all the guns in parallel, numbers two, four and five were able to start opening out the ammunition boxes and sticking them in tidy heaps beside the gun. At 0515 hours orders were given to 'Take Posts', and the subsection took up its position round the gun, making last miunute checks and waiting for the 'countdown'.

I sat on the small round wooden seat just behind the nearside gun wheel with the long barrel of the gun reaching forward on my right side, and I had a strange feeling of exhilaration.

At 0530 hours Hester-Hewitt gave the order to 'Fire'. I struck the firing lever and simultaneously guns from other batteries opened up all round the perimeter. The creeping barrage of concentrated artillery fire was programmed to last for four hours with a twenty minute break in the middle.

The range was set at five thousand two hundred yards. After every five rounds gunfire, the range was increased by twenty-five yards. The recoil on a twenty-five pounder is savage and, occasionally when fired, the gun will kick into the air, and will be thrown off line. After every round, therefore, the gun has to be layed afresh and adjusted by relining on the aiming point or reference object.

No one was wearing a tin hat. We reckoned that tin hats were an uncomfortable waste of time unless we were being attacked by salvoes of 'airburst'. A piece of shrapnel travelling at three thousand feet per second or a bullet would cut through a British Army tin hat like a dart through the sports page of the 'News of the World'.

Sitting there on the gun layer's seat in the dark dawn and with my hand firmly controlling the firing lever, I had an uncanny and a slightly frightening feeling of high elation and power.

Every fifteen seconds, from our regiment alone, twenty-four shells were fired off into the darkness, and the ground shook with the pounding vibration. Each gun was programmed to fire no less than five tons of high explosive shells during the bombardment.

Ahead of us, in the early morning darkness, the clattering and screeching of the heavy caterpillar tracks of the Matilda tanks could be heard as they progressed forward into the close battle area. This was followed by the thunder of the enemy guns as they hunted for our gun positions. An early shell landed very adjacent to our tight sweep of territory, followed by another even closer, and then a cluster of four just ahead of us and another salvo hard by on our left. The enemy shelling was getting too close for comfort and the air stank of smoke and cordite as the flames of vengeance hurled themselves upwards in this blizzard of steel.

Then a hot blast of air like a dragon's breath and a rushing roar, like an express train. Hot furious shell splinters coursed through the air and made vicious music in the deep blue dawn. This latest explosion seemed to be at our very fingers end, and there was the scream of a wounded man close by on our left. We soon perceived that number four gun had been hit.

When the smoke cleared a little, there were bodies on the ground. Sergeant

Don White, whose wife had left him for another man, lay sprawled across the trail of his gun and he died with the wooden ramrod, which had thrust hundreds of shells into the breach of his gun, lying across his chest. Don White, who had narrowly escaped death at Bardia, had been a ideal gun sergeant. He was steady and brave and took endless trouble nursing his detachment along. The plundering civilian who was sleeping with Don's wife in the safety of rural England would never know.

Lance Bombardier Alan Bolingbroke, the gunlayer, was still cast on the blood soaked gun seat and slumped over his smashed dialsight, killed as he adjusted the micrometer head to increase the range.

Gunner 'Nut' Humphreys, a trainee baker from Long Melford, was cut down and sent to his last account with a shell in his hand as he prepared to ram it in the breech.

Gunner Jonathon Hancock and Gunner Sidney Cook were still alive but badly wounded, and there was little hope for either as they tottered on the brink of life.

An experienced battle trained crew, irreplaceable in the short term, wiped out in that sudden fleeting obscene moment. We all had a mind to go over and help our stricken comrades, but we had to shut our ears to the cries of the wounded as we were in the middle of a programmed barrage and there were infantry out on the start line.

We were so busy and occupied, and so fully absorbed in the fire programme in the gun pits, that we scarcely noticed two drivers from the Battery waggon lines, gently lift the bodies of our three dead comrades into the back of a fifteen hundredweight truck and drive off. Neither had we witnessed the overworked, dust covered, field ambulance removing the two badly wounded men. Somehow, in these concentrated moments, on our small tight patch, we seemed remote from all the thews and tension of the outside world.

Just after daybreak six Gloster Gladiators flew overhead in the dawn sky at great speed from west to east. Well, I say at great speed but when at maximum speed they could only fly at 250 m.p.h. at fourteen thousand feet. Peter Bristow, the Signals Sergeant, looked up and said, 'They ought never to let our pilots fly those sodding things, these bloody biplanes were obsolete ten years ago. I know they've about half a dozen Hurricances out here, but they want to send fifty Spitfires out here as well. My brother-in-law is out here with 33 Squadron and all they've got are these clapped out Gladiators. My sister would do her nut if she knew how slow they were.'

At a quarter to seven the Aussie engineers loosed off Bangalore torpedoes in two places to blow gaps in the wire, and shortly afterwards Matilda 'I' tanks ploughed through the gaps followed by the Australian infantry. Once again our forward troops were inside the enemy outer defences.

*   *   *   *

It was just after ten o'clock and the main fire programme was over. My eyes were sore from peering into the dial sight, my right arm ached from the firing lever and my ears were ringing behind a dull, persistant headache. We were thinking about a mug of tea and a smoke.

Sergeant Major Evans footed it in sharp steps over to our gun, and asked me if I could drive a Bren Carrier. He knew as well as I did, that I had been on a week's course on Bren Carriers at Haifa, so I said, 'Well, I didn't come top of the class, but I reckon I can get one along.'

'Well,' said Sergeant Major Evans, 'Mr. Kershaw has just returned from the O.P., as the wireless set on the carrier has packed up, and he has come for a replacement. Mr. Kershaw is anxious to return to the O.P. as soon as possible with the new set.'

'What is there to stop him?' I asked.

'Young Summers, his driver, has lost his nerve. He's been sick twice and Mr. Kershaw says he's useless.'

'So Mr. Kershaw wants me to drive him back to the O.P.?' I said.

'That's the general idea,' said Sandy Evans. 'Bombadier Underwood has just come back from the M.O. and he is ready to take your place as layer on Number One Gun.'

*   *   *   *

I gathered together my haversack and bedroll and made my way over to the Bren Carrier which stood by the Command Post. Lieutenant Kershaw was there and he said, 'Morning Bombardier Cooper, so you're going to drive us back to the O.P.'

'Yes, sir,' I replied.

'Are you happy driving Bren Carriers?' he asked.

'No trouble at all, sir,' I said, 'went on a week's course in Haifa last June.'

'Well, this will be a little different from a week's course in Haifa,' laughed Lieutenant Kershaw.

I liked Adrian Kershaw. He was a good soldier and got on well with everyone and, believe it or not, I was really looking forward to going through the wire.

I topped up the carrier with petrol and checked the oil and water levels, loaded up my bedroll and hard rations and stuck my water bottle under the driver's seat.

Our O.P. party consisted of Lieutenant Kershaw, Ralph Bowman as O.P. ack, Ernie Briggs as signaller, and myself. I squeezed into the driving seat and started up the powerful Ford V-8 engine.

'Right away,' said Lieutenant Kershaw, and I slowly let out the clutch. I was glad to be driving a tracked vehicle again as they seldom got stuck in the sand. It took me a few seconds to get used to the steering as the steering wheel was sensitive, and it was easy to over correct and get into a skid turn.

The Bren Carrier was stirring up a lot of dust and, as the carrier was open topped and low to the ground, we collected great clouds of fine, powdery trash from other vehicles. A squadron of Crusader tanks was moving beside us to the windward. They were creating their own private dust storm and we seemed to come in for most of it.

Within ten minutes we had reached the minefields. A white tape was pegged either side of the lane where the mines had been lifted, and I kept my eyes skimmed on the centre of the narrow corridor. Closely following the white markers we came to the second minefield. 'You want to be careful here,' said Lieutenant Kershaw, 'the Ities have laid poles across three mines, and if you drive over the pole all three mines go up at once. That would be enough to knock a tank out and would blow us to smithereens.'

Just ahead I could see the bridge that the engineers had flung over the tank trap two hours earlier.

The enemy artillery was planting a couple of shells every fifteen seconds or so at close quarters to the tank trap bridge. As we drove across, some shrapnel crashed against the armour plate by my right shoulder. 'Glad I wasn't in my quad,' I said, 'that lot would have gone right through us.' This was certainly no place to hang about.

Several platoons of the Australian infantry were wearily making their way in single file back into reserve. These were men from the 17th Brigade and they had taken part in the first assault wave. The 19th Brigade was now moving forward to take their place in the spearhead.

There were groups of dishevelled and dejected looking Italian infantry around with their hands up. They were like a flock of bottle fed broody hens. They didn't know where to go to surrender and we had no time to pay any attention to them.

We found the Australian Battalion Commander and he said that there were a couple of mortars over the hill, and they were holding up his infantry. He asked Mr. Kershaw if he could bring fire down on them.

Lieutenant Kershaw said, 'We shall have to go forward a bit to try and get a sight of them. Drive on Bombardier Cooper.'

I drove the carrier forward nearly three hundred yards and suddenly we were met by a hail of machine gun fire. Lieutenant Kershaw, who had been standing up in the carrier, bobbed down very quickly as the bullets thudded against the side of the carrier.

'Hard left hand down,' shouted Lieutenant Kershaw, 'and make for that bunker with the mound on top.' It was a time for quick decisions.

I put my foot down and did a U-turn, and slewed the carrier round behind the bunker and hit the brakes. We all scrambled out, with Ernie carrying the wireless set, and dropped into the trench which was connected to a small concrete pill box. The enemy machine gun was still stuttering away and we kept our heads down, I can tell you.

Once in the bunker, which had been hastily abandoned by the Fascist infantry, only brief minutes before, Ralph and I found two observation slits in the concrete parapet. We both spotted the machine gun at the same time.

The gun was cunningly placed in a depression half way up the south facing slope of the rising ground. It was between three hundred and four hundred yards away, and it was being fired through camouflage netting.

'Here it is, sir,' I said, and Lieutenant Kershaw moved to the observation slit with his binoculars, while Ralph took a compass bearing to the target.

Ralph pulled out the map and he and Adrian Kershaw agreed the map reference of the machine gun position. Ralph made a red cross with his chinagraph pencil on the cellophane map cover. The position of our guns was clearly marked on the map. By drawing a line on the map from the guns to the map position of the enemy machine gun, Ralph was able, with a protractor, to measure the bearing and range from guns to target.

'What do you make it Bombardier?' asked Adrian Kershaw.

'Zero plus two four degrees, four thousand six hundred.' Lieutenant Kershaw quickly checked Ralph's work.

In the meantime, I had helped Ernie Briggs to set up his wireless set, and within three minutes we had the batteries in place and the aerial up and were in radio contact with the gun command post.

'Through, sir,' said Ernie.

'Take posts,' shouted the Lieutenant.

'Take posts,' Ernie Briggs relayed down to the guns.

'Target machine gun, zero two four degrees, four thousand six hundred.'

'Number One Gun ranging one round gunfire.'

'FIRE!'

I thought of Harold Reeve, standing there at the trail of his gun, and Philip Underwood, taking my place as gun layer, setting the switch and range and angle of sight.

Ten seconds later we heard the gun firing behind us. The shell whistled over our heads and landed about one hundred and fifty yards behind the target and slightly to the right.

'Less two degrees four four fifty.'

This time the shell landed directly behind the machine gun, but it was still a plus.

'Drop fifty, five rounds gunfire.'

The response from the troop was exciting to watch. Since the morning disaster on No. 4 gun there had been only three troop guns in action and they sent over fifteen shells which completely obliterated the target area.

'I think that's done the trick,' said Adrian Kershaw, as he lowered his binoculars.

'Briggs, send back "Target destroyed, stand easy"!'

'Good shootin' fellas,' said a voice behind us.

We had not noticed the Australian Major slip into the bunker beside us.

'Now,' said the Major to Lieutenant Kershaw, 'can you do anything about those two mortars? They are holding us up.'

By now our signal section had laid a line up to the O.P. and we were in contact with the guns by telephone. The signallers, Ernie Chapman and Stan Palmer, had bravely come through shot and shell to reach our bunker with the reel.

There was a lot of shelling and mortaring going on and the two enemy mortars were still lobbing bombs over our heads into the Australian infantry. The mortar on the right hand side seemed to be at least three hundred yards away, but the one on the left was so close that Lieutenant Kershaw decided that he dare not risk ranging shots as there was a danger of shells falling among our own men.

Lieutenant Kershaw then made the decision to attempt to knock out the mortar on the right and, as he was unable to see the mortar position from the bunker, he announced that he was going to crawl forward to try and spot its exact location.

He said to Ernie, 'You come with me, Briggs, bring the telephone and run out some cable as we go. If we can reach that burnt out half track over there I think we shall be able to see the mortar.'

We helped them both out of the bunker and they crawled forward towards the half track, with Ernie dragging the telephone wire.

The Aussie Major then said: 'I don't think your officer will be able to do anything about this mortar on the left. The bastard's a lot too close.'

I don't know what came over me at that moment but in the corner of the bunker, in a green wooden box, were about a dozen hand grenades. They were Italian grenades and resembled small red money boxes but the spring and firing pins were very similar to the Mills bombs I had thrown during a live ammunition practice session in a wadi at Beer Sheba, in Palestine.

My mind was working very clearly and, to tell you the truth, I was getting a bit scared sitting in the bunker and doing nothing, so I said to the Aussie Major, 'I reckon I could crawl round the edge of those rocks over there and get behind that mortar, and I might get a chance to chuck one or two of these cricket balls at them.'

The Major laughed when I called the grenades 'cricket balls' but I recalled that when I used to play cricket for Newton Green I could throw a ball back to the wicket keeper better than anyone. I used to aim at the wicket keeper's head and the ball nearly always went straight into his gloves. I didn't tell the Major that, but I said, 'I've thrown dozens of these, sir.' Well it wasn't any good telling him that I had only pitched two grenades in my life.

The Major said, 'Well cobber, you're not under my command and I reckon I can't stop you.'

Ralph, who was watching Lieutenant Kershaw and Ernie worming their way forward, heard our conversation and said, 'I'll see you get a State funeral, Albert.'

I said, 'I don't reckon it will come to that Ralph.'

I picked up three grenades and stuck them in a small Itie haversack which I had tied to my waist, and scrambled up over the sheltered side of the bunker.

'Good luck, cobber,' said the Major.

My hands were shaking with apprehension, and with the fantasy of it all.

I could clearly hear the Italians on the mortar being given fire orders and, every few seconds, a mortar bomb flew over our heads and burst two or three hundred yards behind. I kept my head down and ran flat out for about fifty yards and flattened myself on the ground behind a pile of ammunition boxes. My heart was pounding away like a woodpecker at half cock.

I was beginning to feel really keyed up and my mind was itchy with the raw edge of fear, but I told myself to steady up and not to do anything addle-brained and foolish. There were to be no more ill-judged deeds of rashness and I certainly didn't intend to run forward any more. From now on my purpose was to crawl along carefully and guardedly on my belly.

It was awkward crawling along with the small haversack of grenades which kept falling down and hanging in my way. I wished that I had tied them closer to my belt at the back.

Four single ranging shells exploded over to the right, followed by five rounds gunfire, and I hoped that it was Lieutenant Kershaw putting paid to the other mortar. A little light breeze had sprung up and the dust got into my eyes and mouth, and I regretted that I had not been wearing protective sand goggles, but I was able to crawl forward another fifty yards unseen while the dust was swirling around.

And then suddenly I saw them in a shallow pit with a tight ring of sandbags round the top. There were three men in close fitting steel helmets behind the mortar, and they were still intensely absorbed with loading and firing off the bombs. They were half hidden by a small rocky outcrop. I wormed my way out to the left and was able to get round behind and within forty yards of the mortar. It was like creeping up on a feeding rabbit. It was dead easy. Everything had been in my favour. There was quite a lot of machine gunning from our lines, and a considerable amount of noise over on the right, but nothing fell anywhere near.

As there was still a bit of dust blowing about, I felt very tempted to stand up and rush the pit yelling at the top of my voice, but then I thought, 'This is not a bayonet charge. For Christ's sake don't panic.' I was keyed up and no mistake, but they had not spotted me and I was able to move forward the moment they fired the next mortar. It was a bit like a game we played in the school playground, called 'Grandmother's footsteps', when we tried to get closer to someone standing in the front. If they turned round and caught you moving, you were 'it' and you paid the penalty.

I was now within thirty yards and spurred by a desperate all embracing excitement, I decided to have a go the moment they fired the next bomb. Lying on my left side I felt round with my right hand and took a grenade out of my haversack, keeping my eyes riveted on the pit. I pulled the pin and held the grenade and spring tightly in my right hand. My breathing was faster, and now there was a pause which seemed to stretch into infinity. The mortar crew were still intent on their work.

Immediately the next bomb was fired I stood up, weighed up the distance and tossed the grenade into the bowels of the pit. It was the easiest thing in the world, it really was. I flung myself on the ground as the impact of the high explosive charge ripped through the pit.

I couldn't believe what I had done, neither could I assume that I had put all the mortar crew out of action, so I took out another grenade, pulled the pin, and suddenly realised that I had been foolish to stand up to throw the first grenade. In fact I had behaved like a rookie. It should be no trouble to toss the second grenade with a good right overarm bowl, lying on my left side just like the marines do in the pictures. But my second grenade hit the sandbagged parapet, rolled a little way down the slope and exploded a good ten feet away from the pit. It was a pitiful shot.

I lay there for a few seconds and then tried to stand up, but I felt so bloody weak and my legs seemed incapable of movement. When I got up on to my hands and knees I found my knees had gone right through my trousers, and my elbows were bleeding with all this crawling around. I was shaking like a leaf and the sweat was runnelling down my face. I said aloud to myself, 'Pull yourself together Albert, you're acting like a big girl.' But I still couldn't stop shaking and my teeth were chattering. I must have looked a short-winded, drivelling goat out there on my hands and knees. I hadn't received a scratch but I was still filled with nerve stretching tension, and I was so bloody tired.

Gripped by a spasm of determination, I had just decided to make another attempt to stand up when someone grasped me by my shoulders and said, 'Are you all right mate?' and there, standing above me, were two Australian infantrymen wearing the 6th Australian Division shoulder flashes.

One of them, a corporal, said to the other man, 'Just go over and have a look at the mortar pit Snowy, and be careful that none of the bastards slips a bullet into you.'

The corporal sat me up and pulled out his water bottle and said, 'Take a swig of this mate.' To tell you the truth I felt more like being sick than drinking, in fact I didn't know what I did want.

I took the bottle from the corporal and held it to my lips and I soon discovered that the water bottle was half full of Italian brandy. I gulped down two large swigs of the heavy potent liquor and my stomach burned. I hadn't realised that my insides had been so cold.

Snowy shouted over, 'Not much to worry about here, Jim, these bastards have been blasted all over the fugging miadem.'

'Good-oh, well done mate,' said the corporal to me, helping me to my feet. I stood up and started to walk back round the little hill, between the corporal and Snowy. The Australian Major came out to meet us. 'Well done, Pom,' he said. 'I reckon you'd have run out half the Australian team the way you threw those grenades.

I was still carrying the haversack, and there was one grenade left, and the Australian Major, who they called Lew, gently took the haversack from me and put his arm though mine, he could see that I was just about all in and said, 'Take it easy, Sport, you've done a dinkum job.'

A strange, warm feeling came over me for these tough, friendly fellow kinsmen from the other side of the world who were getting me back to base.

When we reached the bunker Ralph was standing beside the bren carrier and checking that the connections in the signal wire to the guns were all in one piece.

'So you've come back then, you old sod,' said Ralph, 'I've been looking at the controls of the bren carrier in case I might have to drive it home.'

'Sorry to disappoint you Ralph,' I said.

The intense activity and racketing in our sector had now slackened off and we were left with the busy background hum of war. The Infantry had moved up over the hill. Ralph pulled out his bed roll from the well of the carrier and half unrolled it.

'Come on, Albert,' he said, 'park yourself down here for a bit, you look shagged out.'

He went on, 'Kershaw and Ernie are on their way back from the O.P., they should be here in ten minutes. The relief O.P. party is on its way up to spend the night at the Australian Company Command Post and we should be back on the gun position before dark.'

When Lieutenant Kershaw and Ernie arrived they were looking flushed and pleased with themselves. 'We got the mortar with four ranging shots and five rounds gunfire,' said Lieutenant Kershaw.

'Blew the bastards to smivvereens,' said Ernie, with a wide grin.

'I reckon the other mortar was knocked out by a Matilda of the Infantry,' said Lieutenant Kershaw.

'No. Albert knocked that one out,' said Ralph.

Lieutenant Kershaw just laughed, and he didn't know until the next morning that I had popped a couple of grenades into the mortar pit.

When the relief O.P. truck arrived we climbed back into the carrier and I squeezed into the driving seat. 'Right Bombadier Cooper. Start her up,' ordered Lieutenant Kershaw, 'and head back towards the guns. I want to get back through the minefields before it gets dark.'

I pressed the starter and the carrier's engine burst into life. The drive back to the guns, sitting low down, and tightly wedged into the carrier, was a bit of a dream for me, as I was deadly weary and could hardly keep awake. It was almost two days since I had had any sleep and my five hour stint in the gun layer's seat for the early morning barrage was beginning to take toll of my senses. Half-an-hour later, as darkness was closing in, we found the gun position and drew in to the Troop Command Post. Harold Reeve and Kevin hurried over from the guns and Kevin said, 'Well I'm glad to see you back in one piece, Albert. We were getting a shade uneasy about the O.P. party.'

'We're O.K., Kevin,' I said, 'but between us all we've had a regular day and a half.'

Harold said, 'Albert, there's some hot stew in the cookhouse truck.'

'Harold,' I said, 'I'm too tired to eat a bloody thing.' So they laid me down on some blankets in the corner of the gun pit. I pulled a greatcoat over my ears and slept like a dead man for fourteen hours.

CHAPTER SEVENTEEN

Albert Gets a Gun

IT WAS MID-MORNING when I awoke. There had been a few spasms of firing but I had slept right through. Now all was subdued and quiet after the chastening rawness of the previous day. Kevin was sitting on the rolled up camouflage net at the end of my blankets.

'I don't reckon you needed much rocking to sleep,' he said.

'What time is it Kevin?' I asked.

'Soon be ten.'

'What's going on?' I said, reaching for my cigarettes.

'This little bit of war seems to be over,' said Kevin. 'I reckon that over four thousand prisoners came through here this morning.'

Kevin struck a match and lit my cigarette.

'I hear you were rorting about round the O.P. yesterday,' he said. 'They tell me that you knocked out a couple of mortars.'

'Only one,' I said.

'Don't think Julie would be too pleased if she knew that I'd let you go rorting about playing soldiers,' said Kevin. 'What did you think you were? A bloody platoon of infantry. You're a silly Bugger, Albert.'

Troop Sergeant Major Sandy Evans came over and said, 'Lance Bombadier Cooper, Major Coleman wants to see you at the Battery Command Post at twelve o'clock, so smarten yourself up and get some of that hair off your face. I'll be back for you in about an hour's time.'

Kevin brought me a mug of hot water from the cookhouse truck.

'See you stand close to the razor,' he said.

When T.S.M. Evans and I arrived at the Battery Command Post, Major Coleman was standing by the Wireless truck with his hands in his pockets.

'Morning Sar'nt Major. Morning Cooper.'

'Morning Sir,' we said, and we both saluted.

King Cole had spent a lot of the previous day at the B. Troop O.P. He said: 'I hear Cooper that Mr. Kershaw had a good day's sport yesterday.'

'Yes, sir,' I said. 'He knocked out a mortar and a machine gun.'

'I'm afraid,' said Major Coleman,' that my birds didn't fly too well and I had rather a blank day.' He had obviously been unable to see much of the enemy from his O.P. and said, 'The reason I have sent for you Cooper concerns Number Four gun. As you know, yesterday we lost Sergeant White and the whole of his subsection.'

'Yes, sir,' I said.

'Well,' said Major Coleman, 'Number Four gun was so badly damaged that it has had to be sent to base workshop for repairs, but a new gun is arriving from Ordnance later this morning. How would you like to take over as Number One on the new gun?'

'But I am only a Lance Bombardier, sir,' I said.

'Cooper,' went on the Major, 'you would be be made up to Lance Sergeant and I hope you will take it on.'

Well, I don't think anyone could be more proud than to be Number One of a gun subsection with three stripes up and all, so I said: 'I'd certainly like to do that, sir.'

'Good,' said Major Coleman.

'But there is one thing that I would like to ask for, sir,' I said.

'And what's that Cooper?'

'I'd like to have Gunner Porter on my gun as gunlayer.'

'I understand that Gunner Porter is going to be your brother-in-law after the war?' said Major Coleman with a smile.

'That's what I understand as well, sir,' said Sandy Evans.

Now, how in the hell did they know that.

'Yes. I'll have a word with Captain Kershaw and see if he can arrange for you to have Gunner Porter on your gun.'

'Thank you, sir,' I said, 'but did you say Captain Kershaw?'

'Yes,' said the Major. 'The Colonel made Mr. Kershaw up to Captain yesterday and he is now going to be your A Troop Commander. 'There's one other thing, Cooper,' he went on, 'the Australian Company Commander of the Nineteenth Brigade had a word with me this morning and he said you did a good job on that mortar pit yesterday. In fact he was very pleased with his gunner support and he has recommended that both you and Captain Kershaw should be put in for a medal.'

I had never had twenty-four strange raw hours like this in my life. It was another surprise, another turn of the unexpected and I was almost unable to believe my compass of thoughts.

'Thank you, sir,' I said.

'If I were you I shouldn't say anything about a medal to anyone. It may not come to anything.'

'I won't mention it, sir,' I said.

'Right, that will be all Sergeant Major.'

We saluted, did a right turn and walked back to the Troop position.

Sandy Evans said, 'You'll be able to join us in the Sergeant's Mess when we get back to base camp, Albert.'

I was as happy as a kitten with wool.

Back on the gun position when Sandy Evans told them that I was going to get the new gun, Harold Reeve came up and shook me by the hand and said: 'Congratulations, Albert. I shall be sorry to lose you from my gun and, if you are going to take Kevin away from me as well, you might be able to lick into shape a gun sub as good as mine.

I then realised that I was joining a very special conclave of Men at Arms.

You wouldn't find three sounder, first rate, gun sergeants than the Numbers One of A Troop if you combed the British Army. On Number One gun there was Harold Reeve, on Number Two, Neville Steele and on Number Three, Brendan McLean. I swear that there were not three better Sergeants in the Artillery in North Africa and every one of them would have died for his subsection. Now, here I was, Sergeant of Number Four gun and I was in duty bound, charged with the task of making my subsection as efficient as the others. Although we were confident that we had the best troop of guns in Africa none of us could forget Don White, Alan Bolingbroke and 'Nut' Humphreys who, only two days before were fighting Number Four gun and who would soon be laid to rest somewhere in the cemetery in Tobruk and Curly Hancock and Sidney Cook who were now in hospital somewhere in the Nile Delta with terrible wounds.

By shortly after mid-day the few remaining pockets of resistance had been shelled into submission and, during the afternoon, the Australian Commander of the Nineteenth Brigade entered Tobruk and accepted the surrender of the Italian Admiral and General in charge of the Fortress. Great columns of smoke rose from the town, over thirty thousand prisoners had been taken and we had captured two hundred and thirty-six enemy guns.

Even if we did no more fighting we had experienced enough, during the battles for Bardia and Tobruk, to last us for the rest of our lives. We were not to know at the time that the 51st (West Suffolk Yeomanry) Regiment, Royal Horse Artillery had many months and years of desert warfare ahead and that the Regiment was to play a major part in battles which were to make history in the years to come.

The next morning I felt as though I'd just come into an estate. I was the proudest man in the Western Desert Force. With three stripes up I was summoned to the Command Post and there stood a brand new twenty-five pounder gun, complete with limber and gun towing quad. Everything had been newly painted in the desert camouflage colours and the limber was full of charges and ammunition. I had always thought that Harold Reeve was half in love with his gun and somehow I felt like I did that afternoon on the farm, three years earlier, when the foreman told me I could drive the new tractor.

Sandy Evans said, 'This is your gun, Albert, don't lose it and mind you don't scratch the new paint!'

'I reckon we'll soon burn the paint off the barrel,' I said. 'Where's the rest of my sub?'

'Your driver is over there in your Quad,' said Sandy Evans, 'he's from New Zealand.' He shouted, 'Gunner Barrowclough, come over here and meet your Number One.'

A tall, bronzed young man with a mop of unruly fair hair climbed down from his Quad and came over and held out his hand.

'Glad to meet you, Sarge,' he said.

'Welcome to the subsection, Gunner Barrowclough,' I said. 'How does a Kiwi come to find himself in the British army?'

'Well, Sarge, I was over in Britain looking for a few decent Romney rams to import into New Zealand when war was declared, so I sent my Dad a wire to say that I wouldn't be home for a few weeks and then I wangled into the second draft of Militia.'

'What happened to you then?' I said.

'I got sent to Oswestry for training, passed out as a driver and then spent the next few months buggering about round Woolwich, doing guards and fatigues and sod all else.'

'The barracks at Woolwich should have been bulldozed into the river years ago,' I said.

'Too right,' said Gunner Barrowclough.

'Done much driving?' I asked.

'Well, back in New Zealand my father has got thirty thousand acres of high country in Otago in South Island and I've got an old Holden four-wheel drive utility, and I reckon I can get that old crate over most of it.'

'What's your first name?' I said.

'Ross,' said Gunner Barrowclough.

'Right then, Ross,' I said, 'come and have a mug of char.' I liked the look of my driver and my emerging subsection was beginning now to take shape as I had Kevin as my gun layer and, what is more, he had been told to put a stripe up.

My first ammunition number reported to me during the afternoon and said that he was being transferred from the water cart on to my gun. He was Jock McKinley who had joined the troop as a reinforcement at the Bagush Box in October last year. We all knew Jock. He was a determined ginger haired Scotsman with fair, bushy eyebrows and a pugnacious face. We knew that he had scant patience with authority and he had a short fuse and sometimes got into fights when on leave. In spite of loud and frequent moanings about the Army in general Jock wouldn't hear a word against the Royal Horse Artillery when in the bars of Tel Aviv. You could almost say that Jock didn't give a damn about anybody. In civilian life he lived in a 'back to back' in a small town in Scotland, called Plean, which lay between Stirling and Falkirk. Plean, he informed everyone, was only a mile or two from Bannockburn and Jock never tired of reminding everyone what King Robert Bruce had done to the English at Bannockburn over six hundred years ago. He was barrel chested and as strong as an ox and he was said to enjoy humping ammunition. When the water cart wasn't out he would often be taken back to the Ammo dump to help load up the Battery three tonners. I thought that Jock would make a good Number Two on the gun.

My second ammunition number arrived later that evening. He had just joined the regiment from the Artillery Base at Almaza, near Cairo the day before. His name was Francis Ellington. He was dark and handsome looking. In fact, he looked more Italian than English. When he spoke it was with a faint lisp and, when I asked him what he did in civvy street, he said that he was one of Ivor Novello's dancers. This was a turn up for the books and this piece of somewhat staggering information produced many scandalised comments from the soldiery who cast sniggering reflections on the supposed morals of Francis who, they had decided, was a queer. They couldn't understand how a male dancer could be anything else.

Jock was, as usual, the most outspoken and he said, 'If he's not a poof, then my prick's a bloater. He should have stayed at R.H.Q. and been the R.S.M.'s bumboy.'

Philip Underwood said, 'Don't be so coarse, Jock. I've had a long chat with Francis and I don't believe he's a "fairy", but I can tell you one thing and that is, as far as Ivor Novello is concerned, Francis thinks that the sun shines out of his arsehole.'

I agreed with Philip and I was convinced that the boys were wrong about Francis. Over the next few weeks Gunner Ellington proved to be very strong and always did his share of the work and, when you come to think of it, you have to be fit and strong to dance around for an hour or more on the stage at Drury Lane. I certainly never saw Francis sodding around with anyone and he was a lively member of my gun sub until he was killed in the desert war many months later.

*   *   *   *

If you run the eye over the map of Libya and bring into focus the eastern province known as Cyrenaica, you will see that a substantial land mass some two hundred miles long and one hundred miles wide juts into the Mediterranean. The coast road runs round the northern edge of this bulge through the small colonised town of Derna and on to the capital city, Benghazi. From Benghazi the road courses due south for one hundred and fifty miles to the southern tip of the Gulf of Sirte and then leads into the Western Province of Libya, known as Tripolitania. The scattered remains of Mussolini's Italian army were now in full retreat and were fleeing towards Benghazi and then south along the narrow coast road, intent on reaching the comparative safety of Tripolitania.

Our Commander, the British General, O'Connor, a small resolute Irishman, decided to take his greatest gamble and the game was in his hand. The master plan was that the Australians should pursue the fleeing Italian forces round the coast road, while the Seventh Armoured Division, of which we were a part, should make a forced march south and west across the northern edge of the Sahara Desert to cut the enemy's escape road a hundred miles south of Benghazi.

This was a bold and spectacular plan and there was intense activity, checking equipment and loading stores as the Regiment prepared for the long cross country march, at the end of which, we should be called upon to fight a battle. The logistics of getting a full armoured division across two hundred miles of virtually unknown, and much of it unmapped desert territory, were horrendous.

All trucks were issued with five days emergency rations and we drew a week's emergency supply of water. Forty gallons of petrol in four gallon cans were stacked high on the roof of each quad and made fast with hessian ropes. With all this inflamable fuel and explosive ammunition aboard, our quads had the potential of transforming into a massive fire bomb.

At daybreak I took Kevin, Ross, Jock and Francis out into the desert to calibrate my new gun. Each Battery had what is termed a 'standard' gun which had been absolutely calibrated and the other guns in the unit were comparatively calibrated by firing against the standard gun. The object of the calibration is to ensure that the muzzle velocities of all the guns in the Regiment are known so that it is possible for all the guns to engage a single target which has been registered by one gun only. Harold Reeve's gun was K. Battery's standard gun and our two guns stood side by side on the measured range. We each fired eleven rounds at different ranges and using different charges and the gun fitter made the necessary adjustments to the gun. Afterwards, Kevin, who was my gun layer, patted the sleek yellow-painted barrel and said: 'She's a beautiful gun, Albert.' I could already detect that mysterious reflective bond between my gun crew and their new gun.

Our blood was running high and we were raring to go. There was an all pervading and sharpened sense of excitement. I had to keep reminding myself that two members of my subsection had not yet witnessed any fighting, Ross Barrowclough and Francis Ellington still had to learn that every noisy, nearby explosion, every enemy aircraft and every burning vehicle was not, of necessity, a signal for danger. There was no way I could warn them of how to distinguish when a distant swarm of enemy aircraft really meant business at close quarters. There was no way that I could prepare them for the experience of having salvoes of shells hurtling towards them in pitch darkness, when fire and thunder and steel leaped up from the murky blackness and smashed danger into the night.

CHAPTER EIGHTEEN

Crossing the Plateau of the Jebel Achdar

The first objective of our heavily armoured mobile force was to capture the Italian stronghold of Fort Mechili, which lay some 70 miles to the west, but when the spearhead of the Armoured Division arrived at Mechili, the Italians had flown. It was now late evening, the Division laagered at Mechili for the night.

At first light on the 3rd of February 1941, the whole of the 7th Armoured Division took to the desert and headed west. Our guns were moving in the centre of a highly trained, powerful formation. Ahead of us and on either side were fifty British cruiser tanks and eighty light tanks and it was a spectacular, majestic and thrilling moment to be part of this desert worthy, battle hardened British Division streaming out across the desert with pennants flying. It was like a fleet of harsh, droning hornets with iron wrapped buzzing engines. In this great, tangible mood of expectancy and the quickening of pace and movement, it was as if we were sailing a turbulent dust squall. The next purpose and intention was for the Division to rendezvous, before nightfall, at the small, insignificant Arab settlement of M'sus, which was a further hundred miles to the west.

The maps showed very little detail of this area and much of it was uncharted. There were no tokens of the works of man. There were no roads, not even a goat track and we were on the very edge of the Sahara.

The overland march throughout the course of the next day, driven by the spur of necessity, was something of a pressed pioneering expedition. The travelling conditions experienced during that long day were the worst that the Regiment experienced during the whole of the war. The desert was incredibly rough and strewn with massive boulders and the swaying, straining vehicles were bouncing and slewing over the craggy, notched earth. For the gunners in the bucking gun tractors in what seemed to be a boulder strewn Goliath's playground, it was as if they were being vigorously tossed on a hard bottomed runaway trampoline.

The dust thrown up by the massed, advancing columns of tanks, guns and supply trucks was sometimes so thick that at times it was necessary to come to a halt as it was impossible for the drivers to see through the yellow clouds of powdery sand.

General O'Connor and General Dorman-Smith, wearing open-necked shirts and red-banded caps, were there with us in their camouflaged staff car. At a brief halt to top up with petrol General O'Connor had a few words with Major Coleman. He said that our journey was a race against time and that it was essential for us to be astride the Benghazi escape road as early as possible on the following morning.

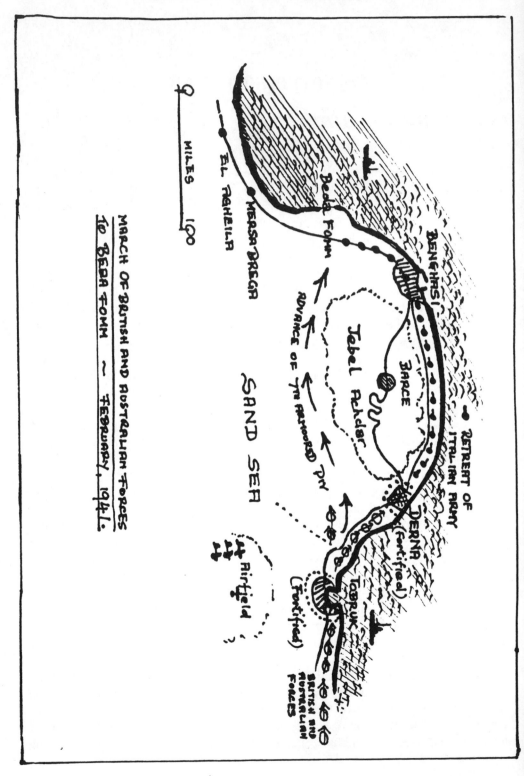

MARCH OF BRITISH AND AUSTRALIAN FORCES
To BEDA FOMM — FEBRUARY, 1941.

After the first fifty, torrid, dust laden miles the going improved but there were more treacherous dunes than before and, as we winched our gun out of the soft clinging sand for the third time that morning, it was easy to appreciate why the Bedouins had a preference for camel transport. Many tanks and trucks were being almost shaken apart in this wallowing, buffeting expedition and the hardest worked members of the Troop were the mechanics and fitters who were trying to set their collective will against the face and cunning of the desert. Most of the broken down vehicles, however, were repairable and able to join up with the Division later.

Ross from his High Country, New Zealand sheep farm, nursed our heavily laden, dust covered quad as it crept forward like a great sand beetle. The hot discomfort and the deep sounding, continuous roar of the churning engine gnawed at our patience and at our endurance.

Over this rough, bouncing country the gun and limber would occasionally become uncoupled from the quad. Punctures were another problem with the sharp rocks cutting into the tyres. Kevin, Francis and Jock sat on the wide seat behind me and for them it was hot, suffocating and very rough. During one sequence of massive jolts when the quad ran over a succession of rocks and deep potholes Jock, who was always ready with a droll quip, claimed that he and Kevin found that they had changed places without knowing it.

As the desert night slowly began to envelop the parched earth we arrived at our rendezvous in the area of M'sus and formed a laager. The protective tanks and armoured cars closed in around us. The lame duck vehicles were trickling into the bivouac area in threes and fours all night. There was a constant hum of engines. Without taking off our boots we sunk down on to our blankets and groundsheets, dog tired and full of weariness. We submerged into a kind of happy, thoughtless relaxation as we felt the yielding, bonding kindness of the earth.

*   *   *   *

Well before first light the whole Division was astir in a fever of keen anticipation and impatient for the fight. Tanks, armoured cars and guns were primed and checked. This was to be the day of battle. Our powder was dry and we were there to measure and join issue in a clash of arms. We were sure and confident that in this approaching contest we held the vantage ground and would prove to be more than a match for the enemy and that we should mark the day and lay our account.

CHAPTER NINETEEN

Beda Fomm

THE SQUADRON OF the 6th Royal Tank Regiment and the armoured cars of the 11th Hussars glistened dully in the morning light. Jock had managed to make a can of tea by somehow lighting a small Italian oil stove under the cover of a blanket. As he handed me my battered mug of steaming tea he said, 'Real Sarn't Majors brew, Albert.'

'Thanks, Jock,' I said, 'my mouth is like the floor of a broody coop.'

The information was that three long columns of the Italian army were streaming southwards and, if we got a move on and made the best of our time, we should be in a position to bar their retreat. Before the white light of the cold dawn began to encroach across the flatness of the Jebel Achdar Plateau, the Division pulled out from its overnight laager and headed into the curtain of quickening suspense and uncertainty. At just after nine o'clock our leading tanks and armoured cars had reached the Benghazi-Tripoli road and we, in the West Suffolk Yeomanry, armed for the fray and made ready for the test, had driven up tight behind them. The Troop Gun Position Officer, Lieutenant Hester-Hewitt, whose mother said his men adored him, had gone ahead of the troop and selected a gun position some three hundred yards to the east of the road. He had stuck in four marking pegs to indicate our individual gun positions. Ross drove to within forty yards of the number four gun marker and, while the quad was still moving, I leapt out, ran and stood over the marker signalling to Ross to make a wide sweep and to come up on me, at the same time giving him the rough direction of the zero line.

Ross slewed the gun round at great speed, slap over the marking peg and jammed on his brakes in a hell burst of dust. The gunners who were already holding the two quad doors open leapt out of the quad and doubled round to unhook the gun and uncouple the ammunition limber. I was then able to stand across the trail of the gun and heave the heavy back end closer to the zero line bearing. Ross tore off with the roaring quad to the waggon lines, two hundred yards behind the guns and, in the meantime Kevin, instructed and trained to master the essence of speed, had jumped on to the layer's seat to take angles from the G.P.O. The heavily loaded limber had been pulled round with its ammunition lockers open and within five minutes the four guns were ready for action with their long snouts reaching for the north.

Everything had gone like clockwork and, in this barren waste in the Libyan Desert, A Troop had swept in at full drive. The guns had been cut away into action with as much speed and precision as the well trained regular gunners of the King's

Troop, Royal Horse Artillery when they galloped up to fire their guns for the salute in Windsor Great Park on the King's birthday. But this lonely footing was far away from Windsor Great Park. It was a dreary, arid quarter of the globe on the Gulf of Sirte, called Beda Fomm.

The gunners were toiling like beavers to unload the limber and to prepare the ammunition. Ross and Francis, who a short ten days before had been hitting the flesh pots of Cairo, were about to hear for the first time in their lives, the ear splitting crack of a troop of twenty-five pounder guns which, at this time of springing impatience and braced tension, stood up like accusing dark monuments against the sky.

The morning was still and airless and we were quietly spinning out the time. There was that tense, unnatural calm when you felt you might hear a dormouse stir. We were all staring in the same direction and hardly took our eyes off the northern distance. It was like waiting by the net for a ferreted rabbit to bolt.

Up at the O.P., a mere six hundred yards ahead, Captain Adrian Kershaw, hard eyed and coldly watchful through his field glasses, saw a distant windscreen glinting in the morning sun.

He drew his breath in sharply at what he saw. An advance armada of M13 tanks and guns with scores of lorries, Lancias, Biancis and Fiats were streaming towards him in three wide columns. It was a lustrous and threatening scene, like a wide cinema of fiction.

We were standing in fascination at the coming battle's edge. Ross found that his palms were moist and Francis seemed quiet and anxious, but their confidence would steadily increase as they warmed to the task.

Licked into shape by training and preparation the decks were cleared and the foils were trimmed as we lay in wait. We were custodians of the line.

Captain Kershaw waited until the distance between the O.P. and the leading enemy vehicles decreased to two thousand yards and soon we were joined in fitful and fierce communion with the battle. The first of our shells landed among their forward vehicles as the morning sun began to yield its thin warmth. The enemy tanks deployed on either side of the road as they prepared for battle. It was as if the tide was coming in.

Perhaps the Gods of War, looking down on us, would approve of what they saw. Perhaps they would glory in the stance of these two opposing armies and would relish the inevitable spillage of blood. On the one hand was an army, which in two indelible, feverish months had carried all before it in its direct and devastating path and was totally confident of victory. The other army, numerically superior, but having lost most of its will to fight was now in impending struggle against the guns and armour of the desert soldiers of the feared 7th Armoured Division. None-the-less the Fascist army was about to attempt the desperate expedient of making a determined effort to smash their way through.

The guns roared as they burst into renewed life and we could almost be assured of lasting deafness in the shattering proximity of four dark pieces of concentrated thunder.

By way of reply, the Italian gunners sent over a canopy of shrapnel, like bursting leaves to penetrate the ice blue near air. The enemy shells, like hissing wildfire, crashed to dry earth like rattlesnakes inflamed with whisky. A distant heavy enemy gun made its incisive statement in a dark note of menace. The enemy gunners, blind to the insanity of their rulers, stood to their hopeless mission as the fireballs whizzed through the flashing brilliance of the morning.

In the near distance among the enemy assemblage, clearly seen through the doorways in the drifting smoke, rising above the battle were two towering plumes of fire as our shells stuck home as we turned the misguided Fascist bandits to their unbending fate.

Our dust-smarted eyes were watery and tender, our stiff, chilled muscles were gripped with dull pain and our strained molested ears were blunted.

There was more dead land to be won.

*　　　*　　　*　　　*

The 7th Armoured Division stood its ground that February day as, over on the flank, the grey puffs of smoke panted into the common air as our anti tank gunners bit into the first wave of enemy M13 tanks. The enemy were trapped, and they knew it. Their only faint hope was to break through our solid wall, but if we stood firm they had little faith and would blench in attrition, like a drought ridden sapling. They were condemned to be netted like a float of market pigs. The smell of the day was drenched in fire and smoke and, at nightfall, we waited to our guns with sharpened attention for a night attack.

On the second day the enemy artillery reduced its pressure and eventually faded out altogether. Another victory sang in our ears.

We were visited by the Battery Clerk, Bombadier Benson, an unlit cigarette clinging to his lips.

'Anyone die in the night?' he asked.

'Not that I know of,' replied Sergeant Reeve.

'I bloody well hope not,' said Benson, 'when anyone kicks the bucket the bloody paperwork is enough to drive you up the wall.'

During the afternoon of victory, with the main stream of battle over, the demoralised remnants of the beaten Italian army were rounded up and our tanks and Infantry were engaged in mopping up the small pockets of resistance. My subsection of gunners had done well. We had been trained to proficiency and disciplined to accuracy. This was the first action in which we had taken part together as a subsection. Kevin, rock steady, had layed the gun as if he had done it all his life. General O'Connor's bold plan had been entirely successful. Another twenty thousand prisoners had been taken, together with the capture or destruction of one hundred and twelve medium tanks, two hundred and sixteen guns and fifteen hundred vehicles.

At about three o'clock in the afternoon, still flushed with the tide of success, we were sitting on the overturned body of a wrecked Fiat lorry, waiting for orders to move when, high above us, we observed a reconnaisance plane spinning out its thin vapour trail. It flew around us at great height for about twenty minutes. Lieutenant Hester-Hewitt put his binoculars to his eyes.

'That kite's a German Dornier,' he announced. 'I can just make out the black crosses under the wings.'

There had been numerous reports of German troops, tanks and aircraft landing at Tripoli but this was the first hard evidence we had that the Germans were about to enter the war in North Africa.

Later on in the afternoon the Regiment was ordered to move north along the road to Benghazi. We passed right through the nucleus of the battlefield of the past thirty-six hours. Hundreds of abandoned tanks and transport vehicles lay scattered in total confusion on both sides of the road. Many had been smashed by the British guns, but others had been destroyed by the defeated army to prevent them from falling into our hands.

The Battle of Beda Fomm may not rank in importance with Waterloo or the Ardennes, or even with Alamein but I swear that anyone who could have witnessed these ten miles of doom laden, abandoned and destroyed military equipment, the still burning fires and the shuffling, bewildered prisoners, the dead and dying, would remember Beda Fomm for the rest of his days. Francis, who had seen nothing before of the destruction of war, began to speak.

'I can't believe ... ,' he began, but he was riven into silence, his mind was shuttered.

As we crawled northwards, through this giant outdoor lumber room of agony, it seemed that a great bell should toll among the debacle as a bitter warning to the perpetrators of war. The muffled drums should roll and roll in this graveyard of past hopes and easy greed. The German and Italian people should be made to follow a dead march through the folly and homestall of death at Beda Fomm.

*   *   *   *

The first twist of the unexpected, on driving into the newly captured town of Benghazi from the south, was to witness Italian policemen at the crossroads, serenely directing the British military traffic. The policemen were smartly dressed in grey uniforms with red epaulettes and shoulder flashes. Their matched peaked hats had a broad red band and they wore smart, grey breeches and knee length jack boots. They had little to lose by co-operating with their new masters as they marshalled their enemy of yesterday through their newly captured city. It was a strange war. We pulled our battered guns, chafed and galled from battle and from the long haul across the Jebel Achdar into an orange grove to the east of the town. There were trees, grass and water, there was time to inspect our gun and quad in readiness for the next round in the desert war. The quad was dirty and bruised from its long, rough, rugged overland journey and it was scarred and pitted with shrapnel. The gun would have to be cleaned and the firing mechanism and dial sight would have to be stripped down, inspected and reassembled. We were warned that we had only three days to acomplish the work and to complete the maintenance schedule.

On the second night at Benghazi, Gunner Charlie Briggs and Lance Bombardier Ernie Chapman, two of our troop signallers fixed up an Italian radio set and we were able to listen in to London. John Snagge was reading the B.B.C. news in his deep toned, measure voice and he said:

> 'A British armoured column of tanks has made a forced march of one hundred and fifty miles in thirty hours by a little known desert track across the Jebel Akhdar, which is the plateau running westward from Derna, and has cut off and destroyed the remnants of the Italian army in Cyrenaica. The capture of Benghazi was the culmination of one of the most brilliantly executed campaigns in military history, during which, within two months, the army of the Nile, after throwing back the Italians from the firmly entrenched positions one hundred and thirty miles inside Egyptian territory, advanced over five hundred miles in country devoid of roads, water and food, subject to blinding sandstorms and with steadily lengthening lines of communication. In this period at least one hundred and ten thousand prisoners, excluding those taken at Benghazi, were captured, including nineteen generals and an admiral, as well as a vast amount of war material and stores.'

I said, taking off my earphones, 'Well! That should cheer them up at home.'

'They say,' said Philip, 'that John Snagge always puts on his evening dress to read the news.'

'Well,' said Francis, 'by the sound of things we are getting more publicity than Ivor Novello ever did at Drury Lane.'

On the third day of our refreshing and undisturbed respite in the Benghazi orange orchard, a massive delivery of mail reached us. The first for ten long weeks. A long letter from Julie brought sad news. My cousin, Derrick, had been killed as a second pilot in a Wellington over Kiel. Derrick was four years older than me and he had always been my hero. He always rode his tuned up motor bike flat out and once, when I rode behind him on his pillion, I was scared out of my senses. Derrick had done well at school and had won a scholarship to the Grammar School at Woodbridge, passed his School Certificate and was awarded his matric. Aunt Millie, being a widow, had a hard time keeping him at the Grammar School, what with the school uniform, the bus and with Derrick not earning anything. After leaving school he took a job as a clerk in the Auditors' office of the District Council. When the war broke out he joined the R.A.F. Almost before we knew what was happening he was flying a Tiger Moth and he got his wings while we were stationed in Palestine.

The way he used to ride his motor bike, he should have been on Spitfires but he was drafted to a squadron of Wellingtons at a bomber station near Bedford. Julie said that he was shot down over the Kiel Canal on his first trip and Aunt Millie had had a very nice letter from his station commander.

The news about Derrick really shocked me. It was now February and Derrick had been killed back in November. I was really sorry for poor Aunt Millie as

Derrick was her only son. She had lost her husband in the first Battle of the Somme in 1916. In fact he was killed before Derrick was born.

A large and heavy parcel had arrived for me, addressed in Miss Bonner's firm hand. It contained two books and a large Christmas card addressed to me and signed by all forty-one pupils in the village school.

'What have you got there Albert?' said Jock, as I opened the parcel and revealed the books, 'some sexy books?'

'Well, as a matter of fact they are,' I said, showing Jock 'War and Peace' and a pocket edition of the Oxford English Dictionary.

'Fuggin useless rubbish,' said Jock disgustedly. 'There's more sense in the Glasgow Woman's weekly.'

Kevin came and sat down beside us. Jock had read his one letter from his mother and he said to Kevin.

'Albert's risen above himself. He's got two books he canna understand and he's bumin his load.'

'No he's not,' said Kevin loyally. 'Albert likes reading and thinking and all that. Miss Bonner reckoned Albert ought to be a sodding professor when he was at school. She used to make him read the Classics.'

Ernie Briggs was passing and he said, 'I fort the Classics was the Derby and the St. Leger.'

Philip Underwood also came to my aid and said, 'The trouble with you Jock is that you suffer from a poverty of the intellect.'

'Get knotted,' said Jock as he spat on the sand, 'the trouble with you so called educated twerps is that you know bugger all.'

Philip said to anyone that was listening, 'There is no doubt at all that our Jock possesses a blessed and delicate gentility of expression.'

*   *   *   *

The logical road ahead for us seemed patently clear and unfolded before us like an endless rolled out red carpet of reason. The Axis Base of the Port of Tripoli was only some three hundred miles to the west. It appeared obvious that we should follow up our succesful battles along the North African coast with a final push up to Tripoli and on to Tunisia. As the Desert Army had advanced five hundred miles in two months there seemed to be no just reason why there should be any impenetrable obstacle to finishing off the Axis forces in Tripolitania, opening up the Mediterranean to shipping and shortening the war. What is more, if no time was wasted, we were confident that we could get the whole thing over and done with before the hot Summer weather.

Then there leaked out the most disagreeable news that had come our way in a very long time.

Back in England Winston Churchill and the British War Cabinet had ordered that a large proportion of the Middle East Forces, fighting in the desert should be withdrawn and sent to Greece and Crete to help the Greeks against the Axis invasion. Some units had already left the desert and were on their way. We were wild with rage and disillusionment. With only three hundred miles to go, the headlong race to reach Tripoli was halted. Our anger was mingled with bitter disappointment. Perhaps we had been over confident but I know that we were all techy and fed up and that feelings were running high. We had a navy in the Med'. Surely they could land some troops further up the coast while we bashed away inland. In no way were we going to get home by sitting on our backsides in the desert with the hot weather coming and all. Suddenly the whole world seemed to have no purpose.

Whisps of dust scudded across the open countryside. Jock brought over an empty packing case which had contained tins of tuna fish and sat down beside us.

'It's a balls up,' said Jock, 'the fugging generals don't know whether their arseholes are punched or bored. They've got us all the way up here and now they are sending half the troops back to Cairo.'

'You can't blame the generals for that Jock,' I said. 'Captain Kershaw says that General O'Connor wanted to push up to Tripoli but Winston Churchill and the bloody politicians decided that it was more important to help the Greeks.'

'Bugger me,' said Jock. 'They've got two and a quarter million men in the army in England. Why, for fuggs sake, don't they send some of them to Greece. They are doing sod all in England.'

Jock went on, 'Anyway, I hope that my mother's got her hat on.'

'What does your mother want her hat on for?' asked Ross.

'I don't know,' answered Jock, 'but my mother always puts her hat on when she goes to bed.'

We laid out bedrolls and thought of soft pillows and listened to the night wind.

Epitaph

I have often thought,
The desert is a hateful place,
A lonely space for men to die.
So dun a waste of sand and sun,
To be the tomb of any race.
Perhaps it does not matter much,
For death is friend, not always foe.
And I who long for trees and rain
In death may get them back again.
It does not matter over much.

Morley Brooke.

CHAPTER TWENTY

Encounter with the Afrika Korps

THERE WERE STRONG rumours circulating that large enemy convoys had broken the British naval blockade and that German Panzer Divisions had been landed in Tripoli. It was also being put about that two hundred German dive bombers had already flown in and landed on Libyan aerodromes to the west. On March 20th the West Suffolk Yeomanry was ordered to relieve a gunner regiment at a small deserted Arab village one hundred and fifty miles south of Benghazi called Mersa Brega. The village was a few miles to the west of Agedabia and was at the very gateway to Tripolitania. At a brew halt on this southern route we met up with an Infantry Regiment on its way back to Cairo. A machine gun sergeant told us that things were hotting up at Mersa Brega and that the Luftwaffe was very active, bombing and straffing the front line.

During the afternoon we once again began to hear the old familiar sounds of the distant rumble and growling of guns and occasionally, the louder crunch of bombs.

When a fighting unit approaches the forward area everyone becomes just a little wary. There is a slight straining of the eyes and ears. Every now and then a column of smoke rifts up into the sky. There is no telling what it is, it could be a burning vehicle or a petrol dump or a smoke shell. Neither can you identify the rumbles and the distant bangs. But as the troop draws nearer to its gun positions the picture becomes clearer and it is possible to identify whether the grey bursts of anti-aircraft fire spilling out into the blue sky have been fired from a British three point seven or an enemy eighty-eight millimetre.

And so, in the late afternoon, tightly closeted within the confining tin and canvas of our labouring vehicles, we came to the small, battered Arab village of Mersa Brega and set up our guns on the southern tip of the Gulf of Sirte.

It had been a comfortless and plaguing afternoon as an unwelcoming dust storm was blowing and nothing made us more tetchy than this continuing, beating stream of yellow dust. It penetrated and invaded our mouths and our eyes and crept into our clothes and the quad and gun were covered in a film of fine powder. We were unhappy and in low spirits as our hopes of pushing on to Tripoli had now withered. What was also self evident was that there were few troops in the forward area to hold the line at Mersa Brega.

On the following morning the dust storm was still raging. We had had a miserable night in the streaming dust and the only consolation was that the enemy must have had a miserable night as well. For breakfast a spoonful of half cold, chopped up, greasy Canadian tinned bacon plus a dollop of lumpy biscuit burgoo, jam and tea. Back into the quad or under a blanket to eat it, away from the worst of the dust. Christ! This was a miserable place and we were in a painful sea of trouble. We cursed the desert and we cursed the dust. One thing, there wouldn't be much action this day. A dust storm just brought the war at Mersa Brega to a full stop. They were able to observe nothing from the O.P.s and the swirling dust would keep most of the enemy aircraft on the ground.

By the next morning the wind had filtered down to a whisper of air and, before the brazen red sun had cleared the eastern horizon, we knew that this would be a day of action. The air was as clear as lucid crystal and, from our exposed positions behind a gradient of rising ground we could gaze over the apron of fine sand into the far distance, like a desert Bedouin. To the north was the sea, to our south was the British line, very thinly held, to the east were friends, reserves and supply columns and to the west, the unknown enemy.

The guns had been manned since daybreak. There had been some desultory firing and the O.P.s had called for some registration of targets. It was all bloody normal. A Troop of 'K' Battery were, like the other gunners in the line, a long, long way from the main supply bases for ammunition, so shells were not to be wasted.

At about ten o'clock, two dark looking twin engined fighter planes dived like thunderbolts out of the sky to a few hundred feet, flattened out and proceeded to plough the earth with machine gun and cannon fire. The earth was ripped and shredded like a violent hail storm on a fish pond. The fighters seemed to be right down among us and flew along a deep wadi to our right, shooting up everything they could see. They were so low that, from where we stood on the side of a hill, we could look down on the ugly black crosses on the top of their wings. The Bofors dare not fire on them even if they could. These were the first German fighters that we had seen and they left three lorries on fire in the wadi. One of them was a three tonner loaded with four gallon cans of petrol. The thing went up like an exploding fireball. Captain Kershaw said that the planes were Messerschmitt 110's and they were the latest German fighters. They had a speed of 340 m.p.h. at 23,000 feet and were powered by a couple of twelve cylinder Daimler Benz engines. They were armed with two 30mm cannons, two Mauser cannons and a twin machine gun. They were cudgels of punching fire power.

'If they hadn't been so quick I'd have let them have a few rounds from my rifle,' said Jock.

'I don't think that a rifle would be much use,' said Captain Kershaw, 'there is 60mm armoured glass in the windscreen in front of the pilot, a 10mm armoured plate around the cockpit and another armoured plate under the floor.'

Several times during the morning we saw Messerschmitts with their deadly weapons, prowling and pussyfooting around looking for targets. They seemed to hunt in pairs.

The afternoon produced a totally new experience for us. The ack ack guns were letting fly and, up there, at about ten thousand feet were the ingredients for an air raid. A string of enemy planes slowly edging towards us, black and ominous. We counted at least thirty and they came at us right out of the afternoon sun.

'Junkers 87, dive bombers,' shouted Captain Kershaw, 'take cover.' The leader of the formation waggled his wings and went into an almost perpendicular dive, followed by the others at five second intervals. They were ugly and evil looking with heavily cranked wings and a big, square cut rudder. They were as black as a rook's feather. As they peeled off, the dive brakes were opened and, attached to the wings were high pitched, screaming banshee sirens which made a noise like a tortured monster. As they screamed down towards us I really cannot say that we were terrified. The main sensation was one of curiosity. It was incredulous and unbelievable. We almost mistrusted our senses. We were filled with pure limitless wonder and were totally fascinated by these terrible happenings around us.

Down they came at full, screaming power, diving at an angle of 80 degrees and releasing their murderous bombs at three thousand feet. We took cover in the slit trenches behind the guns and watched the Stukas come hurtling down towards us. Only two of the planes attacked our position and we soon spotted the two that had us in their sights. They came at us from opposite directions, but the first pilot appeared to lack courage and pulled out of his dive much too early and the bombs drifted away into open country, at least four hundred yards from us. The second enemy aviator, however, kept diving down towards us with the warplane accelerating in its screaming, downwards thrust like some eagle winged black arrow.

'Get your bellies on the floor,' I shouted to Ross and Francis who hadn't been bombed before.

Perhaps the War Office should lay down a standard procedure for position and posture when being dive bombed. Should our hands endeavour to protect our ears and eyes? Jock always said that when he was under fire he didn't know whether to put his tin hat over his head or over his private parts. We turned our faces into the earth and closed our eyes as the thundering plane released its screaming bombs. Already several bombs had exploded around us but these were clearly intended for our special purpose. As the crashing roar and vibration smashed through our tiny trench and we felt the tongues of flame burning over our heads, we knew that the bombs were dangerously close.

Again the painful assault on the ear drums, the dust and the smoke and the stink of high explosives, again the feeling of slightly surprised relief. A quick glance around the sky to see if other machines of war were hellbent committed to destroy us as their intended quarry. Then, suddenly, a wild blazing fire thirty yards away. The canvas roofed 15 cwt command post truck, loaded with specialists equipment and signal gear was well alight. Captain Kershaw was already out with a fire extinguisher but a petrol fire with a few seconds start has a whip hand on those who seek to stem the flames with slim resources and another solid British truck, made in Birmingham, was already quartered with a burning roof and blazing inflammable tyres.

It was easy to be despondent and heavy hearted at the depressing effect of having no air cover and not enough anti-aircraft guns. There appeared to be no answer to the Luftwaffe at Mersa Brega.

Ernie Briggs was cheerful enough. 'It's better than watching a Western on films,' he said.

Kevin said, 'It's a pity those bastard pilots don't black out when they dive and bury themselves in the sodding desert.' Lieutenant Charles Hester-Hewitt, who had been briefed on the Stuka dive bomber since its use in France and Poland, said, 'If the pilots black out during the dive it is no problem. The Stukas are fitted with an automatic pull out mechanism. The pilot just has to aim the nose of the plane at the target and the automatic pull out does the rest.'

All in all we had survived the boiling turmoil of our first attack by dive bombers. We had been driven into the earth by the angry, black whirlwind above us. It was rough and it was destructive, as by Pagan gods, and our pulses were running hard, but we were remarkably undestroyed. There was a new demand on our understanding. We knew the score with the Axis Powers and understood why the air was filled with iron in these desolate sands. Our lives and minds were being enlarged in a strengthening resolution and, if these swooping air sharks thought that they had us by the throat, then they would have to return to their starting point and reassess their wayward estimate.

The daily temperatures were rising rapidly and the flies harried our existence with the tenacity of a lion to a young buck's windpipe. They clung to our faces and to our bodies and our mugs of tea were rimmed with the crawling insects.

The enemy had total air superiority and there was no sign of the R.A.F.

The Battery Commander, Major Coleman, called the officers and sergeants to the Command Post. What he said was unbelievable.

He confirmed that there were three crack German Divisions in the line at Mersa Brega and that two of these were Panzer Divisions equipped with Mark IV tanks and 88mm guns. He went on to say that we had a secret master plan. The Africa Corps were about to attack and, when they did, the Regiment was going to take part in a planned withdrawal south, into the desert. When the enemy came forward into our vacated positions, we were to attack from the flank and blow him to bits between the desert and the sea. He ended up by saying, 'I know the whole damn plan and, all I can say is, "God help the Germans".'

King Cole, with his bent shoulders, seemed war worn and seedy, with his red rimmed eyes and a droopy moustache. He had done his best to sustain our confidence, but to us, the master plan to trap the German Divisions, sounded like blind and desperate reasoning and we were filled with nagging doubts and scepticism.

For one thing, the 7th Armoured Division had returned to the Delta and ahead of us were only the 9th Battalion of the Rifle Brigade and a detachment of the Northumberland Fusiliers with machine guns. Also in the line were the 2nd Armoured Division, but we knew full well that this Division was fresh out from England and that most of the tanks they were using were repaired Italian Mark 10's salvaged from previous battles. It was difficult to appreciate how these few fighting units in a thinly held line could smash three German Divisions plus several new Italian ones that had been sent as reinforcements from Italy.

When I returned to the gun and told my crew of the 'secret plan', Kevin said, 'I reckon that King Cole has taken it into his head that he's shooting partridges and he's planning the afternoon drives.'

On the afternoon of the 25th of March, after a quiet morning in which there had been a feeble exchange of shells, Kevin and I were shaking out our blankets and rolling them tightly into our groundsheets. It was a hot and cloudless day and, apart from the weapons of war, there was no sign to be discerned of the works of man in this punitive expanse of wilderness.

Ernie Briggs drifted by, with a Don Five telephone in one hand and a mug of tea in the other. Ernie Briggs from Billingsgate market, shirtless and cheerful, who had told us that his father wore a bowler hat and a knotted scarf and who said that he always visited the hot pie stall with his girl friend after the pictures on a Saturday night.

'What do you fink of fings Kev?' he shouted.

'Well!' said Kevin, imitating the fruity voice of Major Coleman, 'all I can say is God help the Germans.'

'And do you know the whole damned plan,' went on Ernie mockingly.

'Ernie,' said Kevin, 'Albert and me set the whole fugging thing up.'

'Mind 'ow yer go,' said Ernie as he strolled off.

We had been keeping an ear cocked for Stukas, but it wasn't a Stuka that came hurtling out of the dazzling afternoon sun. It was a lone Messerschmitt fighter and it dived straight for the gun position with its cannons and machine guns blazing, and it release four bombs. Kevin and I just had time to throw ourselves into a slit trench before the bombs hit the deck. The four explosions merged into one tremendous bang.

'Christ!' said Kevin, 'they were close.'

It all happened so quickly. Lieutenant Hester-Hewitt, who was just returning from B.H.Q. and had narrowly escaped death, was calling for help and for someone to call up the M.O. A voice from Number Two gun shouted: 'The Command Post has been hit.'

The Command Post was sited in a ten feet square hole in the ground and was some five feet deep. One bomb had landed right in the middle of it. It was a shocking sight and the three men inside wouldn't have known a thing. Bombadier Ralph Bowman, the G.P.O. Ack was killed as he pencilled fresh switches and ranges on his artillery board. Driver Edward Meade was killed as he sat on the steps of the Command Post writing a letter to his sister in the Wrens who had just received a posting to Beirut. Ernie Briggs had just made the Command Post with his Don Five and his mug of tea. We had run towards them but could only stand back with concussed senses, shocked and raw. Three of our comrades lay in unrecognisable death. We had never thought to see the day when Charlie Briggs would cry. 'Ernie ain't done nuffin,' he sobbed, 'E ain't done nuffin.'

It had been a bad day and a sad day for the Troop. Not since that first day of the battle of Tobruk had the troop lost three men in one single hideous afternoon.

Kevin said, 'You know Albert, I feel fugging browned off, like I've been dragged down the sink plug hole.'

Ross said, 'I've got something to cheer us up.'

'A brew up wouldn't come amiss Ross,' I said.

'No,' said Ross. 'It's better than that. I've got a bottle of whisky in my pack. I bought it off a wog in Mersa, on my way up.'

We were interested I can tell you.

Ross made off towards the quad, which had been dug into a pit towards the rear of the guns.

'Get your mugs out,' he said. He brought out the bottle which had been wrapped in an old, dirty towel and proceeded to break the seal.

'Christ!' said Jock, 'it's Johnnie Walker.'

Having broken the seal, Ross pulled the cork. We were watching him like four Labrador puppies at feeding time. He poured a little from the bottle into his enamel mug and said: 'I'd better sample it to make sure it's vintage.'

Ross raised the mug to his lips and sipped the amber liquid. His face puckered up like a child's when it takes bitter medicine. He spat out the unsavoury fluid. He was bursting with anger.

'The thieving bastard,' shouted Ross, 'the rotten sodding boss eyed, thieving wog.'

'What's up?' I asked.

'Fugging cold tea,' said Ross hurling the bottle with all his might in the direction of Egypt.

'You know,' said Jock, 'that wog had done a really good job on the seal of that bottle.'

So we made a can of tea. We had run out of tinned milk and Francis, who had made the brew, told us that this was the last of the sugar.

CHAPTER TWENTY-ONE

Exodus from Mersa Brega

ON MONDAY 31ST of March 1941, it all began to happen. We had been shelling enemy positions since dawn and then, at nine o'clock, the O.P. reported tanks approaching them in all directions. The nearest German Mark IVs were only a thousand yards from the O.P. and they had machine guns with a range of two thousand yards. The O.P. was withdrawn nearer to the gun positions and the Infantry outposts were brought in.

The guns had opened up at dawn at seven thousand yards and the range we were now being called for was down to four thousand yards and steadily getting less. We didn't need to be told what was happening in front of us. If the enemy tanks continued to come forward the gun positions would be within machine gun range and that could produce a wildfire situation of crisis proportions.

At ten o'clock we found ourselves in the eye of a German Blitzkreig. The whole of the British forward area was attacked by scores of dive bombers. There must have been a hundred planes with their evil looking black crosses diving and twisting and bombing all around us. The Stukas were joined by about forty Messerschmitts firing at anything that moved. It was like being in a huge, upturned basin, cursed with the scath of a hundred demented wasps. We were in great danger and we were unable to seek shelter as the enemy tanks were still advancing. The screaming sirens and the banshees of the Stukas could be heard above our gunfire. A Bofors crew shot down two Messerschmitts within five minutes of one another. We continued our firing through clouds of smoke and dust.

B Troop, our sister troop, on our left flank had also been firing non-stop since dawn and we suddenly saw their four gun-towing quads tear up to their guns at tremendous speed. Within seconds the gunners had hooked up their guns and limbers, scrambled aboard the quads and raced off eastwards in a cloud of dust. Where now were the cameramen of British Movietone News to film and witness this superbly trained troop of gunners of The Royal Horse Artillery carrying out the spectacular manoeuvre of a speedy, but orderly retreat under heavy enemy shellfire and air attack? B Troop would be falling back into action and cover our withdrawal. That is if they weren't too late.

A Stuka scored a direct hit on a Matador full of ammunition not two hundred yards away from us and the exploding shells added to the ear splitting racket of shellburst and thunder. Up at the forward O.P. Captain Kershaw, together with his Ack, his signaller and his driver, all wedged into a Bren carrier were watching with gathering fascination the relentless and malevolent progression of the German armour with each tank fast in its own creation of swirling dust.

Salvo after salvo from the troop rent and tore at the raking, pressing, heavily armoured Mark IVs as they drove forward in battle formation. The tanks and their highly trained crews were spaced about sixty yards apart. Adrian Kershaw knew that each Company had three sections and in each section there were five tanks. The Africa Corps Company Commander, therefore,. has fifteen tanks under his command, and it was well known that, unlike our own tank commanders, he could call up the Luftwaffe over his radio, for direct support.

Stuck up there at Mersa Brega the thin British line was outnumbered, out tanked and out gunned and totally without air support.

Back on the gun position, half a mile behind the O.P. the gunners were firing five rounds gun fire repeatedly to endeavour to stem the enemy advance but the settings on the range scales were sliding. It was hairy all right and shells from the Panzer guns were already bursting to our rear. All around us pillars of smoke boiled upwards. Christ, I was proud of my gunners. Kevin, brother of my darling Julie, sat on the layer's seat, eye to the eyepiece of his dial sight, hand on the firing lever, never flinching or moving in awful responsibility. Kevin, who had been brought up to hoe sugar beet, riddle potatoes and harvest corn in the peace of his father's smallholding was now casting forth burning steel harbingers of destruction from the fiercely hot rifled barrel by his right shoulder. Francis, Jock and Ross were working like demons to ram the dense rigid shells, that weighed like concrete, into the hungry breech. They showed no signs of fear or of the sudden blind instinctive desire for flight that sometimes possesses all men under fire and when the natural wild impulses are screaming, 'Drop everything and run'. No one was conscious of glory, but glory was there. My subsection boys of yesterday were lions of men.

The Stukas had left to refuel and rearm. Four Infantry carriers and two Crusader tanks blundered across our troop position. I shouted to a sergeant in one of the troop carriers, 'Where are you going?'

He shouted back, 'I don't bloody well know. I wouldn't be surprised if we didn't stop until we reach Cairo.'

A lieutenant standing in the turret of one of the Crusaders leant down and shouted to Hester Hewitt, 'I shouldn't wait here if I were you. There are forty enemy tanks just over the crest to your front and we are outlflanked to the north and the south.'

Close on the heels of the last Crusader came Captain Kershaw and his O.P. party and, with an order for five rounds gun fire at a range of two thousand yards be blazed off and then came the order, 'Cease fire. Prepare to withdraw'.

The quad drivers had already been sent back to the waggon lines in anticipation some ten minutes before with orders to start up and keep the engines running and, as they roared up to the guns with shells bursting all around and machine gun bullets flying it was a miracle that nothing was hit. Ross headed straight for us and slewed his quad round and backed on to the gun. He already had the quad in first gear as we clambered aboard. It was a long way from being easy.

At that moment there was a scream of shells over our heads and they crashed into the desert between ourselves and the enemy. B Troop were in action, covering our withdrawal. They were firing smoke, and creating a thick, black screen to shield us from the enemy. We knew that the smoke from smoke shells clears in about one and a half minutes, even if there is no wind. There was no time to lose and our nerves were stretched on a fine thread. As we pulled away a hail of machine gun bullets whined around us from a tank firing blind.

'Put your foot down Ross,' I said, 'and for Christ's sake, don't stall the engine.'

Way behind us the Libyan village of Mersa Brega was burning furiously in a mass of smoke and flame and those of us who were there will never forget the sight of the tall, slim minaret of the old Moslem mosque which had been hit by German shell fire, wreathed in smoke and burning hot in the evening sun of March 31st 1941.

'Well!' said Kevin, as we bumped and jolted our way eastwards in our hot, noisy and comfortless quad, 'everything seems to be going according to plan.'

'Yes,' said Francis, 'according to Rommel's plan.'

Jock said, as we became mixed up with a retreating company of the Tower Hamlets and a detachment of the Northumberland Fusiliers, 'If this is what they call an orderly withdrawal, I hope that I never take part in a disorderly one.'

We had escaped complete encirclement by the skin of our teeth as the German Infantry, to the surprise of our Generals, had moved through the sand dunes to the north, between the road and the sea. I expect that for the Generals this was an interesting chess board, but for us, we had the feeling of floating in something sticky.

Darkness was now closing in and the guns eventually dropped into action some twelve kilometres east of Mersa Brega. It was past midnight and we realised that we had had nothing to eat but dry biscuits all day.

Out to the south and south-east flashes of gunfire and the crump of shells could be heard. We could almost feel the presence of the enemy. The guard was trebled and lookouts were to be placed at vantage points on the contorted crest in the forefront of the guns. It had been a tiring day and I told Ross to get some sleep as he might have a lot more driving to do the following day. I was in charge of one of the three men listening posts until 2 a.m., when I was relieved by Harold Reeve.

He said in a low voice, 'You all right, Albert?'

'Yes, Harold,' I said. 'Have you had any kip?'

'Not a lot.'

'What do you think of things Harold?'

'Well,' he said, 'the withdrawal was a shambles and we damn nearly got surrounded back there and the British Army were bloody nearly four guns light. We should never have been left in that position without Infantry support.' He went on, 'You know what today is Albert?'

'No,' I said, as stiff chilled and full of weariness I spread out my groundsheet.

'April Fool's day,' said Harold.

'The daffs will soon be out then,' I said. 'Good night Harold.'

'Good night, Albert, and don't forget that it is "stand to" at half past four so don't oversleep.'

I could almost laugh, I was so bloody tired.

Perhaps one day a determined student of military history will set down for
posterity the remarkable, full blooded story of those eleven highly charged days
and nights between that first searing blitz by screaming dive bombers on our thinly
held line at Mersa Brega on the 31st of March and the threatening passage of
reverseless destiny which culminated in the West Suffolk Yeomanry moving inside
the perimeter wire of the Tobruk Fortress on the 9th of April. My memory of those
hectic momentous days is hazy and my recollection is blurred. Even with the
memory jogging assistance from my desert veteran comrades it is impossible to
recall the sequence of the fearful mash of happenings and to split into coherent
sections the vast, confused web of disorder. Embalmed in the recesses of my mind
are shadowy visions of a regiment of twenty-four guns, lightly protected by two
armoured cars, feeling their torturous way eastward through the small Libyan
mudwalled villages of Agedabia, Sidi Saleh and Msus, and of ferrying our precious
guns up the rough, narrow track of the steep escarpment leading once again on the
Jebel Achdar, that loftiest of the tiered plateaux of the Cyrenaican mountains.

There was evidence in plenty that the Panzer Divisions had already crossed our
path from south to north as we criss-crossed the deep rutted tracks of their
armour.

On the second day of the withdrawal, after many tank alerts, two M13 Italian
tanks, in a fit of reckless and ill advised bravado nosed in behind us. 'A' troop were
covering the retreat of the remainder of the Battery and Number One and Two
guns took on the tank on the left and Number Three and Four the tank on the
right. We all got off three rounds of armour piercing shot and blasted the M13's
over open sights. We were too quick for them and our nerves were like cat gut. It
was kill or be killed. It was the high, momentous zenith of the day. The enemy
knew where we were but they would now have a healthy respect for the killing
power of a troop of twenty-five pounders and would probably keep their distance.
The main threat to us was from an Infantry attack but the Africa Korps would
have other matters on its mind.

I recall that on that same day, within the period of half an hour, I had swung
the trail of the gun to firing positions to the east, to the west and to the south of us.
All in all we were treading the high ground of experience and, on occasions, there
rose the stark instinct of panic. Some nights in the encircling blackness of the desert
we could hear the clatter of tanks, squealing their way eastwards. There was no
way of knowing in that tense, black circus whether these night formations were
friend of foe. We held our breath in these still hours and the clock could be
entombed in quicksand as time reeled and whirred on our spinning earth in these
witching hours of peril.

Other nights were hushed and quiet as we seemed to ride at anchor in the
muted purr of the desert and the spidery hiss of the wind. Throughout the early
spell of the night hours, as we lay by the guns, we listened to the weird creaking of
the close packed vehicles as the metal cooled. Time and again the guns were
prepared for action and, when the urgent call came from our deep sleep to 'Take
posts', our pulses raced in our heavy weariness. Hardened, as we were, the
suspicion of a combined tank and infantry attack on our poorly defended night

laager, which could boil into a nest of disaster, brought to the surface those unwelcome, involuntary, tiny icicles of fear.

Although we did not know it at the time, three motorised and armoured columns of the Afrika Korps were sweeping across the open desert and threatening to cut off a whole Division of the Western Desert Force. One enemy column was heading straight for the Egyptian frontier. Due to the misguided decision of the British Government to drain the desert of a large proportion of its fighting troops to sustain the abortive campaign in Greece, the whole position had changed. The floodtide had turned against us and our main bases in Egypt and around the Suez Canal were in dire peril.

On the morning of the fifth day of this fluid rear-guard battle, Kevin had taken his after breakfast walk with his shovel and was returning to the gun, when a dusty, low slung, staff car drew up beside him. One of the back windows was being wound down and Kevin could make out two men in the back dressed in field officer's uniform and, in particular, he noticed the red bands around their hats.

One of the officers shouted to Kevin, 'Where are your Headquarters?'

Now, Kevin was a cautious soul and we had been repeatedly warned to watch out for Fifth Columnists and spies, dressed as Bedouins or in British military uniform. So Kevin, who was shirtless and hadn't shaved for six days or more, nor had a haircut for as many weeks, leant on his shovel and shouted back, 'What do you want to know for, and who the bloody hell are you?'

The occupant in the back of the car, according to Kevin later, went a sort of blue colour and, also according to Kevin, was pretty mad and no mistake. He leaned forward and roared, 'Don't you know who I am? I'm General O'Connor. Where's your Colonel?'

'Christ,' said Kevin.

By this time Lieutenant Hester-Hewitt had arrived on the scene and proceeded to humble himself before the General. Although he hadn't got his hat on, he slung up a flabby salute and generally minced about.

The General, who was looking tired and harrassed and who probably felt betrayed by Churchill, said to Hester-Hewitt, 'There will be no more retreat once we arrive at Barce.'

As he drove off, looking for the Colonel, he barked, 'And God damn that gunner of yours.'

He was, of course, referring to the intrepid layer of my gun, Lance Bombardier Kevin Porter, who had quietly slid off, high with his tale of what he had said to the General.

On the 5th April, the sixth day of the retreat, the West Suffolk Yeomanry, still mostly intact and in good order, broke out of the rough terrain of the Jebel Achdar, into the open country eighty miles or so east of Benghazi. Slowly and carefully, heedful of our irreplaceable vehicles and guns we moved into the pretty little colonised Italian village of Barce, with its green trees and grass and its tidy olive orchards. The Italian colonists were keeping well inside their neat white houses but the native Libyans were running wild. A large, noisy group of bickering, jostling Libyan camel drivers and blanket-wrapped herdsmen were looting the village.

Their camels and donkeys were being loaded with bulging sacks of flour from the co-operative central granary. A mile outside the village boundary, on a barren tract of land, there was a vast prisoner of war cage containing some three thousand recently captured Italian prisoners. They were being guarded by men from the Australian 9th Division. A heavy duty Bedford truck with a mounted machine gun and manned by grim faced Aussies was placed at each of the four corners. The machine guns were trained on the prisoners who were fully aware of what was happening and were pacing up and down inside the many stranded, barbed wire compound. In a few minutes time, when we had passed through, the Aussies would fire a few rounds into the air and the prisoners would be left to their freedom, probably to fight again.

One of my never to be forgotten recollections of those distressing, comfortless but exciting days of the retreat was of being very, very tired. Sometimes the Regiment would travel throughout the night and on one weary stretch Ross and I took turns at the wheel and we drove for twenty-seven hours, only stopping for a ten minute halt every two hours. The pace over the rough terrain had been painfully slow. There were no hot meals of any kind, bully beef and biscuits plunged into a new, monotonous dimension. A treasured moment of rejoicing occurred when a flight of M110s were straffing the road and we had scattered away from our vehicles. Kevin spotted a ditched Bedford truck from the Australian 6th Division, some two hundred yards off the road. It turned out to be a broken down N.A.A.F.I. truck and contained about sixty thousand 'Players' cigarettes in bulk cartons.

'Fugg a rook,' said Jock, 'they'd be worth a thumpin' barrow load of siller at a shillin' for twenty.'

We decided to give B Troop ten thousand and shared the remainder amongst A Troop. We calculated that, if everyone was careful, the fifty thousand cigarettes would last the troop for about a month. As we luxuriantly inhaled lungfuls of warm smoke from brand cigarettes made in England, Kevin said, 'They're a fugging sight better than those sodding army issue gaspers that we get from the by-products of King Farouk's stables.'

There were rumours of the fall of Benghazi and Derna and the High Command was obviously in a state of confusion. It would seem that they had no idea of how and where to try to halt the enemy advance.

Everything was counter to reason. Here were Australian sappers on the coast road waiting to blow up the roads and bridges behind us to delay the enemy. These were the same roads and bridges that they had helped to repair and rebuild after the Italian retreat of two months earlier.

We were flesh and blood and we were living and breathing but we were tired to exhaustion. There was no obvious higher intelligence guiding us or controlling our earthly destiny. There seemed to be little security of further existence. Were we soldiers of the King or were we transient, flitting men of straw? It was, perhaps, a good time to face extinction and blank nothingness amid this strange feeling of suspension and wonder in, what was after all, a markedly short lived flame of life.

Having swayed and clattered our painstakingly laborious way for seven days across the Jebel Achdar from south-west to north-east orders were received to evacuate Barce with all speed and head south-east along the rough, battle worn desert track to Mechili, which lay some one hundred and ten miles distant. It was stressed that it was imperative that the Regiment should arrive at Mechili by first light.

'Ross,' I said, 'it looks as if we shall have to average nine miles an hour, driving all night, so I hope that you don't feel tired.' His eyes were like two red balls of pain.

'Aw, it's no problem,' he said. 'I always know when I've fallen asleep at the wheel when I hit the truck in front up the arse.'

We were joined by eight Australian machine gunners from the 6th Division, travelling in two Bren Carriers, and they stayed with us throughout the night as we headed towards Mechili.

At first light, weary with drowsiness through the heavy hours we were still seven miles short of Mechili when our leading trucks ran into a detachment of the Northumberland Fusiliers. They informed us that Mechili was now in enemy hands and that General O'Connor, our finest expert in desert warfare, had been captured and taken prisoner. A youngish looking Captain, harrassed and weighed down with fatigue, advised us to head east towards the main road and Tobruk. He warned us to keep a sharp look out for enemy tanks.

★   ★   ★   ★

Loose sand drifted over the road as Colonel Buchanan-Spooner led his regiment up to the concertina barbed wire defences of the Tobruk outer perimeter.

Walter Hobbs was the Colonel's driver and from his driver's seat in the 8cwt Morris truck he could see a hundred yards ahead, a sandbagged Infantry machine gun post by the side of the road. The post was manned by Diggers of the newly arrived 9th Australian Division.

An Australian soldier appeared out of the post with his tin hat cocked over one eye and his rifle slung. He stepped out into the road and waved driver Hobbs down.

'Slow down, Hobbs,' said the Colonel.

Driver Hobbs slid back the oil and sand coated window and gazed up at the sentry, who asked, 'What mob are yew?'

'The West Suffolk Yeomanry,' answered Hobbs proudly.

'Never heard of em,' rejoined the Digger and, pointing at the Colonel, he went on, 'and who's this joker with the belly?'

'This is our Colonel, Colonel Buchanan-Spooner,' replied Hobbs stiffly.

'Aw,' said the Digger, 'you're havin' me on. You bloody Pomms are all the same. You'd better come on in.'

'Drive on, Hobbs,' said the Colonel urgently.

Within twenty-four hours the long siege of Tobruk had begun.

CHAPTER TWENTY-TWO
The Siege – The First Part

"WHAT'S THE TIME?' asked Kevin.

'I don't know,' answered Jock, yawning oafishly, 'but I think it's Thursday.'

Number Four Gun section had spent an uncomfortable night in a flea infested bunker which had been constructed by the Italians for the defence of Tobruk. The bunker was immediately behind some concreted gunpits which had been prepared and used by a troop of 105mm Italian artillery. The vicious, hardy desert fleas had given us a disturbed night, the morning heat was oppressive and a sandstorm raged in the hot, dry westerly wind.

Tobruk was surrounded by cock-a-hoop enemy armoured divisions and there were strong rumours that the leading formations of the Afrika Korps were now down at Sollum and on the Egyptian frontier some eighty miles to the east. We certainly felt more secure inside the beleaguered fortress than we had been when mixed up with the prowling enemy on the Jebel Achdar, but there was still a rush of blood and the adrenalin was still flowing.

'As we are neatly surrounded by enemy troops, some eighty miles behind enemy lines,' said Kevin, examining his beard in a piece of broken mirror, 'what do you suggest that we do today?'

'I think that I'd better go shopping,' said Ross, his burned sun-beaten face still drawn from the long pull from Mersa Brega, 'I've got a long list.'

'Yes, for beer and bints and bints and beer,' said Jock, emptying sand out of his boot.

'Well,' said Francis, 'I think that I'll stay home and paint the bathroom.' He went on, 'I'll paint it a sky blue and then we could hang some lavender or ultramarine curtains, with a delicate apricot pattern.'

'Yes,' I said, 'and to give it local atmosphere we could have a rat coloured loo and a wog coloured bath.'

'My aunt's already got a wog coloured bath,' volunteered Jock.

'Keep the coal in it?' asked Kevin.

'Aye. It's a long step to the shed in the Winter.'

Jock found a cigarette in his boots and struck a match. 'I'm sorry ta disappoint ye all,' he said, 'but I dinna think I'll be staying in to help with the bathroom. I'm off tae see Stirling play Rangers,' and he added with misty eyes, 'and I intend to have a fair few pints first.'

After all that we had been through during the last few months morale could have been a lot worse.

I said, 'You know what we really must do if we get half a chance?'

Kevin stared into the bottom of his mug before throwing the dregs of his tea on the sand. 'What,' he said.

'We shall have to get rid of the fleas in this bunker.'

'If the Sergeant wants us to get rid of the fleas, maybe I'll no go to the fitba,' said Jock.

'A red hot cigarette is the best way,' said Kevin. 'We've got plenty of fags to burn their arses with.'

There was one thing that we had no illusion about as we busied ourselves bringing our gun pit into order. Soon the Germans would do their hardest to break in and overrun us in Tobruk. Still, there were two obstacles to impede their course and progress. Firstly, we had in Tobruk, manning the weapon pits around the perimeter, the whole of the 9th Australian Division which had been further reinforced by the arrival by sea of the Seventh Armoured Brigade of the Seventh Armoured Division and it was inconceivable that the Nazi Divisions would walk over the Aussies. We also had in Tobruk three well trained and battle hardened regiments of British Artillery, of which we were one. Although, during the retreat from Mersa Brega, the Regiment had lost in killed, wounded and taken prisoner, some seventy men and over fifty vehicles and three guns complete with crews. The Regiment was still armed with twenty-one guns, manned by experienced desert worthy gunners with stacks of ammunition, heaped and sheeted, at hand.

The Tobruk fortress, which we had helped to capture a few short months earlier, was bounded on the north by the sea. The main defences facing east, south and west were defended by an anti tank ditch, a barrier of wire fences and minefields. Round the perimeter there were more than a hundred concrete dug-outs and fortifications, used as Infantry posts.

Just inside the perimeter, because the terrain was so flat, the Italian constructors of the fortress had set up a number of tall observation towers for use of the gunners as O.P.s. Some of the gun positions were more elaborate than others and were constructed of concrete and steel. 'A' Troop were now occupying one of these concreted positions which we had christened 'The Marble Halls'.

During the first two days of the siege the gunners improved their gun positions, the drivers dug pits to protect their trucks from bomb and shell, the Infantry put up more wire and the sappers laid more mines. Large holes were dug to protect our supplies of petrol and ammunition. The heat was oppressive and we waited in the gun and weapon pits in the dark lee of the forbidding and desolate sand dunes with tingling anticipation.

The first enemy attack came on the 13th of April on the south-west sector. We clearly heard the clanking of enemy tank tracks. They were greeted with hundreds of shells from our Battery. After losing seven of his twelve assaulting tanks and more than eight hundred of their infantry, the enemy withdrew. On the 18th of April a second determined attack took place on the same sector. As the sun drew out long shadows, the sky was lit up by British gun flashes as a rain of shells screamed down on the enemy attack. The Australian infantry were using their two-pounder anti-tank guns to good effect and the attack was repulsed and petered out by nightfall.

We began to grow more and more confident. The Germans were unaccustomed to not having their own way in the desert, but we knew that, when they were ready, they would try again. It was a matter of arrogant vainglory and pride for the German generals that Tobruk, now cut off from the main force, should be expurgated and crushed. In the meantime the main British army in the desert were falling back further and further eastwards and Mersa Matruh eventually became the British forward base, while the enemy held the high ground above Sollum. It was not lost on us that the nearest friendly troops and fighter bases were nearly two hundred miles away.

Back in the foul smelling bunkers and dug-outs of Tobruk we fought off close clinching lice and fleas which bit and harrassed our bodies. Our stale, soiled blankets hadn't been disinfected for many months. Our stained, bleached clothes were grimy from sweat and musty from wear, grease and gunsmoke. Washing water was unobtainable. Our total ration of water, which had either to come from the sea water distillery in Tobruk or come up by lighter all the way from Alexandria, was three pints per man per day. This covered cooking, drinking and washing. Every night, at last light, Ross brought the quad up and parked it near the gun so that, if there were an enemy tank attack during the night, the gun could be moved into an anti tank position. The gun position, around which we spent our days and nights, was our world.

Every day hordes of Stuka dive bombers, programmed to kill, ranged the skies in ominous procession. They drifted and they hovered and they dived to fill the air with screaming thunder to startle the uneasy vitals of the desert. They attacked the forward positions, they bombed the harbour and they bombed the aerodrome to converging percussion. No longer did we feel that we were spectators of a horror film. The Stuka parades just became part of our daily life. The few Hurricanes had evacuated the aerodrome and the air over Tobruk was bequeathed to the Luftwaffe for the Nazi pilots to debase, to adulterate and to use for their own purposes.

On the 28th day of April enemy planes dropped thousands of leaflets on Tobruk with the following veiled and cryptic message:

Proclamation

The General Commanding the German Forces in Libya hereby requests the British Troops occupying Tobruk to surrender arms. Single soldiers waving white handkerchiefs are not fired on.

Strong German forces have already surrounded Tobruk.

It is useless to try and escape — remember Mechili. Our dive bombers — Stukas — are awaiting your ships which are lying in Tobruk.

*   *   *   *

It was clear that the enemy was about to strike a major blow at the fortress and, during the still, starless night of April 29th the distant purr of engines and the eerie, ceaseless hum of motor transport blew over the desert wind from the direction of the Derna Road.

The first major, and carefully planned attack on the Fortress, commenced at 8 o'clock on the night of April 30th, as the moonlight lay cold on the desert levels.

The German gunners laid down a two hour, pulverising barrage and, when the intensity of the barrage slackened, enemy tanks could be heard rumbling towards us, putting the defenders to the test. All next day was one of heavy black fighting. Ground was conceded and several of the Aussie forward posts were overrun. Our gun fired over four hundred rounds and the gunner's half naked bodies were caked with sweat. The guns gave us a strange and uncanny sense of power and all through the day, the black clouds of battle into which we continued to pour endless rounds of gunfire, enveloped the devilish cauldron ahead. The air resounded in power and urgency with a blitz of steel. On that day alone fifteen thousand shells were launched into the advancing enemy infantry and armour by the British defenders cannonade.

The booming racket of the artillery was overspread with the high chatter of the Australians' Vickers guns, the crashing of their anti tank two pounders and the heavy crump of mortars. Hard pressed, tin hatted stretcher bearers were bringing the Australian wounded down the wadi and on to the waiting ambulances. One disfigured stretcher case was burnt and shrunken from the scorching fire of a German flame thrower. There were small groups of walking wounded and one Digger with red rimmed eyes said; 'It's crook up there mate.'

These fighting Aussies had come from their far distant homeland, half way across the world, to this nameless arena of seething desert. They were men of courage and defiance and valour and, in these wild moments, they could have been present at the turning of the tide. Never before in the years of this war had the Nazi Divisions been unable to thrust forward in battle. The German tanks and infantry had penetrated some four thousand yards into the outer defences on a front of five thousand yards and there was a real danger of an enemy breakthrough.

Although our artillery and anti tank guns had knocked out eleven Mark IV tanks during the morning, the general situation became more serious as the day went on.

A company of Aussies put in a determined counter attack which was unsuccessful and the ground was serried with their corpses. It was a considerable relief to us when reinforcements of tanks and guns arrived from the eastern sector. However, by this time the Germans had dug themselves in and it became impossible to dislodge them. This 4000 yard salient, which bit deeply into our positions remained for the whole seige. From then on there was a stalemate in the enclave. There was no escape from the encompassing ring of steel. No means of slipping the collar. The R.A.F. had long since disappeared from the skies over Tobruk and the Australian infantry and the British gunners settled down to the long and weary seige.

★   ★   ★   ★

Perhaps the most irritating wretchedness in Tobruk was caused by the hot

Khamsin sandstorms which raged almost every other day in the suffocating hot desert wind. The gunners cursed as they inhaled the choking cast off rubbish of the earth reduced to a fine spawning powdery mould, as it racked and filtered into their mouths, eyes and lungs. With desert stained handkerchiefs bound tightly around their mouths, they coughed and wheezed and sweated in the stifling, oppressive maelstrom. The outpouring of yellow ash and frothy clouds of dross on the surface of the desert were beaten, pulverised and pounded by the turbulent hustling vehicles, trucks and shambling tanks which churned the desert floor. The grey faces and shirtless bodies of the gunners were stung and buffeted by the burning Khamsin in the slough of this wretched, sweltering dust hole.

On a typical sandstorm day, the Tobruk soldier would wake to find the hot blistering sand beating into his face like a cheese grater. His war worn blankets would be covered in an inch of fine dust. It would be tempting fortune to venture far from the gun as there would be a fair chance of getting lost in the nightmare of yellow fog. It was impossible to consume any food or drink without swallowing large quantities of sand and by mid-day everyone had heads that throbbed and spun and there was a feeling of tightness around the chest like a band of iron.

Although some sand storms lasted three days, it was more usual for the storm to blow itself out in the evening, but there was never enough water in which to wash. The gunners would use perhaps a half a cup of water, to gargle, clean their teeth and bathe the eyes, after the storm was over.

April went out and May came in with some really hot weather. My memories flooded back to May in England. In the warm May evenings my father and I would dibble in a few Red Kings or stick the 'runners' and then, about half past seven, when I had had a wash in cold water and eaten my supper I'd go and help roll the cricket square.

On the farm the spring corn would cover a hare when she squatted and they'd be chopping out the beet on piecework at a week's pay for an acre. I've seen the time when the daymen, using long hoes, would do three acres in a week. My father always turned his horses out to grass on the first day of May and they would kick up their heels and snort down their nostrils as they stretched their winter legs and galloped around the horse meadow with flying manes. If Watchman came too close to Sam's mares or started to nuzzle their necks, they'd lay back their ears and squeal like a rabbit. Here, in the forward areas of Tobruk, far from the crank of my mother's butter churn and far from the peace of rural Suffolk, except for small clumps of brown, withered camel thorn, nothing grew. There were no trees or any green thing; just jagged broken telegraph poles and man made stork legged observation posts, dirt, rock, sand and dust.

We fed on the torrid crutches of hope and rumour. One day, or so we supposed, the British army, which was some two hundred miles away at Mersa Matruh, would sweep westwards across the desert, with its armoured might and relieve us from the restraint and confinement of this steel bounded stronghold.

It was a time, however, of a flat heaviness of morale. Greece had been evacuated and over three thousand of our men had been lost. One aircraft carrier and several cruisers had been sunk during the evacuation. It was a disaster and it was our belief that, if those troops which had been sent to Greece, had been left with us in the desert, we would by now be half way to Tripoli.

After the debacle of Dunkirk, the continuous sequence of military and naval disasters gave us little confidence in the direction of the war.

One day Francis was collecting up empty charge cases and stacking them behind the gun. The sun was at its hottest and rivulets of sweat ran down his dark face. The flies were tormenting his eyes and his mouth. I could feel that the blood was boiling in his veins.

He laid the last of the sun hot brass charge cases on the neat pile and came over to sit beside me on the trail of the gun.

'Fag Albert?' he asked, holding an opened packet towards me.

I pulled out a cigarette and tapped one end on my thumb nail before placing it in my mouth.

'Thanks Francis,' I said.

As he struck a match he said, 'You know Albert, the way things are going, we could lose this fugging war. We are on our Jack Jones and the Krauts are getting it all their own way.'

'We always win the last battle,' I said.

'Don't come any of that Albert,' he said blowing out a stream of smoke. 'Rommel is running rings round our Generals. He has three times as many war planes out here as we have. A German Mark IV tank is worth a squadron of our Crusaders. Those undersized shells from our two pounder anti tank guns on the Crusaders bounce off the hull of a Mark IV like peas off a pig's bum. They are only pop guns compared with the 75mm and 88mm guns on the German tanks.'

'Who's fault is that?' I said.

'Why, those bloody politicians at home who said years before the war that there was no need to rearm. Those bloody left wing pacifists ought to be sent out here and made to get into a Gladiator and see how they get on against a Messerschmitt 109 at ten thousand feet. Or they should be stuck in an anti tank pit on a forward slope and see what they make of trying to knock out a hull down Mark IV with one of our piddling pea shooters.'

'Well, Churchill warned them,' I said.

'Yes, but no one seemed to care a bugger. Everyone chose to believe the stories that half the German tanks were made of cardboard and that a few Territorials with searchlights would stop the German bombers from reaching London.'

Secretly, I had to agree with a lot of what Francis said. However I was a bit miffed with him as he had been a lot better educated than any of us and had been to what was known as 'a good public school.' His father was a clergyman in Hampshire and it was his wish that Francis should become a teacher or go into the Ministry. When Francis had announced that he wanted to become a dancer, his father had given five bad sermons in a row. However, when Francis appeared in the back row of the chorus of 'The Dancing Years', the Reverend Ellington and his wife had made a special journey by train to London to see a matinee performance. When the curtain lifted they were full of apprehension and misgivings but, by the first interval, they were completely captivated by the show. After the final chorus the vicar, in his dog collar, and his wife in a pretty hat had gone backstage and Ivor Novello had shaken them by the hand and Miss Evelyn Laye had given them a ready smile. When they returned to their parish, Mrs. Ellingtons enthusiasm for 'The Dancing Years' encouraged the Mothers' Union to book a bus for all to see 'master Francis' doing his stuff.

So I felt that Francis, one way and another, had had a fair run and should be among those who should set an example, so I said, 'For Christ's sake don't let anyone hear you talk like that about losing the war. You'll be up before the Battery Commander for causing alarm and despondency.'

'Well I feel alarmed and despondent,' said Francis. 'We're like an under powered scarab beetle trying to push too big a ball of dung.'

'I'll bet you a quid that we are relieved and out of Tobruk within four weeks,' I said.

'I wouldn't have the heart to take your money,' said Francis.

CHAPTER TWENTY-THREE

The Aussies and the Stukas

THE FIRST MAJOR attempt to relieve the Tobruk garrison commenced just over two months after the onset of the siege. The plan was for the 7th Armoured Division to be the spearhead of the assault on Halfaya Pass on the frontier. The first B.B.C. reports said that it was a reconnaissance in force and that things were going well.

OVER ON THE western sector we were dug in under the Pilastrino ridge and the Troop was preparing to bed down. The guards, hands in pockets and with their rifles slung, had begun their stint for the night's tedious hours of idle drudgery. Everyone was moving around in a timeless, hypnotic dawdle. Any sense of urgency was dormant for the time being. Jock was whistling for lack of thought. Like an unexpected clout round the ears, Sandy Evan's loud voice rang out, 'Prepare to Move.'

'Fuggit,' said Kevin, who was straightening out his bedroll and looking forward to a few hours sleep before his stint on guard at 4 a.m. 'As usual, perfect timing, I think that they do it on purpose.'

'You know what this means,' I said.

'A phantom pregnancy?' said clever sides Francis.

'No,' I said, ignoring him. 'It means that we shall be breaking out tomorrow to meet the 7th Armoured.'

'Yes, if Rommel gives them a free passage,' said Francis, taking a mouthful from his water bottle.

'I told you yesterday that we should be out of Tobruk within four weeks,' I said, 'pity you didn't take my bet.'

'We're not out yet,' said Francis.

'I'm getting browned off with you Francis,' I said.

The next seven night hours were spent threading and straggling our guns along the narrow, deep rutted, wheel eaten tracks across to the Eastern sector. K Battery was directed to a deep, fissured wadi a mile from the sea coast, where we lay low under our camouflage nets to await the dawn.

The Western Desert Force had already begun its push westward but, what we did not know at the time, was that Rommel was more than ready for them. During that next long anxious day over a hundred British tanks were destroyed by the German 88mm guns. Because of these heavy losses, due almost entirely to the inferior British tanks and anti tank weapons, the battle formations withdrew behind the Egyptian Frontier and we continued to be beseiged in Tobruk.

'I expect,' said Kevin with heavy sarcasm, 'that the so called Reconnaissance in Force will be hailed as a great British victory and that our forces around the frontier are carrying out a planned tactical withdrawal to Mersa Matruh to regroup for a major attack.'

'Don't you start Kevin,' I said.

'All I know,' went on Kevin, 'is that I've been in this sodding desert, within range of enemy guns for over nine months and all we get is Stukas, no beer and too much bloody propaganda.'

We all had a bit of a laugh because Kevin didn't often fly off the handle. None the less, after raised hopes and a half a promise of being able to fight our way out, we were'nt too happy at the bleak prospect of another, soul wearying spell of the daily grind inside the Tobruk perimeter.

*   *   *   *

The next day Captain Kershaw sent for me. When I reached the Command Post truck, he held out his hand to me and said, 'Congratulations Sergeant Cooper. Your Military Medal has come through and the Battery Commander wanted me to tell you.

I'd nearly forgotten about that Italian mortar when we had taken Tobruk, four months earlier.

'Thank you Sir,' I said, 'and what about your medal Sir? Did that come through as well?'

'Yes,' said Captain Kershaw, 'my Military Cross came with your medal.'

'Well, congratulations to you Sir,' I said.

'You know,' said Captain Kershaw, 'getting a medal is a matter of luck really. They seem to have a certain number to dish out after a successful batle and, when we took Tobruk, we got two of them.'

'I know Sir,' I said. 'One of the bravest things I've seen out here was when we were being shelled and machine gunned by those Mark III's at Mersa Brega. A badly wounded corporal from Tower Hamlets lay in front of my gun, screaming in agony. A Field Ambulance drew up and stopped by my gun. An orderly got out and I heard him say to his driver, "You stay here mate and take cover in that slit trench. There's no bloody sense in both of us risking getting killed." Then he walked as calmly as you like, carrying his First Aid haversack up to the wounded corporal. He was as composed and unruffled as if he was going to tend a short sighted batsman who had been rapped on the knuckles by a seam bowler. We saw him bend down, get out his syringe and inject something into the corporals arm. He stayed with him until the screaming stopped and that must have been nearly two minutes. Machine gun bullets were flying everywhere and we couldn't understand why he hadn't been hit. I expect he saw that there was no hope for the wounded man, so he stood and started to walk back to the ambulance. A machine gun opened up and he was riddled. He won't get a medal will he Sir?'

'Well, we were lucky Sergeant Cooper and I've got a little something to celebrate with.' He opened the canvas flap at the back of the truck and he took out a half a bottle of Gin and two chipped enamel mugs. He blew the dust off them and set them down on the flat bonnet of the truck. I thought that his hand shook a little as he poured out the Gin. He handed me one of the mugs.

'Good luck Sir,' I said. I found that my mug was almost a third full and I had never tasted Gin before in my life. The common soldier was supposed not to have a taste for it.

'Good luck Sergeant Cooper,' he said and then went on, 'there's something aesthetically pleasing about drinking from a battered and chipped enamel mug when it is half full of Gin.' Then, to my surprise, he said, 'I wonder what Lance Bombardier Porter's sister would say if she could see us now.'

Everyone seemed to know about Julie and me but I was caught in an unguarded moment and, with a sudden catch of my breath, I realised that I hadn't given Julie a thought for more than twenty four hours.

*   *   *   *

It was the 23rd of June. Sandy Evans, who had betaken himself to the primitive spade handed toilet and was returning to the Command Post, bent his steps and strolled over to my gun.

'Heard the news Albert?' he asked.

'What news?'

'Germany has marched into Russia,' said Sandy.

'Is that good or bad news for us?' I asked.

'Good news I hope,' said Sandy, 'but I cannot for the life of me understand why Hitler has done it. I should have thought that he's got plenty on his hands as it is.'

'Churchill hasn't exactly been praising Russia to the skies,' I said.

'No, but I bet that he'll change his tune now.'

'Heard the news?' I shouted across to Ross and Francis, who were completely naked and rinsing their shorts in a bowl half filled with petrol. 'The Krauts have marched into Russia.'

'Serves the Bastards right,' said Francis. 'Russia invaded Finland, Lithuania and Latvia without being asked.'

'Don't know why she swanned into those places,' said Kevin, 'they're only good for Christmas trees and bloody reindeer.'

'I think that they also might be good for sites for airfields and submarine bases,' said Francis, pointedly.

We became firm friends with the Aussies and we set our horses together. They appreciated the artillery support which we gave them and we, in our turn, were glad to have them with us. We always 'Stood To' when one of their patrols went out through the wire at night and we became used to the rattle of machine gun fire and the tracers and flares lighting up the 'no mans land' a thousand yards ahead. We were always alert for their signal for artillery support and, when we saw two red flares fired in quick succession followed by a green, shot up into the night air we strove to get off our first rounds of defensive fire within twenty five seconds.

The Aussies often walked down through our gun positions, Bruce and

Larry, two Australian Sappers would call in on their way up to lay mines. They were in their bush hats and shorts, but they wore no shirt, socks or boots. On one occasion they brought a live Italian mine which they had found near our Waggon Lines. They stuck the thing on top of an oil drum right beside the Command Post, took out a pair of pliers and proceeded to dismantle it. Philip Underwood was horrified and suggested that they were breaking every rule in the Training Manual and he further suggested that they take it down to the beach and dismantle it there.

'I would rather not die,' said Philip, 'by being blown up by so called friendly troops on my own gun position.'

'Aw, she'll be right mate,' said Bruce, 'this little beaut won't blow up unless you tread on it. It's no more dangerous than taking a watch to bits.' Then he added as an afterthought. 'If I think that it's going to go off I'll stick my hat over it.'

July came, then August and the great red sun was a blazing ball of fire as it poured out its blistering heat, day after day. The broiling rays bored into our skin to scorch and burn. Most days there was a morning and evening 'hate' between the artillery on either side but, during the hottest parts of the day the desert was shimmering with giddy paced mirages blurred in the silvery heat and observation from the O.P.s was not possible. The flies were a curse and they made our daylight hours a misery. They clung to our sweat soaked bodies as they clustered round the moisture of our eyes and mouths. We even swallowed dozens of them in our stew or tea. Some days the heat wearied us to exhaustion and, in this tedious lunar landscape, we yearned for the green meadows and cool rich dairy pastures of Suffolk. One day as the waves of heat assaulted our bodies, Jock said, 'Ye know Albert, it's too fugging hot for fighting. I feel like a haggis straight out of the pot.'

Every day, without fail, the dreaded Stukas flew in with their wicked black bombs and their banshee sirens. They assembled, taunted and pressed, even in the raging sandstorms. They employed most of their powerful energies to attack and bomb the harbour with its installations but every now and then, we never knew when, they would turn their full attention to the gun positions. This was particularly so for those of us on the eastern sector, who were becoming a thorn in the side of some long range German artillery which had been stationed outside the eastern perimeter to lob shells into the harbour area.

One such day occurred in the middle of August, when 'A' and 'B' Troop of 'K' Battery were two of the principal targets. It was a still, hot day and there was an unnatural, shimmering quietness round the perimeter. The sky was transparent, azure and infinite, a leaping light under a swarming sun. It was well past noon and we were brimmed with lethargy. Lizards dozed under the hot stones. The atmosphere was untamed and cruel in its arid meanness.

Kevin spotted them first and gave a long, low, whistle.

'Coulu,' he shouted, pointing at an angle to the south west.

'Coulu' means 'a lot' or 'all' in Arabic and we always referred to a pack of J.U. 87 dive bombers by the word. We always kept a wary eye on a 'Coulu' and took cover if they seemed to be heading straight for us. They always came in out of the sun. We followed Kevin's pointing arm and there, seeming to hang motionless in the air, were about forty Stukas, like malignant birds of prey. These were the Nazi terror war planes. Ominous dark dots in the sky, forbidding and evil favoured, symbolising the lawless blemish of cruel fascist civilisation.

The drumming beat of their engines became louder. We were keeping our eyes firmly fixed on the leader and, when he waggled his black gull wings and plummeted into his dive I shouted to the sub section, 'He's coming straight at us. Heads down in the end dug out.'

We were in one of the 'Marble Halls' gun positions which had been constructed by the Italians and, at the end of the pits there was a concrete bunker which would hold a full gun crew. We had only used the bunker previously during prolonged periods of heavy shelling and, although a bomb would have gone right through the roof, it was the safest place for us in an air attack.

We had eight seconds to make the bunker before the torrenting bombs came down with a skull splitting crash. They were close, very close, and the bunker throbbed and shook as it filled with dust and smoke. We then felt the hot blast of air come searing through the opening. The noise was deafening. We knew now that we were on the rack as one of the prime targets and that the next few minutes were going to be rough.

We heard the screaming plane as it pulled out of its dive a few hundred feet directly above us and we were very concerned about the roof caving in as bits of masonry were falling from the ceiling. There was absolutely no ack ack protection and the bombers could dive as low as they wished.

Five seconds later a second plane screamed down and another four bombs smashed into the gun position.

It was nightmarish as the earth above us shuddered and roared and the whole bunker rocked with the vibration, followed by a hot, indrawing draught. A third plane came down on us in a murderous howl as another four bombs hit the site. Every nerve in our bodies screamed as the choking dust got worse, blinding and suffocating. With handkerchiefs pressed to our noses we craved to get out into the fresh air. There was a pause for twenty seconds and we hoped that the attack on our site was over, but there was more to come as two more planes released their bombs above us. The violent shock waves had partly rent our ear drums, as the raid reached its climax in this awful collision with violence.

Gradually the evil, bloodcurdling banshees sounded further and further away, I staggered to the bunker opening and yelled, 'stay there.' As I shouted, three Messerschmitts with cannons and machine guns blazing, straffed the whole gun position and bullets and cannon shells ripped into the earth above us. We couldn't have taken much more, everyone was choking with dust and, as we climbed out of the bunker on to the gun position our ears were ringing like a thousand bells.

'I don't remember the bloody recruiting sergeant saying anything about this,' quipped Kevin in his dry, salty way as we peered into the thick pall of dust and smoke which hung in the air like a flatulent, copious cloud. As usual the air was filled with an acrid, pungent smell and the strong, tangy taste of high explosives. Everyone was dazed and shocked, the lines on the grey, deep burned faces of the gunners seemed to have hardened. It seemed incredible that any of us, at the very point of attack, could have survived this deadly onslaught. This wrack of savage devastation could so easily have kindled, for us, the fall of the curtain and evoked the termination of our brief and brittle existence.

There was some dry, nervous laughter and fluttering, wry comments. Jock, whose belly was overmuch redundant was heard to say through the dust, "My tummy has contracted into a wee tight ball.'

Ross said, 'with a beltline like yours it will take more than an air raid to do that Jock.'

We all had a laugh and the tension was easing.

Number two gun pit had had a direct hit and the gun lay on its side like a dead elephant. The offside wheel was lifted to the sky and the brass hub cap glinted in the afternoon sun. There were ugly, jagged holes in the limber and live charges had been blown about and scattered all over the gun position. A dirty khaki webbing haversack had been ripped open and its contents littered the ravaged surfaces. A pair of crook backed mess tins and a warped and twisted mug lodged at the bottom of an eight foot deep crater. On the edge of the crater there lay a blackened crumpled spoon and a torn and mangled woollen cap comforter which had been pulverised with shrapnel, which had doubtless been knitted and sent to the Regiment by the good ladies of Suffolk. Loose sheets of notepaper, which had been shredded in the blast blew here and there across the hot pitted sand.

The haversack belonged to Timber Wood, and he was bomb happy and no mistake. Timber was a big lad but he hadn't got much in him. He'd never wanted to be on the guns in the first place. He was sitting by the Command Post, quietly sobbing. He was wrung out and he'd probably get a rocket from the Battery Commander, but Timber couldn't help it. It was a general breaking up and he was shaking with fear and humiliation as his courage ebbed away.

Jock picked up a few of Timber's things and took them over to him. He put his arms around Timber's shaking shoulders and said gently, 'Take a drink of this Timber,' and he held out his water bottle.

Timber groaned and looked about him, without seeing. He was like a dazed child, worn out with crying and he seemed to be encountering all the pain in the world.

'Thank you Jock,' he said at last.

'It's nae bother,' said Jock.

Some of the other gunners were wandering about a bit aimlessly but Jock had taken the air attack in his stride and was doing well. I was proud of him.

The more we examined our gun position, the more of a miracle it seemed that no one was killed. The bombing had been accurate and there were no less than eleven bomb craters within forty yards of the guns. If our concrete bunkers had not been so well constructed by the Italian engineers the Troop casualties could have been horrendous.

The Command Post telephone reverberated in high, echoing notes of urgency. Regimental Headquarters were ringing through to enquire how much damage had been done.

There had been a disaster on our sister 'B' Troop gun position. It lay in a shallow wadi some two hundred yards to our left. 'B' Troop gunners were sheltering in the normal, hand dug narrow 'L' shaped slit trenches and had not got the solid back up protection provided by our own troop's 'Marble Halls', concreted positions. A bomb had landed slap on the corner of the 'L' shaped slit trench behind their No.1 Gun. The whole of the sub section were sheltering there, together with the driver of the water cart and his mate who were delivering the daily ration of water to the troop when the raid took place. They had all been killed instantly and the bodies were now lying a stone's throw away in mangled, distorted death. The dead soldiers were: Sergeant Jack Clifton, 25, manager of a shoe making factory in Felixstowe, married and with a baby daughter that he had never seen; Bombardier Pendril Hattersley, 24, a craftsman carpenter by trade who constructed timber cattle troughs and hen coops for the farmers and poultry breeders. He had come from the entrancing little Suffolk village of Chelsworth, where the River Brett faced the gabled and colour washed houses, sagging gracefully with age and whose bricks and timber stood defiant to wind and weather. Pendril Hattersley's widow would now have to bring up two young children without a father.

The three gunners were Gunner Alfred Clitheroe, rising 20, a shipping clerk who had joined the West Suffolk Yeomanry when he moved from Leeds to Ipswich for his firm. Gunner 'Butch' Maxwell, also nearly twenty, an apprentice bricklayer from Barton Mills and Gunner Roderick Lee, 21, who played the violin and owned a four ten, fitted with a silencer for poaching pheasants.

Also attached to Number One Gun was Driver Nathan Lawson, 22, whose Jewish parents already had good reason to hate Adolph Hitler and the jackbooted criminals of the Third Reich.

The two lads from the water cart were Lance Bombardier Stanley Palmer, a schoolmaster's son from Needham Market and Gunner Douglas Smith, 22, a factory sweeper who was never expected to tackle a more responsible job in the Army than assistant to the driver of the water cart.

The news of our dead comrades weighed heavily upon us and we lunged into an empty, sick feeling of depression.

'This is bloody daft,' said Kevin, 'The bastards know exactly where we are and they fully intend to shift us. It's just asking for another Stuka raid if we stay here.'

'Tell that to the Brigadier C.R.A.,' I said.

Kevin was right in saying that the enemy were determined to shift us. In the middle of the following morning four heavy shells, without any previous ranging, bracketed our guns. This opening salvo was followed by a carefully prepared and highly accurate assault on our guns and gunners by heavy systematic shelling for over twenty minutes. We were forced to remain in the hot claustrophobic bunker until the enemy guns had quietened down.

That night, with some relief, the Troop was ordered to withdraw from the 'Marble Hall' position to one about six hundred yards away. We made up dummy guns from old telegraph poles and wire, and stuck them in the old gun pits and pulled camouflage nets over them. I doubt whether it fooled anybody.

The following day Brigade sent us up two Bofors guns to protect us from another dive bombing attack. We had eight dead men and the Bofors were too late.

*   *   *   *

One morning in August as the sun nudged its way through the haze which still lingered around Tobruk, a Heinkel bomber flew over at about ten thousand feet, dropping leaflets. Jock collected a handful of them which he brought to the gun pit. They were addressed to the Aussies.

AUSSIES

After the Crete disaster, Anzac troops are being ruthlessly sacrificed by England in Tobruk.

Turkey has concluded a pact of friendship with Germany. England will shortly be driven out of the Mediterranean. The offensive from Egypt to relieve you is totally smashed.

YOU CANNOT ESCAPE

Our dive bombers are waiting to sink your transports. Think of your future and your people at home.

Come forward, show white flags and you will be out of danger.

SURRENDER!

Jock handed one to Troop Sergeant Major Evans who glanced at the leaflet and said, 'Well you know what to do with these McKinley. I've heard you say often enough that three sheets of Army Form Blank is not enough and you also complain that the officers have a proper bog roll. Now you've got enough paper to shine up your arse to a high gloss.'

About this time the Troop came into possession of two old Italian 149mm howitzers. These were massive guns with heavy iron wheels and the shells that they fired weighed over sixty pounds. Major Coleman decided that Harold Reeve and myself should examine these guns and find out how to fire them. There were stacks of Italian ammunition in Tobruk.

The firing mechanism was similar to that of our own guns but on these howitzers there was a lanyard, about thirty feet long attached to the firing lever. It was clear that, after setting up the gun and loading it, the crew would retire to a slit trench with the end of the lanyard, as a precaution against gun or ammunition malfunction.

Harold and I took a half a dozen gunners down into a coastal wadi to fire a few rounds out to sea. The gun sights had been destroyed by the Italians before surrender so the best we could do, after loading the gun, was to point it in the approximate direction and give the lanyard a sharp pull from the slit trench. We fired off half a dozen rounds successfully and watched them burst out to sea. The enemy must have wondered what was going on.

It was then decided that the guns should be handed over to the Australian Infantry, Harold and I were ordered to draw two days rations for our drivers and ourselves and to take the howitzers up to the Aussies to train them how to fire them. When we arrived at our given map reference, which was in a shallow wadi some six hundred yards short of the wire, we found five Aussies in battered bush hats, squatting round a small fire. They were wearing shorts and boots and were eating their mid-day meal. Harold and I got down from our quads and walked towards the group. One of them put his mess tin on the ground, got up and said: 'So you've brought our shooters then.'

'Yes,' said Harold, 'my name is Harold Reeve and this is Albert Cooper.'

We shook hands and the Aussie said, 'Pleased ter meet yer. My name's Bill Kearns. I'm the sergeant in charge here. Come and meet my cobbers.'

I called over Ross and Ken Burroughs, who was driver for Harold's gun.

Bill Kearns said, 'Park your arses round the fire. There's plenty of room. sorry there ain't no easy chairs.'

We stationed ourselves around them, squatting on our heels.

'Had yer tucker yet?' asked a thin faced little man who seemed to be cook for the day.

'We've brought our rations,' said Harold.

'Aw there's plenty here,' said the cook, 'fetch your mess tins. It's wallaby stew.'

'Make a change from roo meat and rabbit,' said Ross.

'Listen to that joker,' said one of the others. 'He don't sound like a Pomm, surely you don't come from England mate?'

'New Zealand,' said Ross.

The Australian pinched his nose in mock horror. 'Pig or Penguin Island?' he asked.

'South Island.'

'Have you deserted from the Kiwi Division then?'

'No. I was in England buying some rams when war broke out.'

'Thought perhaps you were in England to learn how to play rugby football,' said another of the men.

'You must be joking,' said Ross.

The cook added three more tins of meat to the stew and scratched his behind with the handle of his spoon. We got out our mess tins.

'I'd better introduce you to these jokers,' said Sergeant Kearns, standing up and throwing the dregs from his mug on to the sand. 'The cook there is Dave, he comes from Normanton in Queensland, straight in the arsehole of Australia. If you take my advice you'll have a good look at him, because you might not be alive to see him again after you eat that stew.'

They all laughed and Dave said, 'Yew wouldn't be wantin any more stew would you Bill?'

Sergeant Kearns went on, 'Next to him is Blue. He was a schoolmaster in Brisbane, but he knows bugger all and he ought to be chucked on the mullock heap. He's a hard case.'

Blue waved his spoon at us.

'Then the fat man, Jack Bradman. Nothin' at all to do with the Don. Talk about Jack hitting a cricket ball, he couldn't hit a sheep shed with a banjo. Jack is stock agent for Dalgetty's and half the time he's covered in sheep shit, but if you want some decent Merino rams Ross, Jack can get them for you.'

'I don't want any sodding Merinos,' said Ross. 'they're all wool and no meat. I reckon I'm going to stick to Southdowns and Romneys. We've got to do our bit to stop The British Isles from starving.'

'Wool's a good trade now that the war is on, they want it for uniforms,' said Jack, 'and you won't get any fine wool from the Romneys.

Sitting next to me was a strong jawed, raw faced looking digger. He seemed to be very tall and when he stood up would probably be the best part of six foot four.

'This,' said Bill Kearns, 'is "Shortarse". He comes from thirty miles north of Kalgoorlie. He's a lazy bastard and he reckons that his grandfather was Mayor of Kalgoorlie, but I reckon that his grandfather was a bastard miner like everyone else and you can bet your last, pox ridden dingo that his grandfather married a barmaid. All the Sheilas in Kalgoorlie were big titted barmaids and half of them were on the game.'

None of Bill Kearn's men seemed to object to his remarks at all.

After we had finished our stew, Dave said, 'How would you jokers like some Australian peaches with a drop of condensed milk on top?'

Apart from a few tins of Italian fruit which we had looted from Bardia in January, we hadn't seen tinned fruit for almost a year. Tinned fruit never came up with the army rations and the most common form of sweet that we had in Tobruk was dried prunes and boiled rice.

'How long have you jokers been out here then?' asked Jack.

'We've been on the desert without leave for eleven months,' I replied, 'and we've been away from England for nearly two years.'

'Jesus Christ!' said Bill, 'you poor bastards. We only left Australia on Boxing day.'

When we had cleared up the peaches, Bill took out a tin of Log Cabin cigarette tobacco and rolled a cigarette, using one hand and then he said, 'Well, let's go and look at our rifle then.' Then he added to me, 'Us five will come with you Albert and there'll be another five with Harold, when they get back from a swim.'

Ross started up the quad and slowly drew the gun a little deeper into the wadi. The Aussies came and helped unhook the gun and then they unloaded twenty of the heavy shells from the quad and stacked them by the side of the gun.

Blue shouted, 'Come on you bastards, don't walk. You always move at the double in the Artillery.' He proceeded to clench his fists and hold them to his chest. Then he ran round behind the gun and dropped to one knee. He said, 'You can see I don't need much training Albert.'

'That's very good,' I said, 'only trouble is that you are on the wrong side of the gun. All the ammo is round this side.'

Jack Bradman ran up to the muzzle and, standing on tip toe, he peered down the barrel and said, 'Pull the trigger Dave and I'll see if I can see anything.'

'Come away Bradman,' said Bill, you'll get your bloody head shot off.'

Shortarse pointed excitedly at the very heavy spade at the end of the trail and said, 'My word, she's even got a plough on the back.'

'Come on,' said Jack, who was a machine gunner, 'Let's give the Bastards a couple of magazines.'

Our first training session began. I had to warn them not to take any chances with the Italian ammunition. Some of it was very unstable and premature bursts were common.

The five men who were to make up Harold's squad had returned from their swim and one of them shouted across, 'Are you nervous Shortarse?'

Shortarse replied, 'You can't be nervous with a great big gun like this. It's the Bloody Krauts thats nervous.'

I saw that it was going to be a waste of time to try to get these Infantrymen interested in proper gun drill, but they were dead keen to fire some shells across the wire. Ross loaded a round and Jack rammed the charge home. Ross slammed the breech and I set the gun at maximum elevation. With Bill's help I managed to get everyone to retire to the slit trench before giving the lanyard a sharp pull. When the gun went off it jumped nearly a foot into the air. It made a tremendous bang and, as it was a low velocity gun, it was possible to see the shell leave the muzzle and to follow its trajectory as it disappeared into the air over the distant enemy lines. Twelve seconds later we were rewarded with a deep crump somewhere in the far distance. Our new 'bush' artillery crew were in a transport of delight. They re-loaded the gun and brought the trail back to its original position and re-aligned the piece. We climbed back into the trench. I gave Bill Kearns the nod and he shouted, 'FIRE.'

Blue pulled the lanyard and nothing happened. They had got the lanyard tangled up in a small thorn bush. After they had put this right, another round was fired.

'Jesus,' said Blue, who was a machine gunner, 'She'll get so bastard hot that we shall soon have to change the barrel.' The next sixty pound shell was loaded into the breech and Bill Kearns stood behind the gun while Jack and Dave moved the trail. Bill shouted, 'Keep her just a bit left of the third telegraph pole Dave.' Shortcase said, 'The gun is all lop-sided Sergeant. I reckon that we ought to dig a bit of a hole for the nearside wheel or stick a couple of rocks under the off side one.'

'She'll be right,' said Bill. Then he said: 'I know what we'll do. We'll put a half a dozen bully tins in a semi-circle in front of the gun and we'll space them about six feet apart.'

When this was done and they had fired two more shells, I heard Bill shout when they were lining up the gun: 'One and a half bully cans to the right Dave.'

As I said to Harold afterwards, 'I don't know what the Master Gunner at the Artillery School at Lark Hill would think of the gun drill.''

'We'd both be reduced to Lance Jacks for a start,' he said.

Again we climbed into the trench and again Bill shouted 'Fire.' When Blue tugged the lanyard, nothing happened.

'Try again,' I said.

Again Blue tugged on the lanyard. Still nothing happened.

'I think that it's a dud,' I said. Dave and Jack jumped out of the trench and began to run towards the gun.

Come back,' I yelled. It may be a delayed fuse and explode in the barrel.'

They stopped running and came back to the trench.

'When there is a missfire, everyone has to wait for two minutes before approaching the gun,' I explained.

'Aw, stuff you Albert,' said Jack, but they reluctantly got back down in the trench. I have to say that even today, when I hear an Australian voice, that it brings back to me the nostalgic memories of those valiant and indomitable Aussies, just inside the Tobruk wire. When, some three weeks later, I learned that Bill Kearns had been killed during a daring night attack on a heavily fortified German Post, I was as sorry as if he had been one of our own.

*   *   *   *

Lo! the evening falls and we, neath a starlit sky
Seek to rest below in the safety of the earth
Whilst coyotes yell to the moon
And planes soar high in the Heavens
The guns boom their ever challenging note
And shells scream their serenade of death
Tis hell let loose as every soldier knows
Then deathly silence for a while
The rustle of the breeze in the sun dried bushes
A scurry of a rat deep breathing within
A sudden burst of machine gun fire
Ah! A sigh, a cough, a flaming sky
Oh! night of turmoil for you and I

Oh! beautiful dawn, a stir within
Still is the morn, fires crackle and burn
Breakfast, sweet hopes for the new day
God in our hearts and Faith to carry on.

J. Hopley, Tobruk 1941

CHAPTER TWENTY-FOUR

The Iron Ring Tightens

INTO THE LONG, creeping months of September and October hovering and waiting and wallowing like becalmed battle galleons, we submitted to the long hours of boredom, mixed during gushes of activity with the heart thumping moments of exposure to insecurity and alarm.

Rocks were flung at cans and bottles, cans and bottles were flung at rocks. Captured scorpions were watched with morbid fascination as they stung themselves to death in rings of burning petrol. Were we emerging barbarians, like the Fascists and the Nazis and exposing our brutish edges? We flipped cards into a tin helmet and stoned the kangaroo rats. We hunted for firewood as the wooden ammunition boxes and the timber backs of crippled lorries were used up. We distilled small amounts of sea water in our home made distilleries constructed from oil drums and copper piping. Oil lamps were fashioned from empty tins with strips of Italian gas masks used for wicks. The dugout stank of diesel and smoke.

The gun position was our world. Hour after hour and day after day the siege ran its tedious course, like etching a furrow to eternity. We were leaner and our lips were drawn finer. The increasing heat pressed upon us, layer upon layer. We were stapled to the desert and harnessed to the war machine in a chain of idle hours. The inevitable end to this drawn sameness of existence, would be a pitched battle, fought with savage ferocity. Death was a clear possibility. This was no bad dream, but a real and stubborn reality drawing on the womb of time. There would be no slick conversion and no vanishing trick. There would be no sudden blessed awakening.

★   ★   ★   ★

Did I once say that we were half in love with our gun? But now, I don't know so much. We had pandered to her and nursed her through these long anxious months, but she was a demanding bitch. She stood in the gun pit like a hungry strumpet. She was a licenced mistress in her panoply of burning gun metal. We were tied to her prescription day and night. We never left her.

Our gun drill became sloppy. There was so much repetition that it became mechanical and slack. One day I had to tear a strip off poor old Kevin. He had found a half a tin of plum jam and he had spread some on a thick slice of three day old, sand coloured bread, made in the Tobruk field bakery. He was anxious to consume his bread and jam before the swarm of flies beat him to it. Unfortunately, at that moment, orders came down from the O.P. to 'Take Posts' and Kevin ran to the gun carrying his bread and jam. He didn't know where to put it so he sat on the layer's seat, operating the elevation and traversing handles with one hand, looking through the eye piece of the dial sight and, all the while, hanging on to his bread and jam with the other hand. I was really riled with Kevin.

'Throw it away Kevin,' I shouted. 'You can't lay a gun like that. Now you've got a stripe you ought to know better.'

'That's right,' said Francis. 'Pull your rank on him Sarge.'

'Shut up Francis,' I snapped, 'it wouldn't hurt you to sharpen up a bit yourself.'

*   *   *   *

Every morning now there was a visit from the grey, lazy engined reconnaissance plane, which glistened in the early sun like quicksilver. We christened him 'The Baron'. Sometimes he puttered around, just out of reach of our Bofors for twenty minutes or half an hour. He was probably taking photographs and generally poking around like a potential, loitering house breaker, casing for opportunity and information. A Hurricane could have disposed of the Baron in a few short seconds, but the R.A.F. had removed themselves to the distant eastern airfields of Egypt.

In addition to our daily ration of shelling and counter battery shoots we could always rely on hearing the deep boom of 'Long Tom'. Long Tom was a very heavy, long range gun which operated from the deep wadis outside our eastern sector. It was reputed to have an eight and a half inch bore and to have a range of twenty-two miles. The shells would roar through the air, high over our heads like an express train and the crashing of the heavy missiles echoed and re-echoed in the dry, rock gulleys. Long Tom was particularly active shelling the harbour on moonless nights when a destroyer might be in, unloading supplies. During the course of the siege 'A' Troop fired hundreds of rounds at Long Tom and, although we were able to make the Long Tom gunners keep their heads down and cease firing for long periods, we never succeeded in destroying the gun. Months later when we had an opportunity of seeing the Long Tom gun site we were staggered by the sheer size of the gun and the bore of the barrel. It was clear why we had been unable to knock him out. The gun was positioned on the face of a deep wadi in such a way that our minusses exploded on the hill in front of the gun and our plusses sailed over into the deep valley and burst half a mile beyond, against the steep valley face behind the gun site. A British gun in the same situation would have been eliminated by a Stuka attack, but we had no Stukas.

One sizzling hot afternoon in September Francis was giving Jock a haircut. The blunt scissors were catching and pulling as they bit into the sand and grit in Jock's ginger, shaggy mane. Everyone had at least a fortnight's growth of beard. Ross, wearing a dirty peaked Italian officer's cap and with a towel around his waist, was sitting on a leather, front seat that he had removed from a Fiat lorry. He was busying himself with needle and thread from his 'Hussif' and was mending a tear in his shorts.

Kevin, burnt black by the desert sun was perched on the edge of the gun pit, thumbing through a tattered magazine.

'Strike a light,' he shouted, 'listen to this, Some poxy Ack Ack gunners in Blighty are trying to cadge some comforts from some bloody welfare fund. They sign themsleves "Lonely Ack Ack gunners, somewhere in England". They say that they are five miles from the nearest pub and six miles from the nearest town and, although they've got a gramophone, a wireless set and a billiard table, they would like some money to buy musical instruments as they wish to form a band.'

'Poor wee laddies,' said Jock.

'Five miles from the nearest pub,' said Francis.

'We must concoct for them,' said Jock, brushing some loose hair off his chest, 'a wee letter of sympathy.'

So this was agreed and Francis was asked to write the letter. He received many suggestions as to the contents and, by late afternoon, was ready with the final draft.

'Dear lonely Ack Ack gunners, somewhere in England,' he wrote, 'we read with interest your request for money to purchase musical instruments. As we are five hundred miles from the nearest town and two thousand miles from the nearest English pub we are, sadly, unable to spend any of our money. We have therefore had a whip round in our troop and we have great pleasure in sending it on to you and sincerely hope that it will contribute to the purchase of a grand piano' (Francis enclosed two worthless hundred lire notes, many of which littered the dug out). 'We would make the humble suggestion that, until enough money arrives for the piano, cheaper instruments like rattles, Jew harps, knocking bones together and a comb and bog paper would make a harmonious combination.

'Hoping that this finds you as it leaves us,' and Francis signed the letter, 'A lonely troop of gunners, somewhere in Libya.'

'You know,' said Kevin with a big grin on his face, 'we're a rotten lot of bastards to send this letter.'

'You're quite right of course,' said Francis with a devlish smirk, 'we really are.'

★   ★   ★   ★

By the middle of October, after thirteen months in the desert without relief and after six months in Tobruk, our senses were dulled by what seemed to be the endlessnes of the task. With a confident, strident enemy all round us and ringed by their artillery we were captives, unwillingly installed on the lid of this barren landscape.

The crust of the Fortress was pitted with craters. The skin of the place was like the hide of the moon, gouged and perforated and engraved and ravished with the violence of it all. The Fortress had suffered like a great whale, wounded by thousands of harpoons. One felt that the whole of the stockaded bastion should be covered by a deep blanket of Fullers Earth and overlaid by a soft bandage to ease the pain.

For our part, I suppose that we were just drained and battle weary. Most of us were well past the fear threshold. The future seemed blunted and bleak. There was little real apprehension. Indeed, there was little feeling at all. The long painful haul had deadened our senses as we slopped into a deep layer of lethargy and idleness. We had had a bellyful and no mistake. The General Officer Commanding Tobruk Fortress received many messages for distribution to his men. The one from Winston Churchill read:

'THE WHOLE EMPIRE IS WATCHING YOUR STEADFAST AND SPIRITED DEFENCE OF THIS IMPORTANT OUTPOST OF EGYPT WITH GRATITUDE AND ADMIRATION.'

Another message from General Wavell said:

'YOUR MAGNIFICENT DEFENCE IS UPSETTING THE ENEMY'S PLANS FOR THE ATTACK ON EGYPT AND GIVING US TIME TO BUILD UP FOR A COUNTER OFFENSIVE. YOU COULD NOT, REPEAT *NOT*, BE DOING A BETTER SERVICE. WELL DONE.'

We may have been moving through special moments of history but, for me, during these last days of the summer's sun, the time register began to fall apart. The tidy sequence of progress and duration was thrown out of gear and our actions were undated. I seemed to have lost track and the period through September and October was just a jumble of faint memories. The day shoots and the night shoots went on.

Perhaps the most heart thumping moments were at night when, from a deep sleep beside the gun, everyone would be thrust and pitchforked into action by the loud, compulsive voice of the G.P.O. yelling through his megaphone, 'Take Posts'. Since the fall of Greece there had been reason to think that, in addition to the constant threat of tank attack, that there could well be an attack on Tobruk by sea, combined with a parachute landing.

I have said that my memories of those night alarm calls to the guns were confused and jumbled. One night, for instance, there was the strident command to man the guns. It was well past midnight and we had just come from sleep. It was flap, fluster and panic. Was it tanks, parachutists or a simple D.F. target? Disconnected thoughts surge through my mind but I hear the order from the Command Post: 'Lay on Defensive Task, Two.'

'I know now that the Aussies are out on patrol.'

Someone mutters — 'Jock, why are you wearing that daft clobber?'

It is total darkness.

I hear the order, 'Fire', and the brilliant flash of guns splits the night.

A voice, someone from No. 2 gun bawls — 'Keep out of the way of the recoil you stupid bugger or you'll get yourself deknackered.'

'What's the time?'

And someone answers in the darkness, 'Half past two.'

There has been no correction to line or range and we get the order, 'Five rounds gunfire. Fire.'

Scarlet jets of flame stab into the darkness. The crack of our guns reverberate round the Eastern Sector.

'One thing, if he gets deknackered he won't be able to perform like Ross's rams. I hear that they shag forty ewes in a night. No wonder they've got fifty million sheep in New Zealand.'

'We shiver in the night cold. Great white flares arch the sky.

The order from the Command Post again, 'More two degrees. Fire.'

We load. There is the crack of exploding propellant. 'God. My head aches something cruel. When I get back to my blankets I'll sleep like a dead man.'

'Oh! No you won't. You're on guard the next shift.'

'Oh sod it.'

There is a pause in our fire programme. From No. 1 Gun there is the faint glow of a cigarette.

Suddenly machine guns stutter and tracers sear the sky. This is followed by the angry crack of small arms fire.

'They say that Rommel himself is outside Tobruk and that if Rommel had been in the British Army he would still be a fugging sergeant. They say he don't speak proper!'

'Pity some of our Generals aren't fugging sergeants. They say the Queen Mary's in the harbour waiting to take us out. If we want to get out of Tobruk we'll have to bloody well swim for it. Shouldn't fancy a swim in the harbour tonight. That bargeful of petrol that the Stukas hit is still burning. Reckon the flames and smoke were two miles high.'

The order comes to 'Stand Easy'. The patrol is not yet in so we must wait another fifteen minutes before we get, 'Stand down'.

We wonder what it is like to bed down in clean sheets and to have a wash in clear, running water.

The next morning Francis received a telegram to say that his only brother, a torpedo officer in a submarine, had been reported 'missing believed killed' when his submarine failed to return from a patrol in the South Atlantic. We did not know what to say to him.

During the middle days of September the enemy became very aggressive and started to move in more closely to our wire. The Australian listening posts in no man's land were driven inside the wire, one by one and the shelling became more intense. The Stukas transferred some of their attention from the harbour to our gun areas.

Then came the news that the Australian Division was being relieved and was being transferred out of Tobruk, back to the Nile Delta. The evacuation was carried out by destroyers when there was no moon. They arrived with detachments of the 70th British Division and a Brigade of Polish troops and returned to Alexandria with Aussies aboard.

The 70th Division consisted of the 2nd Battalion, the Black Watch, the 4th Battalion the Border Regiment and Battalions from the 1st King's Own and the Essex Regiment. These troops had been sent for the eventual 'break out' from the Fortress.

★   ★   ★   ★

A welcome batch of mail arrived. It had been brought through the 'Med' and it had only taken three weeks. Julie wrote:

'My Dearest Albert,

Kevin has written and told us about your Military Medal and the whole village is excited and pleased. You are quite a celebrity. Your Mum and Dad are as proud as Punch, and so am I.

By putting two and two together we are all quite sure that you are in Tobruk, Miss Bonner, who I saw on the way to church, says that the village is a little knot of anxiety for you.

Kevin said that there was no need for you to have gone and thrown the grenades into the Italian mortar post. All of you have done your share and they ought to relieve you and let someone else have a go.

Yesterday evening a blackbird was singing in the sycamore at the bottom of the garden and I had a little cry because you said in one of your letters that you hadn't seen a bird for eight months, let alone heard one sing. I just can't imagine what it must be like having to live month after month near your gun pits out in the desert.

Dad says that Hitler has bitten off more than he can chew by invading Russia and there are some terrible stories about concentration camps for the Jews in Germany. We don't know what to believe.

Your father came up and kindly helped Dad dip the sheep last Saturday afternoon. We now have thirty-one ewes and the last of the spring lambs have just gone to market. Two of the ewes got the gid and one of them kicked the fender. They stagger about and act light headed. The vet says that it's a bladder worm that gets in the brain.

The Harvest Thanksgiving service is next month. Your father has three nice sheaves of Yeoman wheat and three of Plumage Archer barley set aside to take up to the church. The wasps are getting into the apples on the Blenheim tree that's got the canker. I know that you used to go round with a tin of cyanide and do the nests, but we don't seem able to get the stuff now that the war's on. The grey Pippin and Lanes Prince Albert are loaded, we have got some wooden potato chitting trays and laid down a couple of bushels of Bramleys in the cellar.

I can't say that I am really made up with the life of working in an aircraft factory. There's so much noise everywhere. There's turning wheels, rotating cutting blades, whining drills and percussion hammers. Next door, in the tool room, there is a large power press and it makes a terrific racket. To cap it all, there's a great big flood of broadcast music from amplifiers slung overhead and the loud music just pours on to the work benches.

We are definitely making parts for the Defiant night fighter and, two weeks ago, one of the pilots who flies them came round the factory to thank us. Mr Willis, the factory manager, told us that the pilot had already shot down two enemy planes at night, one of them over an airfield in France.

Your Dad says that he will be writing to you. He talks about you a lot.

You are now, more than ever in my prayers.

With my dearest love,

Julie.

P.S. Your brother Weaver has joined the Home Guard and he was very proud when his Commanding Officer told him that he was a very good 'silent approacher'.

Dad's letter was written in pencil on paper torn from an old exercise book.

Dear Albert,

As you know I am not much of a hand at letter writing but I thought I would tell you about the farm, what is going on and one thing and another. We were pleased to hear you had got a medal. I know Mum's brothers, Horace and Geoff, what were killed last time, got three each. They called them Faith, Hope and Charity. Mum has still got them in the drawer.

About the worst thing that's happened is that Watchman died last week. I'd had him and Prince ploughing in Long Ley and he seemed as right as rain at half past three when we knocked off. Tis true he did drink a drop more water than usual but, when I got him to the stable he wouldn't eat his oats and he broke out in a sweat. Sam and me got out the medicine horn and gave him one of Day's drenches, but that seemed to make him wus and when I came up after tea to see how he was, he lay dead in his stall. The vet said that he had a twisted gut, but Sam reckons he was wrung in the withers.

It has properly broke up my team but the Guvnor says he'll get me another, but there are a lot more tractors getting about. They say that there's now one tractor in the country to twelve horses. Let's hope there won't be too many tractors about to stink the farm out.

I shall miss old Watchman and no mistake. I'd had him for close on eleven years.

Sam is getting on now. He's nearly seventy and he got a gammy leg doing his allotment and I shouldn't be a mite surprised if he didn't go on the club.

What's made everyone cackle is that he's moved in along of old Mrs Pendlebury, what lives agin the pump. I dare say it's a case of the oven running after the bread. I reckon she's after Sam's bit of money, he never did spend anything. They say he goes to bed to save the candle. I shouldn't be a mite surprised if Sam wasn't worth all of six hundred quid. I happen to think that old Mrs Pendlebury is a short waisted, sly old sod, but I shouldn't say so to Sam.

Last Sunday morning while Mum was at Church I cut the privet hedge.

Mum was back something late and I couldn't rumble what she'd been up to. I thought that, like as not, she'd been passing the time of day with someone up the road. When I asked where she'd been she said it was parson's fault. The sermon lasted for twenty-five minutes and it wasn't often he'd gone on so. It was a real pudden spoiler.

Your Mum and me think a lot of Julie. She's a real nice gal and she brought me two hand hammered horse brasses for my birthday. She bought them from one of the gypsies on the common that have come down from Yorkshire for the tater picking.

It's getting near the fall of leaf so I shall have to take my bill into the woods and cut a few withies to tie up faggots. Coal is getting very dear.

Well Albert, I reckon this is the longest letter I've ever wrote.

Hoping it finds you in good health, as it leaves me here.

Dad.

P.S. You know I've never told anyone what I used on the horses coats to make the hair grow. Well, it was equal parts of oil of Rosemary, honey and powdered charcoal.

You know, my old Dad had taken a Hell of a lot of trouble with that letter and I shouldn't be surprised if it didn't take him three days to write it.

Reading my letters in the stifling heat I thought of the contrast with some of the days at home when I was ploughing, when it was so damned cold that I had to wear two overcoats and two pairs of gloves on the old Standard Fordson. As like as not I grumbled and created, but I didn't know how happy I was.

*   *   *   *

Throughout October the enemy continued to close in around our Eastern sector. There were more diggings, vehicle and tank movements and in the mornings there were track marks which indicated that the enemy troop carriers were coming much nearer the wire at night. Our infantry patrols were being beaten back by heavy fire from well dug in troops and the enemy dominated the area of 'no man's land' which had always existed between us.

Every time our guns opened up we were shelled by their counter batteries in fierce retaliation and visits from the Stukas became even more frequent. Many more enemy guns had been brought round to dominate the Eastern sector. Everything pointed to an early and a major attack on Tobruk by the Afrika Korps. At the same time we learned that our forces in Egypt, now named 'The Eighth Army' were preparing to do battle and sweep up from the east to relieve Tobruk.

*   *   *   *

Charlie Briggs was perched on the tailboard of the 15 cwt. signals truck mending a coil of broken telephone cable. He had the heavy reel at his side and a pair of insulated pliers in his hand.

Philip Underwood walked across to Charlie and asked for a match. Charlie put down his pliers, fished a half book of matches out of his shirt pocket and threw them over to Philip.

'Well Philip,' said Charlie, 'what do you fink of fings?'

'If you ask me,' answered Philip, cupping his hands around the lighted match, 'this is it.'

'You've said a bleedin' mouthful,' said Charlie. 'This fuggin' telephone wire was cut free times yesterday wiv the shellin' and the signallers ain't too wrapped up wiv crawlin' along the wire to trace the breaks. There's too much shit flyin' abart.'

'It's nothing to what will be flying about in a few days time, when we start to break out or they start to break in,' said Philip.

'There's no dart abart it,' said Charlie cheerfully. 'Fings is gettin' bloody 'ot, and I don't mean the wevver.'

'It's good for lazy bowels,' said Philip philosophically.

'I counted ninety Stukas and Messerschmitts in the air at the same time yesterday. If there had been any birds around they would have had to soddin' well walk.'

Charlie became serious, he was still not reconciled to his brother's death.

'Ron Greenwood was killed and Trevor Partridge and Hubert Loosemore wounded on the 'B' Troop guns this mornin'. Kershaw and his O.P. party were shelled out of their O.P. and had to move to another site.'

'Yes. I know that,' said Philip, keeping a wary eye on a string of Stukas turning in from the coast. 'They keep talking about this so called Eighth Army steaming up from Egypt to relieve us. I'll believe that when I see it. If you ask me Rommel will get in his attack on Tobruk first. The Krauts have shot off thousands of rounds of ammo during the last two days. They are definitely trying to soften us up.'

'We'll soon know, one way of the uvver,' said Charlie.

'Captain Kershaw says that Rommel has got five divisions outside the wire and he intends to get Tobruk out of the way before makin' 'is attack on Egypt.'

While they were talking a Stuka, taking part in a raid on the infantry was in the middle of its dive when a Bofors shell caught it right on the nose. For a split second the plane seemed to shudder and hesitate before plunging on full power with the engine screaming and white flames streaming from its belly, into the yellow earth six hundred yards away. It explosed in a wild ball of flame. It was a spectacular termination to an absolute commitment by the Stuka pilot and a dramatic final act for the Fuehrer and the Fatherland.

Cannon shells and bullets were exploding in the burning wreckage and while flames were licking round the black tail, probing skywards like a blazing monument.

'Poor sod,' said Charlie, 'it's enough to turn yer guts.'

'Well I can't feel sorry for the bastard,' said Philip, 'I agree with the R.S.M. He's right when he says that the only good Kraut is a dead one. That pilot will be put to bed with a shovel.'

'I can remember,' said Charlie, 'the old man takin' me and Ernie to the Hendon Air Display and also to see Alan Cobham's Flying Circus. We paid five bob to go in. Half the spectators were hopin' to see a damned good air crash and about all they saw for their money was an old Short Flying Boat and a decrepit Handley Page bomber flyin' across the airfield. I fink the highlight of the show was a bloke jumpin' out of a Sopwith on the end of a parachute.'

'They'd see more here in fifteen seconds than they would all day at Hendon for five bob,' said Philip, 'and here it costs bugger all.

The burning Stuka was of no further interest to them. They had seen it all many times before. Philip heeled his dog end into the sand.

'Don't do that you stoopid bugger,' said Charlie urgently, 'I've got a tin 'ere for dog ends.'

'Sorry Charlie,' said Philip, 'I didn't think.'

'Grandpa' saunted up wearing his tin hat. 'Grandpa' was Gunner Alfred Potts. he was thirty -eight years old and the oldest man in the Regiment. He was a regular soldier of many years service and an adept at keeping his head down and out of trouble. He drove one of the 'B' Echelon vehicles but he had spent most of his regular service as a batman or sanitary orderly. He kept a low profile and never volunteered for anything. He had a sketchy knowledge of Kings Rules and Regulations and was a natural barrack room lawyer. He and the Battery Sergeant Major had their differences but had settled down to a policy of mutual toleration. 'Grandpa' always had a funny story to tell.

'What's the griff Grandpa,' asked Philip.

'Heard about the bloke in the R.Es on the thunderbox,' asked Grandpa.

'No. We'll buy it," said Charlie.

'Well this young squaddie had just come up from base to join a detachment of the R.E.s and, on his very first morning, he found himself sitting on the rose bowl with his trousers around his knees, beside a sergeant. The young squaddie was scared something chronic and had the squitters and while they were sitting there the German long range batteries opened up on the harbour and the shells came whistling over their heads.

The sergeant said, 'Don't be frightened son.'

The squaddic answered, 'I'm not frightened Sergeant.'

Then a salvo of shells landed just three hundred yards behind thcm and the Sergeant said again, 'Don't be frightened son.'

And the squaddie answered again, 'I'm not frightened Sergeant!'

Then the sergeant said, 'What are you wiping my arse for then?'

'I reckon you're having us on Grandpa,' said Charlie, rocking with merriment.

'No,' said Grandpa, 'straight up. That's the honest truth.' But he was squeezed up with laughing.

TWENTY-FIVE
The Breakout

Winston Churchill had ordered general Sir Claude Auchinleck and his army commander, Major General Ritchie to attack in the desert, although the attack was originally planned for two weeks later, on 18th November 1941, 13th Corps under General Cunningham breached the wire to the south of the main axis positions on the Egyptian frontier and made for Sidi Rezegh, about twelve miles south east of the Tobruk wire.

SO IT WAS the 18th day of November and, by working long hours during darkness of the previous two nights, forward positions had been prepared for battle. The gun pits had been dug and camouflaged, hundreds of tons of ammunition had been moved up, and stacked in big flat heaps and draped in netting. Believe me, preparing for a battle is sheer hard work and it cost us some lard. The following night our blackened and blistered twenty five pounders were moved up to the carefully prepared positions in a very forward area of the eastern sector. It was strangely quiet and it was a slow laborious, rasper of a task, manhandling the guns into position over the rough terrain.

By 2 a.m. all was ready, the stage was set and the guns were laid on the zero line, fully charged for action and awaiting the word of command. The night was cold with a chill breeze off the sea. We spoke in low voices. There was no news of the relieving Eighth Army. Those who could snatched a little sleep, but no doubt there would be frayed men who would lie awake and tremble in this sinister, lurking background of the threatening unknown.

The infantry were in their fox holes on the start line and the tanks had pulled in round our guns. They would not move forward until our barrage was in full drive and the thunder of the guns would drown the noise of their engines and the squealing of their tracks.

Kevin checked and rechecked his dial sight and his aiming post angles. Francis laid out our tin hats on the edge of the pit in case of air burst shrapnel. Ross and Jock were pulling the heavy sheets and nets off the boxes of ammunition and charges.

'Well, we've been waiting for this for seven months,' I said.

'I reckon that we'll be half way to Tripoli by tomorrow night.'

'Anyone would have the notion, listening to you,' said Francis, 'that Rommel isn't long headed enough to have a fair idea of how the land lies and which way the

180

pig will jump. It stands to reason that, if the so called relieving forces are coming up from the south east, any attempt to break out will be from the eastern sector.'

Certainly Rommel had moved a large number of heavy guns into positions opposite our sector during the last few weeks and, undoubtedly there would be scores of hull down enemy tanks in wait for us.

The arrows of reason were sometimes bound in a suspended ring and our spirits were seen as through a magic lens of emboldened inspiration, like pilgrims through the centuries. But, if we missed our footing and our attack was impotent or the battle took an ugly turn, then our foiled and blundering end could be written in blood and ashes.

Zero hour for the barrage was 05.30 hrs. The Gun Position Officer was Lieutenant Hester-Hewitt. Hester-Hewitt had come good, and although his father had sent young Charles to Eton, we felt that our troop of Suffolk Yeomen had contributed a great deal to his further education. But through no fault of his own, he had been brought up to believe that he was superior to us in every conceivable way. When he discovered that the low bred Suffolk Yeomen were not only, at a general level, good hearted, but also had a certain pride and did not relish being talked to as if they were vulgar cider squeezers and dregs of the common order. Hester-Hewitt, according to Francis, passed through various stages of rebirth and renewal, to try to earn the love and respect of his men. At first he was tainted with a degree of insincere, singing small and condescension. He acted over graciously to his inferiors. he enquired after our mothers and he stooped to our unworthiness and we despised him for it. He then indulged in what Francis called, 'a great deal of 'hob nob', and tried to be one of the boys. This also failed because Hester-Hewitt insisted on changing his natural vocabulary to using foul mouthed language and selected oaths and swear words, which although mildly becoming to a Suffolk Yeomen, were obnoxious and uncharacteristic for an officer worthy of being 'A' Troop Gun Position Officer. He would never rid himself of his strained, high pitched upper class voice, like a marble fighting to get out of a well. That wasn't his fault either. His parents, his grandparents and his brother and two sisters all seemed to be determined to push their voice level through a non existent sound barrier.

However, as I have said, when Charles Hester-Hewitt learned his distance and after seven months in Tobruk with Adrian Kershaw as an example and with no further need for the Troop Sergeant Major to see him through his day, he conducted himself with a confident good grace. He was well liked by the troop and was an efficient Gun Position Officer to boot.

At exactly 05.15 hrs. Lieutenant Hester-Hewitt called out 'Zero Hour less fifteen minutes.

The replies came back from the Numbers One.

'Through on One Gun,' from Neville Steele.

'Through on Two,' from Harold Reeve.

'Through on Three,' from Brendan McClean.

'Through on Four,' from myself.

All is set for a heavy shoot and three hundred rounds per gun were to be fired in the first part of this carefully planned creeping barrage.

All the spare drivers, specialists and batmen are down on the guns to assist in this pre-dawn bombardment.

The ground was sliding beneath us as we sensed the brewing of the storm. At that early hour we seemed to be aware of a quiet breathing of the desert, yet, in this distant outpost, the enveloping medium felt raw and unreal. a few red flares were falling in the 'no man's land' in front of us. We could distinctly hear the faint sounds of the infantry preparing for battle.

I again check that Kevin, who is now on the layer's seat, knows the exact location of the aiming point light and the battery picket. It is vital that no mistakes should be made and that all the shells should hit the target in the area predicted.

The G.P.O. shouts 'Zero Less ten minutes.'

Again the acknowledgements from the Numbers One.

I pull out my torch to check the second hand of my synchronised watch. It is still dark and the morning is raw and chilly. The enemy infantry, who we were predicted to blow to smithereens, would, by now, be alert in their weapon pits. The iron had entered into our souls and there was no unease that, once again, we were dipping our hands in blood.

There was no tossed up hassle, we had long learned to endure the tedium of waiting.

The first shell is loaded with the charge rammed home and the breech slammed shut.

Kevin, who will pull the firing lever, sits still and upright on the layer's seat. he is wearing a brown woollen skull cap, which he found in an Italian Quarter Master's store in Benghazi and a German, roll neck pullover which is pulled on over his army issue khaki drill shirt. He wears no socks and his soft brown boots were once enemy property. Kevin is the best gun layer in the troop and, although, as gun sergeant, I am required to check every setting of the gun, never had I found the gun wrongly layed or improperly corrected.

My Number Two is Jock who lived and worked in the little Scottish town of Plean in the County of Stirlingshire, from where, or so he said, he could throw a saxpence on to the site of the Battle of Bannockburn. He never tired of reminding us that Robert the Bruce's thirty thousand men had knocked the daylights out of Edward's one hundred thousand. But on this bleak morning when the gun felt like fresh clay cold marble, the Jocks and the Sassenachs at Tobruk were on the same side of the wire, firmly united to challenge the greed and treachery of the Dictators of the Axis powers.

As soon as the first round is fired, Jock will whip open the breech and the spent charge case will shoot out and clatter on the trail of the gun. My spare number is Ross, and he will pick up the shells and charges from the stacked ammunition and hand them to Francis, who is my Number Four.

Ross, far from his red roofed New Zealand homestead, now had other things on his mind than wool prices and crutching wethers, but Ross, not only drove the quad but he also helped with the ammunition and was an invaluable, efficient and hard working member of my gun detachment.

'Zero less five minutes.'

I just had time to re-read parts of the fire programme which I held in my hand.

We'd be firing 'Rapid' (Four rounds a minute); 'Normal' (Two rounds per minute) and 'Slow' (one round per minute) Three hundred rounds per gun would be fired in the first part of the barrage, which was programmed to take exactly, one hundred and thirty five minutes.

We thrust flimsy cotton wool plugs in our ears, but they are small protection against the hot, crushing blast of the crack of a twenty five pounder. The percussion and roar will drive right into our inner ear. After the barrage our ears and face and jaws will ache for hours. Kevin once said that our ears would want rebushing after the war or we'd be as deaf as a wheatsheaf.

'Zero less sixty seconds.'

I pick up my rammer staff and tuck it under my left arm. Every nerve must be strained to stay watchful and alert. Any diversion from the correct switch and range could be fatal to the infantry who will be following behind our barrage.

Jock removes his false teeth, wraps them in a piece of dirty rag and sticks them in his shirt pocket. He think's they'll be safer there.

Kevin's hand moved towards the firing lever.

'Five seconds, four, three, two, one, FIRE.'

The four troop guns fire as one and, at the same time, other batteries open up all around us. To our right, to our left and behind us, the guns roar and thunder.

Jock whips open the breech and the empty charge case flies out, together with a white sheet of flame.

Francis rams another shell into the breech and another charge. Kevin makes the fine adjustment to the angle of sight and reports, 'ready'. I make a quick check of the settings on Kevin's dial sight and micrometer head.

'FIRE' and another shell hurtles into the enemy front line. We have just fifteen seconds to get each shell loaded, the gun correctly aligned and the firing lever pulled. The range is four thousand, five hundred yards. Fifty yards are added to the range. Kevin makes the correction to the elevation and I check. 'FIRE' and another shell screams away into the darkness. The moving belt of fire is biting into the enemy's forward defences.

Now and again the tell tale, high pitched shriek of a shell that has lost its driving band or the swish, swish of a badly rammed shell is heard.

'Zero plus thirty minutes.'

We have been so committed to the programme that we have not noticed the passage of time.

The rate of fire will now be scaled down to two rounds per gun per minute. The barrel is as hot as a stove. We spit on it and it hisses like an angry snake.

There are slithers of purple in the empty sky and we see the first streaks of dawn which, for many soldiers in Tobruk, will be their last.

The enemy artillery has been sending over salvo after salvo at our old gun positions, but most of them have coursed through the air like wild things to crack and explode far behind us. We are reaping the benefit of being close up behind the infantry and of having moved into new gun positions during the night.

Suddenly we have a problem. There is a jam on my gun and the charge case is tightly wedged in the breech and has not ejected. We know the trouble and I have a large screwdriver at hand for such emergencies. I am quickly able to loosen and lever out the impacted charge case and my gun is able to resume firing in what has become a sweeping and searching barrage.

There is a brilliant blaze on the horizon followed by a massive explosion and furious sheets of flame, shooting skyward in the half light. One of our guns has found a target, an ammunition or a petrol dump. The sky is alight and aglow bearing a powerful testimony to the authority and dreadful destruction of the guns.

Seven, noisy, battle-ready 'I' tanks, clanking and squealing crept steadily forward over the uneven ground, feeling their way like waddling Aylesbury ducks, determined to make the pond.

The enemy gunners were making wide sweeps of gunfire, much of it too close for us to ignore. A rain of shells screamed downwards, hurtling high explosives into our already tortured sector. The desert and the sky became suddenly alive with wicked, rough edged flashes and the earth rolled with deep rumbling concussion.

With daylight, came the persistent rending chatter of machine gun fire and the unholy crump of mortars. The enemy gunners sent a succession of vicious shrapnel burst over the infantry.

The troop is now firing at the slow rate of fire, one round a minute. Clouds of smoke and dust surround us and the dry reek of cordite and high explosives fill the air. Our ears buzzed and rang like a wasps steel band. Lance Bombadier Holgate and Gunner Edward Gibson, two of the Battery cooks, stagger up to the Command Post, carrying between them a lidless dixie of hot tea. One man at a time from each gun walked over to the Command Post and dipped their filthy, cracked mugs into the steaming brew.

The hot, sweet tea plus the claptrap of finding and selecting a much needed cigarette and the solemn ritual of feeling for matches and lighting up, followed by the first deep draw, induced into our being a dimension of brief contentment.

If it wasn't for the fact that a German Battery which was presently shelling our sector had only to drop their range three hundred yards and the shells would land in our gun pits, we could almost have enjoyed this short, ten minute interval.

As it was, after dipping for our tea, we walked quite sharply back towards the slit trenches. While we were sipping our brew, Jock suddenly lifted his head and, standing there with his tea in his hand and his head on one side he said, 'Can ye hear the pipes?'

Through the roar of battle a piper could be clearly heard.

'What's he playing, Jock?' I asked.

'It'll be Highland Laddie,' he said softly.

I had never seen Jock so set astir and, to tell you the truth, my own mind was stretched and the purling of the pipes with their lilting melody ran in my head.

'I thought,' said Francis, 'that the playing of the pipes when going into battle went out in the last war.'

But there was no doubt about it. In the smoke filled cauldron ahead. Scottish pipers were playing their Company into the attack. Until the battle the playing of the pipes had been forbidden in Tobruk, but there was no muffling them now.*

The nostalgic, aching music of those pipes on a bleak November morning in that arid desert battlefield, turned our minds aside and brought our hearts to burn and our throats to tighten.

On that bloody morning of November 19th, as wind fluffed up the loose sand into ribbons and as great crackling explosions lashed the earth, the 2nd Battalion of the Black Watch with bayonets fixed and now candidates for high oblivion, advanced across the sterile, ugly desert behind our curtain of fire. It is true that they took their two main objectives, two heavily fortified positions, code names 'Jill' and 'Tiger' but at a very high cost. In killed and wounded they lost half their men.

The signal on the battlefield for first aid or a burial party is the man's rifle stuck in the sand by its bayonet. Later that morning, when some of the smoke of battle had cleared, as we gazed across this arid garden of death to the strongpoints from our wire, the ground was a forest of rifle butts pointing to the sky.

The plain intrinsic circumstances of that long awaited break out from Fortress Tobruk can be read anywhere in the books of war. Those written by the Generals and their ghost writers in broad sweeping canvas and those of methodical careful study and analysis by the war historians in quiet libraries and War Museums.

The Regimental diaries might tell more, but even they do not tell all. The diaries blimp on of those killed, wounded and mentioned in despatches, but they do not tell of the cold feelings of the men who were in committed action, day after perilous day. It does not tell of those men who missed death by the shadow of a shade, or of the stretched nerves and the real battles of will which were prolonged, raw and bitter. It does not tell of the specific yards of ground which were won and lost, and won again or of the hair breadth escapes, the signals of distress and the constant threat of violent and sudden death.

*   *   *   *

The Eighth Army attacking from the frontier had become involved in fierce tank battles in the desert and scores of British tanks had been destroyed. General Cunningham was seriously considering withdrawing the Eighth Army back into Egypt, leaving the defenders of Tobruk to make their own way out or to withdraw back inside the wire. At this moment of indecision General Auchinleck arrived in the area and immediately relieved Cunningham of his Command. General Ritchie was appointed in his place but Auchinleck took personal charge of the battle.

---

*The tune, 'Highland Laddie', that Albert Cooper heard that morning as the Black Watch advanced into battle was played by Pipe Major Roy and Pipe Sergeant McNichol of the 2nd Battalion.

On the fifth day of the battle the troop, with all its guns, was ordered to move out through the wire into what was pleasurably designated, 'The Corridor'. This corridor was reported to be three miles wide and, with the enemy on either side, we cautiously moved the guns to a very exposed position, three miles out into the line of passage. We felt like chickens, stripped of feathers, moving over exposed, cold stepping stones through the thoroughfare of battle, leaving the comparative safety of the wire and the tank trap well behind us. The enemy was able to fire on us from three sides and there was the constant threat of the corridor being cut behind us.

Attack was followed by counter attack and the guns volleyed back and forth in long artillery duels. To add to our problems, guns from enemy tanks spread casting weight against us and, altogether, the enemy was able to bring a great weight of fire into the narrow corridor and this added to the gathering pressure.

It was touch and go and after two days of confused, bitter fighting and with increasing casualties, together with our infantry we were forced to give ground and to move back nearer to the wire. The relieving force of the Eighth Army had failed to arrive to link up with us.

On the 25th November we tried again. The Battery was once again ordered to press home the attack southwards, towards Sidi Rezegh and El Duda. There was an assurance that this time the 2nd New Zealand Division would be there to link up with us.

Details of the tattered moments in the zenith of this obstinate, case hardened confrontation, for which every yard of ground had to be fought, escape me. I blame the unevenness of my memory plus a total ignorance of the fluid and confused situation around us. However, during the first week in December the Essex Regiment, supported by the guns of the West Suffolk Yeomanry, met up with the 19th Battalion of the 2nd New Zealand Division and a squadron of 'I' tanks on the high ground of El Duda. The next morning a convoy of newly painted vehicles which had travelled from the Egyptian frontier pulled in behind the guns and we knew for sure that, at long last, contact had been made between the Garrison and the Eighth Army.

An embittered tank corps staff officer told us that British, lightly armoured Stuart tanks, or 'Honeys' as they were called, had been ordered to attack German Mark IVs at Sidi Rezegh. The German tanks had much thicker armour and three times the fire power. They destroyed the 'Honeys' before they could get into range. The staff officer said, 'The bastard politicians who had the obsession with disarmament before the war should be forced to come up here with us. The "Honeys"', he said, 'are fugging widow makers.'

CHAPTER TWENTY-SIX

The Deadly Confrontation

I'LL WARRANT THAT none of us who are alive and who were members of the gun crews of 'A' Troop on the 4th of December 1941 will forget that day. The chill of the night was well past and the Winter sun had long since melted the morning mist and now shed a bright warmth over the levelness of the desert. The troop, in full muster was heading south-west. It was fifteen miles outside the Tobruk perimeter and half way between the high ground at Sidi Rezegh and the now deserted El Adem aerodrome.

This flat, barren area was where the biggest tank battle of the war had recently been fought and won. Scores of burnt out tanks and lorries, both German and British, disabled in this violent pitched battle, littered the desert. Many were still smoking from the all consuming fires and there was that nauseating, unforgettable stench of burnt flesh. God knows how many had died here during the last few days, but I do know that such was the carnage, spread over four miles in this field of violent death that our capacity for understanding could not absorb or give credence to the stark and awesome reality.

The troop advanced through the main battle area of this great whirlwind and turmoil of destruction and threaded its way through the tortured huddles of smashed fighting vehicles. 'A' Troop was travelling independently. It had been sent forward, together with two armoured cars, to reccy to the south and west. As usual we were travelling in extended desert formation. Captain Kershaw was in the leading eight hundredweight Command Post truck, followed by a signals vehicle and two ammunition lorries. In diamond formation, surrounding the soft vehicles were the four guns, keeping a distance of at least one hundred and fifty yards apart. Two guns on the right flank and two on the left. My gun was the rear gun on the off side and Neville Steele and his gun detachment were directly ahead. We were travelling at a steady ten miles an hour. All the Numbers One were standing up in the hatches of their quads with an eye for signals from the Troop Leader and generally keeping a lookout.

The area was thought to be clear of the enemy and no real trouble was expected, except from perhaps the odd Messerschmitt which might swoop down and loose off a few magazines of cannon shells.

Suddenly, without any warning, a shell burst about four hundred yards, immediately to my right, and this was followed ten seconds later by a second shell exploding well in front of the Command Post truck.

It didn't seem at all to fit the pattern of artillery ranging on us and I shouted down into the quad, 'I reckon there's a tank about.'

The Command Post vehicle spun round and raced back towards us and Captain Kershaw yelled to Neville Steele and myself, 'Action right, target tanks, gun control.'

The rest of the troop was signalled to disperse and retire to the left, leaving Neville and myself to take up anti tank positions with our guns.

On the order 'Gun Control' the Sergeant takes independent control of his gun, selects his own target and engages it when he sees fit. Gun control is used mainly when the gun is engaging tanks. This can be done over open sights or, more usually, with an anti tank telescopic sight.

Amid a great screech of tyres and flurries of dust we drew to a shuddering halt. Ross reacted immediately by swinging the quad round as it slowed and jamming on his brakes. Within seconds the gun was unlimbered and the limber positioned with its ammuniton doors open. Kevin leapt to the gun layer's seat and I grabbed the hand spike and heaved the gun on to the approximate line. It was stirring stuff and we were riding a tight rein. In the meantime two more shells landed and one of them was dangerously close to the signals truck which was racing away to the left. Then we saw him, a German Mark III, about six hundred yards away. The tank wasn't hull down, as I had expected but was lumbering towards us, like a charging wild beast bearing down on its quarry, no doubt looking for some soft targets.

'Cocky bastard,' I said.

We could now hear the chatter of his machine gun and the deadly spit of lead, but our gun was not the immediate target he seemed to be heading straight for Neville's gun.

It was like a dream really, a wild fallacy of vision, but by now Francis had rammed an A.P. (armour piercing) shot into the breech and Kevin was peering into his tank scope. His arm was stiffly stretched out behind him with the palm indicating which way I was required to move the trail. His palm was facing right and I gently eased the trail to the right. He then slapped his buttock to let me know that he was now roughly on line and quickly and surely turned the traversing and elevating handles to get the tank in the cross wires of his sight. He worked skilfully and adroitly with speed and accuracy.

Five seconds later he shouted, 'Ready.'

At the top of my voice I yelled 'Fire' and Kevin pulled the plug. Once again we experienced the violent crack of the exploding propellant and I held my breath and prayed that this one wouldn't miss. We were unlikely to get a second chance when his machine guns were turned against us.

'Got the bastard,' shouted Kevin, excitedly.

The tank had been hit squarely on the lower part of the turret. It stopped dead and the machine gunning ceased. It was intoxicating. Francis rammed in another round and again Kevin lined up the target in the centre of his cross wires.

'Fire'.

It was another direct hit executed in masterful, absolute precision. Christ, I was glad that we had practised our anti tank drill in Tobruk. We were in a ferment of soul stirring excitement.

'Well done, Kevin,' shouted Francis.

Although the machine gunning from the tank had ceased, he still sat there, now not more than four hundred yards away and we couldn't trust him.

'Load,' I shouted and Francis put in another round, followed by the charge and Jock slammed shut the breech.

'Take your time this time, Kevin,' I said. 'He's winged and very groggy but he might still be dangerous. Hit him between the top of the tracks and the base of the turret.' I knew that, although the Mark III has two and a half inches of armoured plating on the front, it was only half that thickness on the side.

'Ready,' shouted Kevin.

'Fire.' The third round smashed into the armour plating just between the top of the tracks and the painted swastika on the lower part of the hull. Christ. It was good shooting.

Then a strange, unbelievable thing happened. It was like a horror film in slow motion. Firstly, the heavy metal hatch of the turret slowly opened and the tank commander, tottering on the brink of life, painfully and, little by little, dragged himself up through the hatch, toppled and fell to earth. His hair and clothes were on fire. He rolled over once in the sand and then lay still. Smoke started to billow from the turret but the tank commander appeared to be in the final, absolute meshes of death.

Our eyes were drawn to the huge black crosses on the turret. They seemed evil possessed. We were mesmerised, almost as if a spell had been cast upon us, as this steel clad, twenty ton, instrument of war perished before us.

As if on an inexorable time schedule the tank burst into orange spears of pencil brightness as small kindling flashes of flame licked its hard moulded form, and broad, flashing tongues of fire shot out of every slot and flue.

It was another fifteen seconds before the ammunition inside the tank began to explode. Each Mark III tank carried a hundred shells in racks around the turret wall and three and a half thousand machine gun bullets in belts and magazines. Like a fire breathing dragon, convulsed in excrutiating pain, the whole hull seemed to be moving and heaving as it became ravaged with fire and exploding ammunition.

Inside the burning hull we knew that the driver, the radio operator, the gunner and his loader were trapped and perishing in this blazing inferno. It was like the scuttle of a cornered, foundering, pocket battleship which had played its last card.

Thin streams of hot metal began to trickle down the hard side plating on to the sand.

Then the oil and the gasolene caught fire and the great frame appeared crumpled, distorted and shapeless. There was a sharp explosion and noxious clouds of black smoke and burning fire poured out and engulfed everything in this ravaging pyre and the dead body of the tank commander became part of the spreading fire.

From the waggon lines behind us a great cheer went up and we, the executioners, cheered as well. I think that we cheered to express a great feeling of relief from the long minutes of bottled up tension as those last moments of ordeal and danger flashed across our memory.

There was a roar to our left. It was the two armoured cars racing back towards us. One made for the burning tank and the other straight for us and it skidded to a stop by my gun. A young Lieutenant shouted, 'Well done, Sergeant, but I think that your other gun has been hit.'

In the boiling excitement and confusion we had completely forgotten Neville Steele and his crew, some two hundred yards away on our left. We were still high with taut nerves and the adrenalin was racing in the richness of the hour. I kept my gun fully manned and my crew on the alert until we got an order to stand down and also some news of Neville and his men. I looked across and saw that Captain Kershaw, Lieutenant Hester-Hewitt and the two signal trucks were grouped closely around Neville's gun.

'I don't like the look of that,' I said.

'Bloody machine guns,' said Kevin.

'I'm glad we fried the bastards,' said Jock.

I took a quiet swig from my water bottle and lit a cigarette. I began to feel elated that we had killed five Germans and I had an impulse to wish that another enemy tank would come into our sights. I felt strange and inspired, I boiled with intolerance and hate. A German tank had been destroyed by my gun and it had brought a new and widened dimension to my battle experience.

Francis was rummaging in his haversack and he produced three sweet biscuits. They were wrapped in a piece of three-month-old airgraph edition of the Daily Mail and were the remains of a small tin of Huntley and Palmers which had been sent from home.

'We have three biscuits and five men,' said Francis, carefully breaking two of the biscuits in half. 'Now, who is going to have the whole one?'

'You'd better have it,' said Ross, 'they're your biscuits.'

'No,' said Francis, 'we'll give the whole one to the gun layer who got the tank. Here you are Kevin.'

We had just begun to realise that Kevin had probably saved our lives. Although I was Sergeant in charge of the gun, it was Kevin who had sat calmly on the layer's seat and lined up on the tank. If the first armour piercing shot had missed, the tank would almost certainly have turned on us and we could have been machine gunned into the ground. It had been a testing time and the calm, level headedness of Kevin had shone out like a watchfire.

'Thanks, Francis,' said Kevin, accepting the whole biscuit. 'I don't suppose I'll ever have the chance to get a tank in my cross wires again.'

'If you do,' said Jock, popping the half biscuit into his mouth, 'I hope I'm two thousand miles behind the lines.'

Captain Kershaw drove up in the Command Post truck. I noticed that there was blood on his shirt sleeve.

'Well done Number Four gun,' he said. 'Bad news of Sergeant Steele and Gunner Parsons. Both killed in that first burst of machine gun fire. They weren't even able to get one round away. The armoured cars tell us that there are no more enemy tanks within two miles of us and that the one which attacked us must have been a rogue tank on a semi suicide mission. He had probably been despatched to wreak havoc among our soft skinned vehicles.'

We were all given a sharp jolt with the news about Neville Steele and Vincent Parsons. Neville was a first class gun Sergeant. He had been softly spoken with a dry sense of humour. In civvy street he had been transport manager for a small lorry business in Thetford. It was said that he had split up from his wife, but I never heard anyone say a word against him.

I had been at school with Vincent Parsons. We had both joined up on the same day and signed on together in the Drill Hall at Middlesham. That now seemed a hundred years ago.

*   *   *   *

The main battle and the forward troops of the Eighth Army moved past us to the west and we drove back into Tobruk and laagered near the main water point.

Every vehicle which we possessed was riddled with bullet or shrapnel. The guns were worn and blistered and there wasn't a scrap of paint left on the barrels. Everyone had long hair and no one had shaved for at least ten days. Many were wearing the grey, army issue cap comforters and strange oddments of British German and Italian uniform. We looked what we were, uncouth desert pirates.

The guns were unlimbered and were left, just where the trails hit the ground. No attempt was made to line anything up in a smart and soldierlike fashion. Guns and fighting vehicles were left haphazardly pointing in all directions. I wouldn't say that we were at the end of our tether but I really don't think that we could have taken much more.

We were in Tobruk at the beginning of the long siege and we were there at the end. There are few desert soldiers alive today who can say that they saw it all through.

The day would no doubt come when we would say that we were proud to have been part of the saga of Tobruk, but for now, we just pulled out our weathered bed rolls and opened them out beside the guns. We were weighted down by a terrible deadly fatigue.

We had survived the longest siege in British military history and after two hundred and forty days under siege culminating in that last, long, fierce battle we were burnt out, numb beyond caring and we craved some peace and quiet and stillness.

*   *   *   *

Perhaps the greatest of the war correspondents, Alan Moorehead wrote, when he entered Tobruk with the relieving Eighth Army:

> 'It was a memorable moment, driving down into Tobruk. Coming from the east you do not see the town until you are right on it. Then, as you wind down from the El Adem crossroads, the scarred white village breaks suddenly into view. On this day it had the appearance of utter dreariness

and monotony, as though the very earth itself was tired. Every foot of dust was touched by high explosives. Countless thousands of shells, bombs and bullets had fallen here among the rusted barbed wire, the dugouts and the dust covered tracks. You could distinguish the men of Tobruk from the other soldiers. Their clothing, their skin and especially their faces were stained the same colour as the earth. They moved slowly and precisely, with the absolute economy of effort. They were lean and hard and their lips were drawn tightly together. They seemed to fit perfectly into the landscape and it was impossible to tell if their morale was good or bad, whether they were tired after so many months of bombing, shelling and isolation or merely indifferent. They had become identified with their underground and dusty existence. Certainly they were not exuberant at their release, it had been too hard and grim a business for that and the realisation of it would only come after weeks, or even months.

Of the high excitement and the heroism which had held this place for nine months there was no sign whatever. There were no flags, no bands, no marching men. The war seemed to have reduced everything to a neutral dust. Except for the cemetery and its lines of crosses and the occasional passing ambulance there was not even the suggestion of pain. Tiredness and boredom governed this place where no green thing grew, where everything had been designed for death for long over a year of warfare.'

CHAPTER TWENTY-SEVEN
Cairo Leave

KEVIN, LYING IN bed, propped himself up on his elbow and lit his second cigarette of the morning. It was nine o'clock and Abdul had just brought us in a large pot of tea.

'This is the life,' said Kevin, throwing his half empty packet of Players and his book of matches on to the chair by his bed.

Things had taken a distinct turn for the better. Harold Reeve, Kevin and myself were sleeping in a room, three storeys up, in a house in the Kasr el Nil in Cairo. The room was little bigger than my bedroom at home but the Egyptian proprietor had managed to squeeze three beds into it. The place was called the Glenroyal Hotel. It was a potential death trap as there was no fire escape, no fire extinguishers to be seen and only one narrow staircase to the ground floor.

But we were happy, the beds had a bit of spring to them and the sheets and pillow cases were white and clean. None of us had slept between sheets or in a bed for fifteen months and just to lie there, smoking a cigarette and drinking a large cup of sweet tea, was all that we could ask for.

Abdul sat on the floor in the passage, outside our room, ready to minister to our every need.

'Abdul. Get us three Egyptian Mails and forty cigarettes,' ordered Harold.

'Right away, Effendi,' said Abdul and we heard the faint patter of his bare feet on the stone stairs.

A few minutes later he returned with the newspapers and the cigarettes. The news in the Egyptian Mail was that the desert war, which we had now left hundreds of miles behind us, was going well.

'You like breakfast on the balcony?' enquired Abdul.

'In twenty minutes, Abdul,' said Harold.

We took our eggs, bacon, toast and marmalade in the morning sun, sitting on our balcony overlooking the main thoroughfare of the Egyptian capital. Our comfortable cane chairs were grouped round an oval table covered with a spotless white linen tablecloth. The Egyptian proprietor hovered around with jugs of steaming coffee. It felt strange to be away from the hot atmosphere of urgency. There was not a sound of a gun, a mortar or a bomb and no need to cock a wary ear for Stukas. Just the loud murmur of the traffic below, the shouting of the ghari drivers, the street sellers and 'gully gully' men. Somewhere a Mezzuin was calling the faithful to prayer. It was indescribably abnormal and our subconscious was still churning.

A silent waiter appeared to clear away our plates and, as we were drinking our last cup of coffee after breakfast, Abdul reappeared, handomely robed and turbaned, for his job as our unsolicited dragoman. He enquired if there was anything that he could do for us.

We had drawn big pay arrears as we hadn't spent anything for over a year. In fact, we had each drawn over fifty pounds. It was clear that our first, inescapable business was to present ourselves to the barbers.

'Order a taxi and tell the driver that we shall want him all day,' I said.

Fifteen minutes later the taxi arrived and we all climbed in. Although I had sat on smelly tractors, creaking tumbrils, had ridden with the farm waggoners and had even ridden in a cattle float, I had never ridden in a taxi before. Abdul sat in the front with the driver.

'Mohammed very good driver,' he volunteered.

Although we had all managed to get a quick bath the night before, our long hair and stubbly beards were still full of sand and grit. Our visit to the barbers took over an hour and a half. First of all a haircut and, as the barber removed our long, sunbleached locks which tumbled to the floor, it piled around our chairs like a filling haystack.

'I shall miss my busby,' said Kevin, peering into the mirror at his 'short back and sides'. 'It has performed its duty as my home grown head warmer and pillow, all in one.'

The haircuts were followed by a shave, a shampoo and hot towels. We even had a manicure. Christ, we felt better.

'Now then, Mohammed,' I said, 'take us to the best bar in Cairo.'

'My cousin got the best bar in Cairo,' said Mohammed.

'Hullo,' said Kevin, 'they've all got fuggin cousins somewhere. I bet the cunning bastards get a rake off.'

'Of course they do,' I said, 'but it won't be more than fifteen per cent of what we spend. Leave it to Abdul and Mohammed.'

After downing a couple of ice cold Stellas at the bar, we decided to get ourselves in clothes fit for soldiers of King George on leave in the largest city in Africa.

'You know a good tailor?' I asked.

'My cousin very good tailor,' said Abdul and Mohammed together. We had to laugh.

We climbed back into the taxi and, as we sat back in the soft leather seats, we began to become aware of a gathering peace of mind and a surrounding ambience of pleasure far removed from the wring and harrow of war.

Mohammed and Abdul were in a constant undercurrent of controversy as they quietly wrangled in the front seat. They were, no doubt, carving up the percentages.

Mohammed drove the taxi through incredibly narrow streets flanked by high, dull brown, teeming buildings with the street facing windows covered with interlacing wooden screens. The alleys were thronged with people. It was like being in a submarine battling through waves of humanity. The Caireens were thronging the pavements, the shops, the bazaars and the roadway. Mohammed kept his thumb on the horn button to open up the line of way by pushing on to the sidewalk the plethora of goats, asses, cats, cars and bicycles. When he could get no further he stopped the taxi on the side of the pavement and Abdul motioned us to follow him while Mohammed stayed with the taxi.

If Abdul had abandoned us I don't think that we should ever have found our way out of this maze of streets and alleys. Half of the total population of eight million people seemed to be jammed into this teeming, jam packed throng.

Abdul led us for less than a hundred yards, past a butcher's stall displaying newly severed goat's and sheep's heads, before taking a sharp turn to the right into a dark passageway not more than four feet wide. On the left side was a faded, dingy green doorway. The door, with its peeling paint, was half open and Abdul led us into a large front room where a little bald man, with podgy hands and wearing metal rimmed glasses, was sitting cross-legged on the floor, stitching some stripes on to a bush shirt. His short beard was dyed with henna and on his wrist was a string of 'isbah' amber beads.

'This is my cousin, Ibrahim,' said Abdul. 'He is a very good tailor.'

'If he's Abdul's cousin,' said Kevin, 'my wallay's a turnip.'

'Never mind,' said Harold, ever practical, 'let's see what he's got to show us.'

The little bald headed man led us through an open doorway into an adjoining room where two more tailors were working. All round the room were rolls of cloth heaped up against the wall. Much of it was khaki drill.

A small boy in sandals, with close cropped hair came in with three small cups of mint tea on a round, brass tray. Also on the tray there was a small plate of sweet, sickly looking cakes and a finely decorated sugar bowl. There was no milk and Abdul instructed us to place a lump of sugar in our mouths and to suck the mint tea through the sugar.

The old man brought over a roll of cloth.

'Officer's cloth,' he said. 'I make up a suit in twenty-four hours.'

Harold felt the cloth and said, 'Well it looks all right to me,' and so, without even asking the price, we each ordered a bush shirt with buttons down the front and a pair of khaki drill slacks.

While we were being measured up the old man asked, 'You want pips or stripes? I stitch on anything you want. You want to be a Colonel? I fix it.

We knew that with the pips up we could use the Officers' Club, but I said, 'Put three stripes on all of them.'

'I only want one on mine,' said Kevin.

'Shut up, Kevin,' I said. 'You'll be able to come into the Sergeant's Club with me and Harold.'

'You want a nice pair of brown shoes?' asked Ibrahim and he took us behind a partition where there were dozens of pairs of shoes and leather belts.

'I see,' said Ibrahim, adjusting his steel spectacles, 'that you are in the artillery. Yes?'

'We may be,' I said, drinking my second cup of tea.

'How about a red and blue, artillery dress cap?'

'Plenty of caps, all regiments, all sizes,' he said. 'You want cap badges as well? I got all cap badges.'

Ibrahim said that he would send the whole lot over to our hotel and we could pay Abdul for them.

We had fourteen days leave in Cairo and we made the most of it. We certainly put some beer away and drank far more than was good for us. By the time that we had helped each other home and dropped into bed, we were feeling battered and rough. It wasn't so much the beer that we drank that caused our heads to throb and our stomachs to loop the loop. It was the thin local spirit called 'arrak'. It was distilled from fermented rice and jaggary sugar. Christ, it was powerful stuff.

'How do you feel, Kevin?' I asked one morning when the last thing that we wanted was breakfast.

'I feel,' said Kevin, from the depth of his sheets, 'like a shell has exploded between my ears and as if a camel is dragging a bloody great chain round my guts.'

'Well, don't breathe heavily near a naked flame,' I said helpfully.

A major reason for Kevin's drink problem was that every time we ran into Aussies and they saw our Royal Horse Artillery shoulder flashes, they welcomed us like long lost brothers and plied us with drink. We had been their artillery support at Bardia and Tobruk and they didn't let us forget it. We had one memorable night's drinking with Dave, Jack Bradman and Shortarse, who we had taught to fire the Italian howitzers in Tobruk. I can't remember too much about that evening but I know that at eleven o'clock Dave, Jack and Shortarse, after promising everlasting and eternal friendship, said that they were going down to the Berka to say 'G'day to the sheilas'.

We ate food that we wouldn't get in Ipswich and no mistake. Most nights we went down to a small restaurant by the river where Achmud was the cook and he did his very best for us. We relished the baked egg plant, mashed and mixed with sesame paste and flavoured with lemon, garlic and olive oil. Into this appetising mix we dipped toasted bread chips.

For the main course we would sometimes have the Egyptian version of Shish Kebab with its chunks of lamb with spices added and marinated in thin shavings of onions, parsley, marjoram and lemon juice. The marinated pieces of lamb were then placed on a skewer and grilled over hot charcoal. This was washed down with wine made from Alexandrian grapes.

Another of Achmud's specialities were tasty, plump, roasted pigeons broiled on an open spit which gave the meat a smoky flavour. He then added fried rice mixed with currants, nuts and the pigeon livers. We were also offered rice in baskets and joints of sizzling goat's meat. To all this we were able to add delicious grilled prawns, straight from the Red Sea and there was sweet Egyptian sherbert, rich cakes and hot, thick, black coffee laced with a drop of vanilla and some hashish oil. After our long year in the desert we were blissfully content and indulged to the full.

Most nights, after dinner, we visited the cabarets and night clubs of Cairo. Here were the fire eaters, the snake charmers and the belly dancers.

Lulu, the belly dancer, wearing heavy gold bracelets and a necklace hung with tiny bells, wriggles herself on stage to the cat calls and whistles of the half drunk squaddies. Her whole body shakes and ripples in erotic movement, her breasts rise firmly, like desert dunes. She strokes her body, her legs, her powdered bosom and gyrates with incredible sensuality. The accompanying Islamic drums in the oriental and African tempo vibrate with the violin's deep seductive rhythm. There is a subtle interplay between the dancer and the music. To us, from the Suffolk villages, it was heady stuff and our fanciful emotions blew hot and cold and our capricious senses played fast and loose in a girdle of giddy racing passions.

In all the streets and corners of this kicking, unwearied, urgent city, there was noise, voices and hubbub, and in every quarter our nostrils were assailed with wondrous spicy smells.

There were the sharp fumes of burning maize stalks. There was smoke from the glowing charcoal burners, the sensual, racy traces of incense and musk, the reasty scent of hashish and strong tobacco.

We walked as little as possible and rode all over Cairo in ancient, well worn taxis and in open four wheeled garis drawn by thin, rangy horses. You could have hung your coat on their pin bones. Overhead, during the daylight hours, flew and hovered some of the hundred thousand kites which beshitted the city with their indiscriminate droppings.

In our new bush shirts, 'Cairo' slacks, brown shoes and with the red and blue artillery forage caps perched on our heads, we journeyed in the clanging trams to the Pyramids of Ghiza and the Great Sphinx.

We gazed in mild wonder at the last of the Seven Wonders of the Ancient World. We climbed the Great Pyramid on its thirteen acre base and its two and half million tons of stone, each stone weighing two and a half tons. It was no surprise to learn that the Great Pyramid, which stands four hundred and fifty feet high and was built four and a half thousand years ago, took twenty years to build. As Kevin, who always had an agricultural turn of mind said, 'I shouldn't want to turn that lot, if it was a haystack that had started to get hot.'

*   *   *   *

It was mid January 1942 and our days in Mena Camp, which was due south of Cairo, were again taken up with gun drill, route marches, guard duties and fire pickets. All our equipment had been left behind in Tobruk and handed over to other regiments. Soon, however, new guns and vehicles arrived for us and it became 'peace time' soldiering again. There were kit and vehicle inspections, we saluted officers and I became Sergeant; Sarge; or Sergeant Cooper again. But discipline was lightly used and there was no damming of the close friendships forged in battle.

Back in England, Winston Churchill was laying it on the line. In the second week of January he made a long speech in the House of Commons and referred to the desert battles and the breakout from Tobruk in November and December. We read an extract from his speech:

'At the same time as the menace to Persia, Iraq, Syria and Palestine defined itself, General von Rommel, with his army of ten German and Italian Divisions, entrenched at and behind Halfaya, was preparing to make a decisive attack on Tobruk as a preliminary to one great attack on Egypt from the west.

'On the western flank we prepared to meet Rommel. For the sake of the battle in the Libyan Desert, we concentrated everything we could lay hands on and we submitted to a long delay, very painful to bear, so that all preparations should be perfected.

'We hoped to recapture Cyrenaica and important airfields around Benghazi.

'For more than two months in the desert, a most fierce and continuous battle was waged between scattered bands of men, armed with the latest weapons, seeking each other dawn after dawn, fighting to the death, day after day and even long into the night.

'The battle would have been lost on November 24th, if General Auchinleck had not intervened, changed command and ordered ruthless pressure of the attack to be maintained without regard to the consequences.

'But for this robust decision, we should have been back on our line of Tobruk, Tobruk would have fallen and Rommel would probably have marched towards the Nile.

'Cyrenaica is regained. It has still to be held, we have not succeeded in destroying Rommel's army but nearly two thirds of it are wounded, prisoners or dead.

'In this strange and sombre battle of the desert, we lost in killed, wounded and captured about eighteen thousand men.

'We have thirty six thousand five hundred prisoners in our possession, including many wounded, of whom ten thousand five hundred are German. We have killed and wounded at least eleven thousand five hundred Germans and thirteen thousand Italians. The total accounted for is just over sixty one thousand.

'During the battle we have had, in action, more than forty five thousand men against enemy forces more than doubly strong. Therefore, it seems to me, that this heroic struggle in the desert in which there were many local reverses, has tested our manhood in searching fashion. It has been proved that men cannot only die for their country, everyone knew that, but that they can kill.'

Well, we were very pleased to read all this and we knew only too well that we had had a very narrow shave in Tobruk round about the 24th of November when there was a distinct likelihood that the main relieving attack would have been called off and Tobruk would have been overrun.

Old Winston certainly knew how to put it across and we lapped it up, even though we knew that a lot of it was a load of bullshit.

CHAPTER TWENTY-EIGHT
The Gazala Battles and the Runback

IT WAS JANUARY 1942 and Rommel had made a second comeback in the desert and the situation was again serious. After the West Suffolk Yeomanry left the Eighth Army on Christmas Day 1941, after the lifting of the Tobruk siege, the British divisions had pushed on up to Mersa Brega. Mersa Brega was the place where we had first met the Afrika Korps and had had our first experience of a German Blitzhrieg with tanks and dive bombers almost a year earlier.

Rommel attacked with his Armoured Divisions on the 21st of January, rolled back the British 1st Armoured Division and re-took Western Cyrenaica. A line was now being held from Gazala, which is forty miles west of Tobruk, to a desert outpost some fifty miles inland from the sea, a mere speck on the map called Bir Hacheim.

My soldier readers will know that soldiering is often very boring and that the man-at-arms is often tethered in a mire of abstract tedium and lassitude. The Regiment had, once again, been ordered to head west, back to the crazed, savage Western Desert. Driving along that dusty, featureless road of melting tarmac to Alexandria and then along the black burnt strip of the old coast road through Bahig, Bagush, Mersa Matruh and Barrani was flat, soulless and boring beyond its meanest capacity.

Ahead lay a landscape of yawning distance and purple emptiness. None of us would have cried if we had never seen the Western Desert again. All we asked for was to be sent to fight in a theatre of war where there was running water and where trees grew instead of this rotten wilderness. We could almost be excused for thinking that our lives were taking on a pattern of endless repetition and that there was a dreary recycling of our existence.

The Regiment was now newly equipped with brand new Chevrolet lorries and quads, that had been shipped straight from the United States and new guns and limbers which had been transported at great cost to lives and ships by British sailors and seamen, through the hostile Mediterranean.

It took us five, dusty, bumpy days of tedious and irksome travel before we, once again, found ourselves skirting the old battleground of Sidi Rezegh, round the El Adem aerodrome and into Tobruk, which was now some forty miles behind the lines.

Taking up gun positions in the old Pilastrino sector, where we had taken such a battering during the earlier part of the siege almost a year earlier, we found that we were in support of the 29th Infantry Brigade of the 5th Indian Division.

A gusty wind was blowing and we huddled round on the sheltered side of Ross's new quad. The sand was pounding against the paintwork with a ceaseless drumming. We stood, sweating under a brassy sun and the sand engulfed our boots and stung our faces.

'I have a notion,' said Jock, wiping his eyes with his shirt sleeve,' that they are determined to get rid of us. They will not be happy until they can get us trapped in Tobruk again, better still, they would like to see the whole frigging Regiment get into a fuggin great sump of quicksand and sunk without trace. Then we'd be nae bother to anyone. Bugger Churchill and bugger the useless fuggin Generals. They're all bloody moonstruck.' Jock spat at his feet.

'What about the Pope?' said Francis, working mischief.

"Aye,' said Jock, 'bugger him too.'

'And bugger,' said Francis, 'the Moderator of the Church of Scotland.'

We tried to laugh, but morale was low and Jock moaned on.

'It's one great fuggin balls up,' he said. 'Our tanks are useless, our anti tank guns only pea shooters and they've sent us up the desert again when there are four million squaddies in England with bugger all to do.' He kicked the tyre of the quad and spat again.

'The squaddies in England are waiting and training for the Second Front,' I said. But Jock's mind was not in a receptive condition.

'Second Front my arse,' he said. There won't be a Second Front until Hitler is in Moscow and Rommel's in the Persian Gulf.'

At that moment Grandpa sauntered up. He was wearing a pair of thin gas mask eye shields against the wind which seemed to be rotating like a whirlwind circling a bath bun.

'Itma,' said Kevin, 'it's that man again.'

'Cheer up Number Four gun,' said Grandpa, merry as a cricket. 'The army will take good care of you and there's a lovely sunny day coming over the hill.'

'Piss off, Grandpa,' said Jock uncivily.

'And another thing,' said Grandpa. 'The M.O. says that I am to sleep with one eye open and keep a careful watch on your moral welfare. He says that you must all be careful up here not to get the clap.'

'Very funny,' said Jock, who was cleaning his ear with a piece of pencil.

'You want girl,' said Grandpa, imitating a Cairo pimp, 'my sister very clean, fifty piastres, very virgin, plenty jig a jig.'

'I've really gone off you, Grandpa,' said Jock.

'Gunner McKinley,' said Grandpa, putting on his most sorrowful voice and imitating Jock's Scottish accent, 'I crave your good opinion and I'm devastated to ken that you've gone off me. Nonetheless, I shall continue to labour and shall not ask for any reward.'

'Bollocks,' said Jock disgustedly.

Grandpa sighed heavily and limply waved an arm in our direction. 'Bless you my children,' he said, and he strolled off, humming the tune of the well known army ballad, 'Banging away at Lulu'. Grandpa definitely made life better and he did nearly as much for morale as a letter from home.

★   ★   ★   ★

After a couple of subdued and dismal weeks in Tobruk, which we had now learnt to hate, we were packed off forty miles to the west into what was known as the Gazala Line.

As we cautiously approached our gun positions during the weird stillness of a Sunday night, the drivers threaded their vehicles, looking a ghostly silver in the moonlight, through the supply columns, the tanks, the rear infantry and we were soon in position where we could blast and be blasted.

Daylight confirmed our suspicions that we were in an area of utter desolation. Not a hill, wadi, rock or a sprig of camel thorn. Just a flat, featureless, inhospitable landscape dotted with blobs of hull down tanks, vehicles, dark patches where infantry were grouped round their foxholes and weapon pits. The brazen sun was a swimming, leaping light and the sky was as blue as a bat's arse.

Jock was looking into a small piece of cracked mirror, squeezing a blackhead.

'I'm cheesed off,' he said, 'this place is no worth fighting for.'

'Do me a favour, Jock,' I said, 'stop moaning or you'll crack up.'

'I think I'll go A.W.O.L.,' he said.

'No one would notice that you've gone,' I said, angrily.

Throughout April and early May there was sporadic shelling, air raids and enemy reconnaissance aircraft were constantly overhead. Dummy gun pits were constructed and efforts were made to camouflage the guns in this vast open desert space. Attempts were made to fix up tarpaulins and groundsheets to protect us from the relentless burning sun.

About a third of the Regiment was afflicted and tormented with running desert sores. The slightest scratch or graze turned septic. Dry bandages were bound round the ulcers and abscesses as they festered and ran with pus. The myriads of persistent flies made medical treatment more difficult as they clung to the stained and rancid gauze wrappings.

Every second or third day a sixty mile an hour, burning southerly wind shrieked across the desert and would whip up whirling storms of billions of tons of hot, fine red sand. Mirages and a great heat haze shimmered in the glare and the dazzle of the mid-day sun. Water was scarce and we were miserable from the weeks and months of extreme heat and hard rations. The underlying knowledge that we were on the defensive and that there was no sign of us moving into the attack added to the dreariness of it all.

One mile to the south of us simmering in the heat haze and dug in round the slightly higher ground of Bir Hacheim, were four thousand Free French soldiers. God knows where they had come from. Rumour had it that they had crossed the great Sand Sea from Chad.

'If it's their Foreign Legion,' said Kevin, dripping with sarcasm, 'and they've got a shower of stinking disease ridden camels, they'll be just the ticket for squaring up to Rommel's Mark IV tanks.'

'My Uncle Angus,' said Jock, 'was in the Camel Corps in the last war and he told me that riding on camels had given him arthritis in his genitals.'

*   *   *   *

In the middle of May, Rommel began to step up the rate of shelling, the number of air attacks and his tanks began to nose in closer to our infantry. We knew the signs, we had seen them all before. It was apparent that Rommel was gathering for an all out attack.

It was one hour before sun up on the twelfth of June 1942. Red-eyed, grouchy and with stiffened limbs from the night, the gunners climbed reluctantly out of their dusty bed holes. It seemed to us in our yawning weariness that we had been 'standing to' at dawn all our lives.

Our interest in the new day was slightly sprung by an unusual spate of spasmodic gunfire from the direction of Bir Hacheim. We assumed that the Free French were getting over excited and were loosing off some random rounds to let everyone know that they were still there.

'Bloody Frogs,' said Kevin, 'they want to stop frittering away valuable ammunition. It might come in handy.'

The hollow, booming of the gun fire from the south increased in volume and, shortly after the sun had lifted its red rim clear of the desert floor, came the familiar order from the Command Post.

'Take Posts, Target Tanks.'

'Bloody hell,' said Francis, running for the gun in sockless and unlaced boots. 'Where the hell have they come from?'

We had been assured the night before that there were no enemy tanks nearer than five miles from our sector.

'Zero five degrees, seven five hundred, one round gunfire. Fire! ...'

'Hullo,' said Kevin, with his eye to the dial sight, 'here we go again, ranging with all four guns.'

Ranging with four guns of the troop at the same time indicated important targets and we deduced correctly that there were a number of enemy tanks moving towards our O.P. As the sun slowly rose above the new day's distant edge, the world took a hard and brutish shape as the enemy guns retaliated in strength and artillery duels, like wild spitting Fire Gods, volleyed back and forth.

A solitary Bofors gun to the north loosed off a magazine clip of five. Boom, boom, boom, boom, boom. We knew only too well what that meant. The familiar prelude to an air raid. Someone shouted, 'Coulu' and Lieutenant Hester Hewitt, who was relaying fire orders form the O.P. yelled, 'Take cover.' We dived into the slit trenches.

'The bastards are early this morning,' said Ross, 'they must have taken off in the fugging dark.'

The air above us was suddenly filled with a whirling confusion of twisting Stukas and Messerschmitts with their crooked crosses. There must have been a hundred or more and, once again, we were confronted with the devastating combination of Stukas and Panzers. Wave after wave, black and menacing, like vampire bats, bombed and machine gunned targets all around us.

Most of the dive bombers, with their fixed under carriage and with their sirens screaming, were concentrating on attacking Bir Hacheim to our south-west, but two sticks of bombs had exploded perilously close to the gun position and once again we experienced that choking stink of high explosives, sulphur and rotten metal. Once again, we braced ourselves against the shock waves that stun the senses. The rocketing Bofors, joined by its fellows in a collective crescendo, continued to cough up a torrent of vicious air bubble explosions. Once again, in this wild war, we were scudding the pinnacle of awareness and challenge as lives were being snuffed out in this hideous orchestration of death.

A blackened Valentine tank and its dead crew, destroyed by bomb and blast, sat crippled and impotent, with its disabled gun like a broken bean pole pointing uselessly to the sky. Four, grey canvas covered lorries were fiercely burning and an armoured car had been blasted over on its side, the wheels still spinning. Six Messerschmitts were machine gunning a small group of R.A.S.C. vehicles that had just arrived with petrol and ammunition.

A wounded Stuka broke the circle and plummeted down, white flames streaming from its belly. It fell to earth, a flaming ball of fire.

I know that we had been through it many times before but we had never really become case hardened to being attacked by dive bombers. Hundreds of bombs were dropped during a Stuka attack and one of them could be just too close to guarantee your survival. You could be wiped out like a fly on a wall.

By mid-afternoon, when I had counted the empty ammunition cases, my staunch, honest, even handed gun and its gunners had blazed off two hundred and fifty-two rounds of high explosive shells since morning.

It was said that Rommel had five hundred tanks to throw into the battle. There were four more penetrating, rampaging dive bombing raids that busy day and the swooping Stukas lanced through the burning air. We christened the screaming banshee sirens, 'The Trombones of Jericho'.

*   *   *   *

By nightfall, the Free French at Bir Hircheim on our left flank were completely surrounded by German armour which swung south, then east, then north. The French had endured, during the day, more than their share of shelling and bombing and they were ordered to break out to the east.

Our own orders to retire came shortly afterwards and by then many of the German columns had swung round, well behind us and were heading for the coast. Our orders were to make for a map reference point some twenty miles to the south of El Adem aerodrome.

Progress was slow in our bobbing, bucking quads following the dark, blistered and cratered desert track.

'How do you feel Kevin?' I asked above the roar of the engine.

'Like a droopy old hen with coccidiosis,' he said. He had been laying the gun, with his eye glued to the dial sight eyepiece, since day break and was now sitting directly behind me in the corner seat. With a grubby green gas mask case behind his head he was trying to snatch a few moments of well deserved sleep.

'Well, I'd better give you a dose of turpentine,' I said. In the pitch darkness we soon felt the ridges and bumps as we crossed scores of deep ruts and wheelmarks that had been formed by the Panzer Divisions as they ploughed their way forwards and crossed behind us northwards towards the sea.

Ross kept his eyes pinned to the small hooded tail light of the gun ahead. My head ached and my mouth was as dry as a ditch. After four hours I said to Ross: 'Like me to give you a break for a bit Ross?'

'I shall be all right for a bit longer Albert,' said Ross. 'You try and get a bit of shut eye.'

'Not much hope of that Ross,' I said.

The rest of the gun sub, over tired, heavy lidded and weary from the day were sound asleep, slumped in their seats, chins on their chests. I dozed off for a bit but with the overworked quad engine drumming away I could not sleep in the tightly crammed cab. At midnight, in the slow dark hours I took over from Ross in the driving seat and, shortly after this, Captain Kershaw, who had been leading the column, called a halt. He had been reading his milometer and reckoned that we should be at our destination, but where was everyone? He got through on the wireless to Battery Headquarters and asked them to fire some green tracers to give us their position. The Numbers one climbed stiffly down from their vehicles and peered into the darkness. Thirty seconds later a green tracer shot into the air well to the north. We had strayed from our appointed course by over six miles.

It was well past two o'clock when we eventually drew into the Battery night laager and we were guided by the B.H.Q. personel with torches into our designated area and by the time that the vehicles had been checked over and filled up with petrol and we had had a cup of cocoa it was nearly half past three. There would be no more than two hours sleep for anyone that night as 'Stand to.' would be at half past five.

In the morning it was made clear that we were forming a 'Flying Column'. The hard core of the column was to be the Battery with its eight 25 Prs. escorted and protected by a screen of anti tank guns and Bren Carriers. The code name for our column was 'April'. There were three other columns named, March, July, and August. We were now operating well behind enemy lines and our main committment was to harrass the enemy from the south as he drove eastwards towards Egypt.

As the final rays of the sun drew out long shadows after the third bruising day of the retreat, and after sparring all day with loose enemy formations the Battery headed south into the comparative safety of the southern stretches. As we prepared for a watchful night laager the rich dark canopy of the desert night was girdled with myriads of pulsating stars.

The next morning as dawn was breaking Major Coleman held a briefing session for senior N.C.O.s. He stood on a small sand hill as we gathered around him. 'Our present location,' he said, 'is eleven miles south of the Tobruk perimeter. It is clear that Tobruk is surrounded and that the forward enemy troops are already on the Egyptian frontier. The 15th Panzer Division together with two Italian Divisions are lying outside Tobruk. A full scale attack on Tobruk by the Afrika Korps is imminent.'

Old King Cole was hollow cheeked and was beginning to look drudged with weariness. His moustache was droopy and his eyes were red. He had two septic places on his face and, every now and then his right eye twitched uncontrollably. He was unshaven and gaunt. From his dusty boots to his battered hat he was taking on the colour of the desert. Old King Cole had shepherded his weary battery over miles of endless desert and the long months of strain were beginning to show. He went on, 'We have been ordered to head north to try and relieve pressure on the Tobruk garrison. We shall lay up today, get some rest and begin to move up towards Tobruk at nightfall. Ensure that all vehicles are filled with petrol and oil and that water levels are checked. Each quad must carry an extra forty gallons of petrol in cans tied on to the roof. See that ammunition limbers are full and that everyone has three days hard rations. The position inside Tobruk is as follows. Defending the perimeter are thirty three thousand men. These include the whole of the 2nd. South African Division, the 11th. Indian Brigade, the 201st. Guards Brigade and the 32nd. Tank Brigade.'

Then we had the bullshit.

'There is absolutely no possibility that Tobruk will fall to the enemy. We held Tobruk for eight months and bunkers, gun positions and defences are still there. There is an excellent chance that our troops in Egypt will mount a major counter attack and that we shall be required to support them in a drive to knock the enemy out of Cyrenaica.'

We had heard all that before. When I got back to my gun and relayed the Major's words to them, Kevin said, remembering the Major's words at Mersa Brega

'All I can say is God help the Germans.'

Francis said 'Thou shalt not take the mickey out of Old King Cole.'

Jock said 'God help the subsection of number Four gun of 'A' Troop tomorrow, if we start stirring up the krauts round Tobruk.' 'I say "Amen" to that.' said Ross.

*   *   *   *

That night we laagered six miles outside Tobruk. With the enemy all around us it was a very uneasy night and the next morning, before daybreak, the guns were moved up forward, closer to the enemy. What we did in fact, was to stir up a hornet's nest. Before we were able to drop the guns into action the enemy had sent dozens of rounds of heavy stuff in our direction. It was clear that the guns which had been firing on Tobruk had now turned round and were firing on us.

Once we had dropped the guns, our first salvo was away within three minutes and, from then on, as the sand spun in the rising wind we were at the sword's point and the wild, incessant enemy shelling bore upon us. The guns were dancing and shimmering in the morning brightness. For every shell we fired we reaped three in return. It was a one sided artillery battle and it was disturbing to realise that the enemy guns which we fondly thought were busily engaged in attacking Tobruk were free to concentrate on us.

The troop had fired just over fifty rounds gun fire when the urgent order came,

'Cease Fire.' Hester Hewitt then yelled through the megaphone, 'Tobruk has fallen, prepare to withdraw.'

The staggering news that Tobruk had fallen after only thirty six hours resistance hit us like blow on the jaw, but at this burning moment we were riding a whirlwind and, once again, with pounding blood we experienced that high excitement of limbering up under shellfire. There was the urgency to get away. The slight panic if something went wrong and the frenzied desire to distance ourselves from this turbulent and palpitating point of danger in the desert immensity.

I was glad to have Ross at the wheel. He would get every last measure of speed from the thumping quad. Lieutenant Hester Hewitt had moved to the front and was waving a blue flag instructing us to form up in desert formation and to spread out. Shells were exploding all around us and we were living on the high edge of experience and apprehension. Our tentative invasion of the hornet's nest had proved to be a dangerous and useless exercise. However, the enemy shelling soon became well off target and the column was gradually stretching out of range. The sky was an open furnace as the heat of the day gathered strength. The quads pitched, rolled and tossed like wild things, our knees, shoulders and elbows were bruised by being cast and thrown against the metal sides and hard corners of the vehicles. Our jolted bodies were caked with sweat and the rampant swells of summer heat joined issue with the suffocating dust.

We made forty miles by nightfall and, for the next seven days continued to harrass the southern flank of the enemy's drive to the East.

The April column's operations were now shaping their course a hundred miles behind the enemy lines but, with our protective screen of Bren carriers and anti tank guns it would call for a powerful enemy force to risk attacking us in a determined and resolute fashion. Soldiering on a mobile 'Flying Column' was very much to be preferred to sitting in gun pits for weeks on end our Royal Horse Artillery training for short, sharp actions, carried out at very high speed was well suited to our daily hit and run engagements. It made the adrenalin run and called up a blood stirring thrill as we faced the challenge anew. Every new day saw us operating further and further eastwards and moving towards the Egyptian frontier.

One day my gun crew all lay spreadeagled full length under the quad. It was the only scrap of shade during the middle of the day and the heat from the pitiless sun was almost unbearable. The skirts of the blue sky bowl above us, disolved in thinning light. The flies were at their maximum summer swarming. The water in our water bottles was at blood heat and mirages shimmered and danced in the heat of the afternoon.

Jock was lying on his back on a spread towel, a dirty handerchief over his face against the flies. He said, 'They say that Ritchie's got the sack. First it was Wavell, then Cunningham and now, sodding Ritchie. I reckon the Auk's next for the chop.'

'They won't sack the Auk.' I said, moving over slightly to avoid the occasional drip from the sump. 'You can't go around sacking Generals every five minutes. It's not good for morale.'

'Sod the morale,' said Jock, 'my morale's so bleedin' low you'd want a shovel and pick to dig it out.'

'Jock,' I said, 'It's a good thing that there weren't any wee Scotsmen like you at Bannockburn. King James would have walked all over you.'

'All I know,'' went on Jock, 'is that at the rate we are going, Rommel will be in sodding Cairo before us. Let's hope that the Krauts get themselves poxed up in the Berka.'

*   *   *   *

That night, lying under the stars with my hands behind my head, fully dressed and my rifle by my side and with every nerve strained during the day, I was as tired as a hunted fox after a two hour run. I was so tired that I couldn't sleep. Sometimes it was like that and in those waking hours of the night, thoughts are drawn to home and the train of musings flitted and ran over my stretched mind. That night I couldn't get these irrational reflections weaned from my mind. I could hear the clip clop of my father's horses as they plodded home with the check chains jingling. I saw in my mind's vision the late Autumn Suffolk sky, smooth as a duck pond. I could see mighty, thick ribbed oaks in wet fields and I could sense the rough drab smell of wet, rotting leaves. I could see the bats flitting around the stackyard in the soft air of a Summer's evening. I thought a lot about cricket and that magic, hollow knock of bat on leather. An old memory had risen in my mind about a special Sunday game we played at Slades Green in 1939. I had gone in at Number five and we were three wickets down for less than double figures. I admit that I had a bit of luck and was dropped twice in the first over but, in the end I got my eye in and carted the bowlers all round the ground. I made fifty one and was finally stumped going half way down the pitch trying to hit one into the road, but by then I had as good as won the match.

There weren't more than a dozen spectators altogether, but Julie was one of them and she sat on the grass under the score board. She was wearing a blue and white striped cotton blouse and was looking as neat as a tightly packed wheat sheaf. They gave me a little clap as I walked back to the pavilion and I was glad that Julie was there. Now, all that I had was Julie's faded photograph in between the pages of my A.B.64. Although it was unlikely, I knew that I could get killed tomorrow, or even before morning and I felt my two identity discs, one tied round my neck and the other round my wrist. The discs were indestructible and would withstand fire and water and, when the burial party found you they removed one for their records and left the other, inscribed with your name and your number on your body. Lucky up here it you got a winding sheet. Christ! I was getting morbid. Damn it all I was only just over twenty and I ought to be around for another fifty years.

It had been a quiet night but, circling above us in the darkness was the familiar drumming of an enemy plane. You always hoped that it would go away and not start dropping parachute flares which flooded the desert with light like broad day. This could be followed by bread basket bombs to maim and kill.

Kevin turned over.

'You awake Albert?'

'Yes,' I said.

'I wish that plane up there was from Imperial Airways and has come to fly us back to Blighty.

'You'll be back in Blighty soon enough, shearing those old black faced Suffolk ewes again,' I said, 'and don't forget that I can always come over and give you a hand at week ends. Now, get a bit of shut eye Kevin.'

Kevin turned over on his groundsheet with his booted feet sticking out the bottom of his blankets and I soon heard the rhythmic sound of his breathing.

*   *   *   *

Every day, as we drove eastwards, through the wide flat corridors of the sand sea we were confronted with stricken crushed tanks and vehicles with the bodies of men raw and bloody from violent death. There was a smell like a decaying sick room, of blood drying in the sun and corpses with half eaten faces, bloated bodies sprawling ungainly and awkward in the sun's blunt refracted rays.

Crashed and force landed aircraft lay on the desert floor like stranded sharks. Engines had broken away on landing, cannon and machine guns lay askew across the battered wings. Two burnt out quads with guns minus their dial sights still hooked on, stood a lonely vigil over eleven newly dug graves. What had happened only the Devil knew. We suddenly shivered in the heat.

On the twelfth day of our flying column we hit the wire again on the frontier, twenty five miles south of Sollum and here again was a sight to turn the stomach. At first they looked like rocks and small hills of sand. As we moved closer, the blurred indistinct mass which seemed to float in the haze before our eyes, became recognizable as five dead camels and, beside them, lay four dead Bedouin tribesmen. They had ventured on to the minefield.

Eventually, after another week of harassing the enemy from the south and battling against sleep we drew near the line at Alamein.

The main defence system at Alamein was in the north and ran at right angles to the sea. There were very few troops at the southern end of the line, near the Great Quatara Depression of salt flats and this area was defended by mobile units of tanks and armoured cars.

On the morning of the fourth of July a halt was called. A mile or so ahead on the horizon, three blobs could be seen. We were very much on the alert. Captain Kershaw put down his glasses and said, 'Armoured cars. I think they're friendly.'

Five minutes later one of our own Bren carriers returned and informed Adrian Kershaw that the blobs ahead were South African armoured cars. We had reached comparative safety at last after twenty two hectic days since the German armour had turned our line at Gazala. Within an hour we were in behind the line at Alamein.

Everyone in the Battery was unshaven and were topped by shocks of long, unkempt sun bleached hair. Beards were dusty and long in stubble and we were all blackened by the sun. The quads and vehicles were shell and bullet ridden and some of the fresh troops in the line, many of them new out from Britain, showed great interest in us as we drove through.

★   ★   ★   ★

There is no doubt that the Regiment, by delaying the enemy onslaught on the Alamein line, had enabled the defences to be improved and strengthened and, in the late afternoon, weary from the long running fight, K Battery pulled in to a deep sheltered wadi some five miles behind the line. Here, waiting for us, was the Battery water cart full of gallons of fresh, needful water, but there was to be no wild indulgence in washing and shaving until the thirsty vehicles had been filled with petrol and oil and spanners had been taken round to tighten up loose nuts and bolts and everything made ready for instant action if necessary.

During the evening after weeks of hard rations, there was hot stew, veg and dehydrated potatoes for everyone and, as we indulged in this simple luxury there was the promise of beer in the morning. Cigarettes were issued and, when darkness fell, the bedrolls were brought out but we were too full of experiences and sensations, too tired from the long, harrowing exposure on the column to talk a lot.

Kevin, Francis, Ross and Jock had fought the gun, like the good soldiers they were. My sub section had been superb and through it all ran a steel thread of pride. There had been no backsliding, no standing aside and no swerve from duty. When the chips were down and when action was called for, they did not separate themselves from what had to be done.

In the second week in July the West Suffolk Yeomanry pulled away from the Alamein line to a beach by the sea, a short distance from Alexandria. Here we swam in the Mediterranean and rested and relaxed for five palmy days. In the meantime it was announced that Mussolini, the Italian Dictator had arrived in Libya and was ready to stage a grand entry into Cairo, riding a horse and wearing the gilded sword of Islam.

★   ★   ★   ★

The July Summers day was immersed in folds of heat and the murmuring, rolling sea had rippled up to within yards of our two-man tents, pitched in geometric patterns on the white sandy beach. The morning had been spent swimming and our raw limbs rallied as they were massaged and refreshed by the warm pummeling surf. It was quiet, relaxing therapy to our jarred bodies and our humming nerves.

The afternoon leave trucks were due to arrive in half an hour to collect us and to deposit us among the flesh pots of Alexandria.

Grandpa was putting some strong scented concoction of grease on his hair.

'What's Grandpa up to?' asked Kevin, 'He stinks like the inside of a poof's handbag.'

'I'm not suprised at that,' said Francis, 'he's dolling up with his fly buttons at the quick release, to go whoring down Sister Street this afternoon.'

Ross said, 'Grandpa tells me that he's got two special bints in Alex, a Greek one called Rosie and a dark skinned one called Sunshine. He says that Rosie has titanical tits and that Sunshine is as black as the parson's charcoal. He reckons Rosie's been at it for a long time and that she's next in line to become a Madame. Grandpa reckons that Rosie hasn't crossed her legs for thirty years.'

We knew that Grandpa was a lecherous old devil and that he wasn't always over careful and, when we had been stationed in Palestine in 1940, none of us were surprised when be came in for a packet. The problem had been spotted by the M.O. on one of his frequent F.F.I. inspections.

Grandpa admitted that this was the second time he had been caught but he reckoned that the so called arseno-benzol treatment was a great success.

One of the signallers had once asked Grandpa how you knew if you had caught a dose and Grandpa had replied.

'There is no need to wait until you've got a carbuncle on your John Thomas. You know that you've got it when you feel that you are pissing tin tacks and don't delay going to see the M.O., because, if you leave it for a few days, you will feel as if you are urinating half hundred weight rolls of barbed wire.'

*　　　　*　　　　*　　　　*

After five days resting by the warm Mediterranean the Regiment, refreshed, restored and prepared for reinstatement into the Eighth Army, returned to the Alamein Line. The Regiment had, by now, suffered over one hundred and sixty casualties in killed, wounded and missing. We had considered ourselves particularly fortunate that our sub section had been able to stay together as a gun crew for so long.

I don't think that I would have missed the next day for a thousand pounds.

In the reddening silence after dawn, when fires had been lit and breakfast was being taken in the bright morning girdle of sunlight there was the loud, steady drone of aircraft from the east. It would be true to say that, during the last eighteen months, since Germany had entered the war in North Africa, for every British plane that we had seen, there were, flying our sector of the front, no less than three hundred enemy aircraft. But the tide of the war in the air was about to turn.

In tight, steady formation, passing directly overhead with the red, white and blue roundels on their wings flew the R.A.F. in thirty, American built Boston and Mitchell bombers. High above the bombers, in the morning sun, flew twenty Hurricane and Tomahawk fighters. They bustled like liberated cage birds as they tumbled and reeled in the high, thin desert air, thousands of feet above the earth.

From our gun positions we were able to watch with sharp pleasure as the bombers released their bombs on the enemy front line four thousand yards to the west. Never, since the first Stukas and Messerschmitts arrived in the desert, had we had air superiority and, in spite of spending two long years in the desert never had we seen thirty British bombers or twenty British fighters in the air at one time. It was for us, a psychological landmark and we had long and patiently waited in this primitive wilderness for this blessed, burning moment.

As the dense black bomb colums of fire and smoke gushed and split hundreds of feet upwards into the battle stained sky, like devilish thick grey soot fountains. Jock's lips went thin and tight, 'Och,' he said, 'a sicht for sair een.'

All that glorious day and for the three following, our new found R.A.F. flew west and pounded and enemy almost every hour of daylight. We were able to watch with beating blood, the yellow stabs and zig zag flashes of the enemy anti aircraft flak batteries which were grouped round the enemy Panzers as they vainly tried to ward off that rain of exploding steel.

*   *   *   *

The Fitters were changing the barrel of my gun as it had fired over three thousand rounds since Gazala. It was a boiling day and we were stripped to the waist, defying the Summer sun to do its worst.

Troop Sergeant Major Evans picked up the Command Post megaphone and shouted 'Numbers One.' All four of us went doubling to the Command Post.

'Get back to your guns,' said T.S.M. Evans 'try and scrounge a shirt and hat and report back here in a quarter of an hour. Someone is coming to see you.'

'Who's that?' asked Harold.

'You'll see,' said Sandy. He was happy because he knew something that we didn't.

I ran back and grabbed a shirt out of the quad locker and a forage cap which Ross found at the bottom of his small pack. Then I returned to the Command Post.

'Get in line,' said Sandy

We stood there in the blazing sun like four recruits at a training camp.

'It's probably just the old man,' said Brendan McClean. 'I don't know why Sandy's looking so smug about it.'

Captain Kershaw was standing, legs apart, shading his eyes and looking towards B. Troop gun position. After a few minutes a small Dingo scout car appeared, followed by two dust covered Daimler armoured cars.

As the cars moved nearer we could make out the figure of someone standing up in the second car, holding on to the frame of the windscreen. He was wearing an Australian bush hat and, pinned to the up turned brim was a collection of regimental Cap badges. Underneath the hat was a thin, hard faced officer with a long sharp nose and penetrating eyes. He had bony cheeks, a short, clipped moustache and a string of stars and crowns and crossed guns on his epaulettes.

'Montgomery?' I said to Harold.

'Yes,' said Harold. 'That's him alright.'

The armoured car drew up beside us and Captain Kershaw brought us to attention and saluted. A beribboned Montgomery leaned out of his armoured car and shook hands with Captain Kershaw. 'Glad to meet you Kershaw,' he said. 'Now, who have you got here?'

Sarn't Major Evans, Sarn't Reeve, Sarn't Rogers, Sarn't McClean and Sarn't

Cooper.' said Captain Kershaw. 'Our Troop Sarn't Major and our four Numbers One in A Troop. They have all seen over two years service in the desert.'

'Tell them to stand easy,' said Montgomery.

By this time Colonel Buchanan-Spooner, who had travelled in one of the cars had come across and he said, 'Sergeant Cooper got the M.M. at Bardia sir.'

'Did he by Jove.' said the General. 'Then Sergeant Cooper you can have this,' and General Montgomery handed me a day old copy of the Egyptian Mail.

I stepped forward and gave a hurried salute. 'Thank you very much Sir,' I said, noticing that he was wearing longish Khaki shorts and I could see that his knees were still quite white and also that his reddened, sharp features had caught the sun.

'Don't forget you chaps,' said Monty. 'We are just about to knock the Germans for six, right out of Africa. To do that you Sergeants must see that your sub sections are fighting fit and then we shall have no trouble at all. If your men are not fit, it is no good at all. In the forthcoming battles we shall have total victory,' and he repeated 'Total Victory'.

His words were clipped and pruned and his manner decisive, he had the well cast signs of a General who would be capable of putting a few of his Brigadiers on bread and water if necessary.

'Right Colonel, I'd like to see your Headquarters. I haven't got much time.'

As the armoured cars moved off Monty returned Captain Kershaw's salute and we watched the General's party head off into the haze of the afternoon.

'One thing is certain,' said Captain Kershaw, 'the Colonel will not be giving the General a whisky and soda and a cigar when they arrive at headquarters.'

'Why is that Sir?' I asked.

'Montgomery is a non smoker and teetotal,' said Captain Kershaw, 'and they say that he keeps a big picture of Rommel on the wall of his caravan. I think,' he added, 'that Monty will be all right.'

The next time that I saw Monty he was a Field Marshall and had been given a peerage. This was nine years later at the Alamein Reunion at the Albert Hall in London.

CHAPTER TWENTY-NINE

The Build Up

We are back in the line.

More attacks, more counter attacks, more of everything. It is a night shoot and things are slow, only one round per gun per minute.

Orders are shouted out into the night and, between rounds of flaming gun fire, the gunners hold forth with backchat and prittle prattle.

'Never mind, we're on night rates.'

'Worse than civvy street where you work like a dog all hours for Mickey Mouse money.'

A slightly bothered Lieutenant Hester-Hewitt is overseeing and checking the work of Lance Bombardier Alister Fraser who is a newly arrived specialist, pink faced and earnest looking, who has very recently arrived as a reinforcement from Base Depot. The gunners are ever so slightly jealous of the specialists because they consider, quite rightly, that these grammar school types get certain privileges when it comes to doing guard duty and so on.

The gunners watch and listen as Lieutenant Hester-Hewitt watches Lance Bombardier Fraser set the delicate micrometer head on the director, the instrument which stands on three legs and is used for setting the guns in parallel. The reference object for the director is the right hand edge of a derelict tank.

'Swing right and traverse left.'

The gunners comment pithily on happenings they don't properly understand.

'Any Bugger knows that.'

'Convert the grid bearing to a magnetic bearing by adding the magnetic variation if west and subtracting it if east.'

'Bullshit.'

'Subtract the magnetic bearing from 360 degrees.'

Sergeant McClean is not satisfied that he has been given the correct angle and shouts.

'Check back angle.'

Gunner Hobbs on No 2 Gun says, 'Bloody specialists, they know fug all.'

'Load'

'More three degrees.'

'Five four hundred. Three rounds gun fire. Fire!'

A disjunction of words assail the ear. Minor insults are volleyed back and fourth and there is an exchange of abuse.

'Macaroni and sodding beans again.'

'The cook's a bastard.'

'All bloody sergeants are bastards.'

A battery of guns on our right opens up with five rounds gun fire.

'Roll on the boat. Why are we waiting?'

'King Farouk, King Farouk up your pook, up your pook.'

'Less three oh minutes.'

'Fire!'

'He was shook rigid.' The gunners are discussing an unpopular Sergeant Major from another battery.

'He's windy and useless.'

'He's as soft as a barmaid's pussy.'

It is our umpteenth shoot. We suspect we were born in a gun pit.

'Get a move on for Christ's sake.'

'Get down you daft bugger, I can't see the fugging aiming point.'

'I've got a nervous stomach.'

'Five, four fifty.'

'Someone wants to silence those bastard eighty eights.'

From the direction of the Command Post someone is singing the old Royal Horse Artillery refrain;

> 'When the other's are drawing water
> I'll be kissing the Colonel's daughter
> In the little harness room across the square.'

* * * *

It was mid August and we were harrassed by the sun drenched waves of stifling heat which drew rivulets of sweat from our exposed, half naked bodies.

From the extended stretch behind us came the deep steady roar of powerful engines. A dozen, brand new, squeaking matched tanks, each with a formidable looking heavy gun mounted in the turret and with the turbulent dust, spinning around them, pulled in and dispersed just behind us. All were newly painted in desert yellow camouflage. They were like slow moving, belligerent iron forts of combat ready to measure and exchange their power.

'What,' said Kevin, standing up, 'are these wondrous looking contrivances of desert furniture?'

'Those tanks,' said Lieutenant Hester-Hewitt,' are General Grants. They are American built and have recently arrived in the Middle East from the United States.'

'Let's go over and have a shufti,' I said to Kevin.

A Tank Corps Sergeant in a black beret climbed down from the tank nearest to us and he was more than pleased to show us his new toy. The sergeant, who had served in the 7th. Armoured Division told us that the Grant had a powered traverse turret and that they were much more heavily armed than the British Valentines and Crusaders. He also said that, at least a hundred new American made Sherman tanks had recently been unloaded and these would soon be on their way up to the desert. The Shermans, like their counterparts the Grants also mounted a 75 millimetre gun and the thickness of their armour was all of three inches.

Kevin climbed down through the hatch and sat in the gunner's seat. He got himself behind the sights under the watchful eye of the tank gunner and traversed the turret. Kevin, who had sat on the layer's seat of a 25 Pdr. and fired off thousands of shells said, 'Christ Albert, I should be fuggin proud to be behind one of these.'

That same afternoon, three low flying Spitfire fighters. born of the Schneider Trophy and the wealth of Lady Houston, the first that we had seen since leaving England nearly three years earlier, streaked with a thunderous roar across our gun position, hugging the desert contours.

All the signs were, that at long last, we were being given the arms and equipment the equal of those of the enemy and that the desert war had at last turned towards us.

★   ★   ★   ★

On the morning of August 19th 1942, the orders were for everyone to stand by for a visit from Winston Churchill, who was coming to visit his troops in the desert.

Every shoeshine boy and every street seller in Cairo knew that Winston, whose code name was Mr. Bullfinch, was out in Egypt and strong rumours were spread around that Franklin Roosevelt, the President of the United States and Joe Stalin, the dictator of Russia, were going to meet at a top level, summit conference at the closely guarded Mena House Hotel. The desert was abuzz with lurking whispers and disclosures which blew about and took air in every cookhouse and wadi.

'What will we say to Winston, when he asks us how are we enjoying ourselves in the Middle East,' said Kevin.

'He'll no come here,' said Jock. 'He'll only go and have a palaver with the wild colonial boys.'

Some thirty yards away Grandpa, looking deep in blank preoccupation, was under easy sail and was taking his time as he toddled idly across towards the Command Post.

'Grandpa. Come here,' shouted Jock.

Grandpa halted on his leisurely journey, turned towards our gun and plodded over.

'And what,' enquired Grandpa, 'is my wee Scottish friend wanting this forenoon.' Grandpa was rolling his r's.

'Sorry to interrupt your wee walk,' said Jock, 'but we want to know what we are going to say to Winston when he comes round?'

'I can tell you exactly what I shall say,' proclaimed Grandpa, pushing out his chest and sticking his thumbs under his armpits. 'I shall take a smart pace forward, sling one up, and then I shall say, "Sir, I shall not flag or fail. I shall fight them on the beaches. I shall fight them in the desert. I shall fight them in the hills and wadis. I shall fight them sitting on the thunderbox and in the Berka. I shall nevah surrendah".'

We all had a good laugh, particularly when Grandpa said, 'I shall nevah surrendah.'

'Grandpa,' I said, 'you ought to know better than to take the mickey out of the great man.'

'What about a bit of blood, toil, sweat and tears?' suggested Kevin, helpfully.

'I shall serve notice on Winston,' said Grandpa springing limply to attention, 'that I hope that he would give me leave to say that nothing would give me greater satisfaction than to suffer noble and unlimited measures of blood, toil, tears and sweat and I shall conclude by saying,' said Grandpa, knowing that he had our full attention, 'Accord me permission to say, Sir, "God Save the King and Hurrah for the British Empire".' Grandpa was entering into the spirit of the hour.

Jock's considered opinion that Churchill would not be visiting us proved to be correct. He managed to visit the New Zealand Division, The Australian Division and the 51st Highland Division, but there was no time to visit us. Secretly though, we were glad that the old boy had been out to see his troops. He always referred to us in the House of Commons as, 'The Army of the Nile' and we were confident that we would soon have good news of a major victory for the people at home.

CHAPTER THIRTY

The Battle of Alam Halfa

GENERAL HAROLD RUPERT Leofric George Alexander, aged 51, Harrow and Sandhurst, son of the Earl of Caledon, had now taken over the Middle East Command.

General Bernard Law Montgomery, aged 55 and the son of an Ulster clergyman, was in command of the Eighth Army.

Several sharp battles to capture vantage points and to win and consolidate areas of high ground took place during those first few weeks in the Alamein Line. By far the most important was the Battle of Alam el Halfa which raged between August 31st and September 3rd.

It was common knowledge that Rommel was building up his forces for a major attack in a desperate endeavour to reach Cairo and the Suez Canal before the Eighth Army was able to mount a worthwhile offensive.

Montgomery's plan of defence was to form a heavily fortified area against which the enemy would exhaust itself until it ran out of ammunition and petrol.

The northern half of the Alamein line was good defensive country with ridges and wadis from the coast to the Ruweisat Ridge, which was an area of high ground some twenty miles inland from the coast. South of the Ruweisat Ridge there was a vast stretch of desert and in no way were there enough troops to man the whole of the southern end of the line. It will be seen from the map that, running back from the centre of the line, is a dominant hogsback known as the Alam el Halfa Ridge. This ridge commanded a great part of the open country to the south.

Montgomery realised that, if Rommel tried to push his Panzers round the southern end of the line, that he could not ignore a strong force sitting on his flank. In fact, Rommel would have to annihilate the army on the ridge before he dared push further to the east and the vital oil wells across the Canal.

In the middle of the Alam el Halfa Ridge there was a small saddle. If this saddle appeared to be lightly held it was reckoned that Rommel would direct a major thrust at this area.

Captain Kershaw told us that the plan was, as soon as Rommel's Panzers were on the move through the minefields, that we should be taking our guns up into the Alam el Halfa saddle, together with the tanks of the 22nd Armoured Brigade and dig in.

On the night of August 30th the West Suffolk Yeomanry, with its buttress of guns and battle trained men, was lying up about two miles to the north east of the Alam Halfa Ridge. That night, although the moon was five days past its full, Rommel's armour began to move eastwards. There were two large undefended

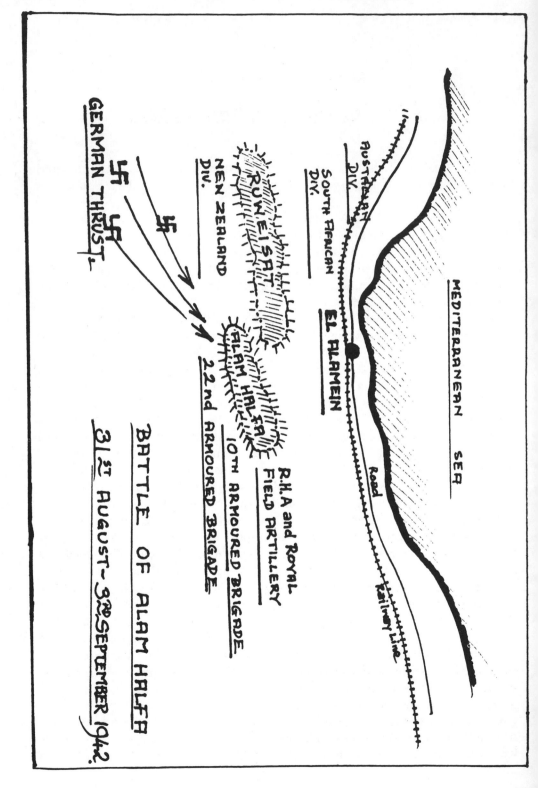

BATTLE OF ALAM HALFA
31ST AUGUST ~ 3RD SEPTEMBER 1942.

minefields out there and, from 10 p.m. onwards, the German Panzers began to move eastwards through them. Just before midnight we were all woken up and over the next four hours as the bright, eastern moonlight dripped on the desert floor we drew our guns up on to the top of the saddle in the middle of the Alam el Halfa Ridge. Here we dug our three batteries in and waited for the impending battle.

A mere three hundred yards ahead of us a brigade of thirty ton Grant and Sherman tanks with their 400 h.p. engines, looking ghostly silver in the moon's bright rays, were in hull down positions. The outlines of the powerful muzzles of the tanks 75mm guns were clearly visible in the moonlight. Immediately ahead of the tanks was a camouflaged, well sited screen of the new British six pounder anti tank guns.

When we had dug in and made ready I went across and had a word with Harold Reeve. I said, 'I like the look of this set up, Harold. I reckon, one way and another, we shall take a bit of shifting from here, even if things gets nasty.'

'I agree,' said Harold. 'As long as we don't run out of ammo we can sit here till Kingdom come.'

Some three hundred feet below us, spread over the vast, treacherous soft spaces of the Quattara Depression, we could hear the continuous menacing hum of the approaching Panzers, pushing relentlessly forward in the bright mantle of the moonlight.

'I think,' said Adrian Kershaw, 'that the enemy will find the going somewhat soft down there and, hopefully, their M.T. will use a lot more petrol scrapping around in the sand marsh than they have bargained for.'

As the night sky dissolved into light we stood to our weapons and at daybreak Captain Kershaw took up a position in his 'Honey' tank on a sand hill behind the guns. Never before had our O.P. been established behind the guns. Captain Kershaw, who was standing up in the turret of the 'Honey', field glasses to his eyes, called out to us that he could see hundreds of enemy tanks, carriers and transport vehicles spread out on the flat plain below. I climbed up and stood on the wheel of the gun and gazed down over the edge of the escarpment on to the apron of distance and I could hardly believe my eyes. Advancing Panzers could be clearly seen in this vast sea of sand like a toy army spreading widely out into the skirts of the distance. Here in the soft sand reaches was a relentless deadly force, a colligation of killing power and hammered steel; an aggregation of fearful weaponry of the most powerful military force in the world. The scarlet sun rose without a cloud in the sky and the wide desert was lit from end to end in brilliant daylight. It was headline stuff and meat for the poet in these tense, expectant moments of confrontation. It may sound corny to say so but I acknowledge to this day my privilege to walk with the honourable and glorious company into the girdle of the gathering imperative intrenched on that lonely exposed feature of sand and rock overspreading the craggy pitched ridge of the Alam Halfa.

★   ★   ★   ★

The first guns to split the silence of that spirit bearing, mean morning were from a squadron of heavy tanks of the 22nd Armoured Brigade, positioned directly ahead of our troop territory. The huge, compact tanks, hull down were firing over open sights and succeeded in convulsing massive, angry, enemy retaliation. It seemed as if every gun on the plain below had opened up on our sector on the summit of the Alam Halfa Ridge. Bright, stabbing flashes from the enemy guns could be clearly seen as they laid fire down on the ridge and lambasted the sector from end to end with raining steel. Our jackets were being dusted and no mistake.

But great as was the firepower of the determined enemy, our own thundering, frightful gunfire at its zenith seemed to know no bounds and we and other gunners, declaring our faith, pumped thousands of rounds of deadly high explosive shells into the engines of the advancing enemy.

There were estimated to be three and a half thousand tanks, troop carriers, armoured cars and transport vehicles spread out in the cauldron below. Forty enemy tanks had dug in immediately below us and were pounding the top of the ridge and another hundred enemy tanks were mustering to the north between the New Zealand Division and ourselves. In the meantime we derived inspiration and encouragement from the heart stopping sight of three formations of Bostons, dropping their bomb loads with perfect precision on the enemy concentrations of tanks and vehicles. All of the bombing and much of the shelling was clearly visible from our position on the ridge as we continued to fire salvo after salvo into Rommel's Panzers. However, in spite of the gunners firing a succession of 'Stonk' concentrations of Divisional artillery, the vast Panzer army continued to move eastwards.

In the middle of the afternoon a Stuka dive bombing raid pasted the whole of the top of the ridge. With their flaps down the Stukas were twisting, weaving and hurtling themselves through the anti aircraft barrage. Two Stukas fell out of the now darkening sky and with air brakes screeching and trailing thick black smoke, they hit the ground in blazing balls of fire. Shortly afterwards four ambulances, their red crosses greyed over with dust, arrived at Battery Headquarters. 'B' Troop had been hit by the bombing and were only firing with two guns. A dazed tank Sergeant was staggering about in this frothing, smoke filled fog with an arm blown off. Immense clouds of smoke and dust hung over the whole blitzed area and the enemy tanks below the ridge were giving us more and more attention. There was no doubt that the enemy were making a determined attempt to take the Alam Halfa and we could take it for granted that their motorised infantry were in the background, ready to assault the ridge when it had been sufficiently softened.

None the less, the enemy out there on the flat desert were at a disadvantage. We were well dug in and our O.P.s had a grandstand view of the enemy targets and there was no shortage of ammunition. On the other hand the enemy were unable to see us properly from below the escarpment and they were taking a tremendous pasting from our bombardment.

It is impossible to draw a fair word picture of the havoc, ravage and sacrifice in the thunderous furnace of the battle. The eyes and ears are so full of sights and sounds, there is always so much more to be said and the tightly rolled, condensed experiences will not fully unfold. I can tell you this though, if we had not learned of war and battle through the long months and years, we should have been awe struck and fearful, welded up to the Alam Halfa Ridge with everything coming at us.

My gun and subsection had performed to a high order of efficiency. Not a round jammed nor a misfire or a badly rammed shell and not a round of gunfire missed. I was surprised to find myself really set astir and roused with a white hot current of rage and hate for the arrogant Nazis in the Quattara Depression below. It rankled with me that I should be in this pit of danger on the Alam Halfa Ridge and that I was being separated from my homeland and the girl I loved. I felt resentment and outrage against these evil Fascists whose foul regimes were like a rat in a corner smothered in blood.

Perhaps I was apprehensive that the German infantry and tanks might surge up on to the ridge but, shouting out orders to my subsection, I was feeling a little wild, like being in a state of mild intoxication. Reckless thoughts danced around my brain like chaff in a drum. It was a static shooting match and we were all highly wrought. We knew that we had to stick it out until the enemy had had enough. We were like cowboys with twenty five pounders in a shoot out at high noon and a scarlet glow was opening in my blood.

*   *   *   *

It was during the late afternoon that Francis was killed. I wish that I could say that he died instantly, but he didn't. Francis took over an hour to die.

A brace of high velocity 88 millimetre shells, probably aimed at our hull down tanks, overshot and exploded just too close to us. At the time we were engaging a small group of Mark IV tanks that were moving in towards the western edge of the ridge.

A piece of white hot, jagged steel, probably travelling at something like three thousand feet per second had ripped across Francis' chest. Why he wasn't dead there and then I will never know, but he wasn't even unconscious.

The force of the impact had hurled his body right up against the wheel of the gun and a horrible red scath gushed blood, which spread all over the front of his ripped shirt and was dripping on to the ground.

Ross was the first to reach him and he placed his open hand firmly over the ghastly wound to try and staunch the flow of blood. A part of Francis' rib cage had somehow pushed its way through the gory mass of torn flesh.

A First Aid kit was carried on every gun. 'Shell Dressing,' I shouted to Jock. Francis was moaning but still fully conscious. I could see that he was mortally wounded but I said, 'You'll be all right Francis.'

Jock brought over the black tin First Aid box packed with bandages, field dressings and one or two large shell dressings.

'Right, Ross,' I said, 'slide your hand away and I'll fix the dressing.' The standard, army shell dressing consisted of a large sterilised pad with long tapes to tie it in position. Francis began to cough up blood and his head rolled over to one side. With the shell dressing in position and the tapes tied as firmly as we could we propped him up against the gun wheel and arranged a folded blanket behind his head. His face had gone the colour of straw and blood was trickling from around the edges of the shell dressing.

Long, anxious minutes dragged on. Time seemed to stand still. I added a rolled up shirt over the leaking shell dressing and tied it tightly behind Francis by the sleeves. Kevin had run off to get the M.O. Some twenty minutes had gone by.

'Where the bloody hell was he? Where were the Field Ambulances?' I was supporting Francis on one side and Ross was on the other.

Suddenly Francis said a few words. 'I've had it, Albert.'

He moved slightly and then cried out in agony and coughed up more blood. We were afraid to give him anything to drink but I took my water bottle and just moistened his lips and bathed his face. What can you do? I couldn't understand why Francis didn't die. I wanted him to die quickly. In no way could he survive with a wound like that.

The other three guns were still firing, what with the noise of the guns, with Francis moaning and crying, with blood all over us and no sign of any medical help coming, it was like a bad dream.

Sandy Evans came running over from the Command Post. 'We can't raise the M.O.,' he said. 'He's still busy with the other Battery. They've got heavy casualties. We've called for an ambulance but it is bloody slow in getting here.'

'Why to God,' I thought, 'didn't they let each gun have some morphia. We could easily have given Francis an injection and that was all that the M.O. could do for him at this stage anyway.'

I was riled. I was riled at everyone. Here was a mortally wounded gunner, drowning in his own blood and dying in agony thousands of miles from his home and there was no real aid for him.

Suddenly Francis cried out, 'Can't somebody do something?'

It is funny how the mind works, but here I was, stuck out in the Alamein line, holding a dying member of my own gun detachment and, when Francis called out, I thought of the time, many years ago, when I was at home sitting in our front room listening to the wireless. King George the fifth was ill and on the point of death. I still remember the words of the bulletin from the Palace. It said, 'The King's life is moving peacefully towards its close.' The bulletin was signed by one of the King's physicians, Lord Dawson of Penn. I thought to myself, 'Christ alive! What sodding bulletin could we give poor Francis, except to say that he was dying slowly and in agony with his mouth full of blood. No Lord Dawson of Penn here, no hospital, not a drop of morphia and not even a bloody nurse.' I don't know when I'd been so riled.

I said to Sandy Evans, 'Can't we put him on one of the signal trucks and take him back to the Forward Field Dressing Station ourselves?'

Sandy nodded his head in agreement.

Kevin had found a stretcher at the Battery Command Post and four of us gently lifted Francis on to it. He screamed to leave him where he was. I hate to admit it but I shouted at him, 'Shut up, Francis.'

We had begun to carry him towards the signals truck when a Field Ambulance drove on to the gun position. The driver ran round the back of the ambulance and threw wide the door to let an orderly out. Another man, who had been sitting by the driver climbed stiffly out and began to walk towards us.

'Where the bloody hell have you been?' I shouted. 'We've been waiting nearly an hour.'

The man replied, 'Don't you dare talk to me in that way, Sergeant or I'll put you on a charge.'

I saw then that he had a crown on the epaulette of his bush jacket. He was a Major in the R.A.M.C. He was not wearing a cap and his cheeks were hollow. He had blood all over his trousers and he was carrying a brown bag.

'Where's your man?' he asked curtly.

'Over here, Sir,' I said.

'While the M.O. was injecting Francis one of the orderlies said to me, 'Your own M.O. was unable to come so we have been sent to you from Brigade. The Major and the rest of us have been on the go since first thing this morning. We've lost two ambulances this morning, including their drivers. The Major and the stretcher bearers are just about all in. He's been doing emergency operations at the F.F.D.S. and there'll be a stack more waiting for him when we get back. From what I can see he can't do your chap any good.'

As they were lifting Francis, now mercifully unconscious, into the ambulance, I went up the the Major. 'Sorry I spoke like that, Sir,' I said.

He said, 'Forget it, Sergeant. We're all fully stretched.'

'Is there any hope for him, Sir?'

The Major shook his head. 'He won't wake up again,' he said.

*   *   *   *

The battle quietened down as night closed over the desert. As I was walking back to the gun with Francis' blood still on my hands and clothes, I could have done with a stiff drink. I wished that I had stored up some of the weak tots of rum with which we were issued from time to time. Christ, I was depressed about Francis.

We swabbed off the gun wheel with the grey blanket that we had used as a pillow for Francis. The worn blanket was already stiff with dried blood. No hope of washing it up here. I folded it neatly and laid it beside his pack and haversack. I was glad that most of the gun fire had stopped.

The red glow faded from the sky and the cool, grey dusk seeped across the desert. I felt slightly sick. Kevin brought me over a mug of tea.

'Thanks, Kevin,' I said.

'Poor old Francis. He'll never dance at Drury Lane again.' Then I added, 'Did you know that it was Ivor Novello who wrote "Keep the Home Fires Burning", in the last war?'

'No, I didn't,' said Kevin. Then there was a pause and he added, 'Didn't Francis have a brother who was lost in a submarine earlier on?'

'Yes,' I said.

A replacement for Francis arrived later that night. An R.H.Q. truck had brought him over and he was dumped with all his kit outside the Battery Command Post. I was called over to collect him.

Captain Norman Kingston, the Battery Command Post Officer said, 'Sarn't Cooper. Here's Gunner Proudfoot. He's a replacement for your sub section.'

I could see by the light of the Command Post hurricane lamp that Gunner Proudfoot had dark curly hair, and that he was short and thickset, with a body like a phone box and hands like shovels.

As we walked away I asked him, 'When did you have your last meal?'

He replied, 'Oh. I'm all right sergeant, when I left Almaza last night they gave me two days haversack rations and the cook at RHQ gave me a meal earlier this evening.'

As he spoke I saw that he had buck teeth. He seemed to be a cheerful customer with a ready smile. If he did his work on the gun, was cheerful and didn't moan all the while, I couldn't ask for anything more.

'How long have you been out here?' I asked.

'Only a week. We came round by the Cape and, after six weeks at sea, we were all Damned glad to get off the boat.'

We threw his kit in a corner of the gun pit and I said, 'It may get very noisy here tonight or at first light and if there are some loud bangs, don't worry. I'll tell you when to take cover.'

'I heard the gunfire on my way up this afternoon,' he said. 'It was a bit frightening really, as we got closer, but, to tell you the truth, I can't wait to get into action and see some real fighting.'

Jock, who was opening up his bedroll said, 'You know something. I once thought that I'd like to get into a bit of action myself.'

'Shut up Jock,' I said. 'You're a Bloody no hoper.'

We had just got our heads down, we were still fully dressed and ready to man the guns at a moments notice, when the ammunition three tonners turned up from B. Echelon and we were kept fully employed unloading three hundred and fifty rounds and boxes of charges into our gun pit.

'Don't worry,' said Jock to our new member, 'We get time and a half for this.'

'Well', said Gunner Proudfoot, 'In civvy street I was getting one and fivepence three farthings an hour and I never could work out what that came to at time and a half.'

*   *   *   *

In the morning at first light I again stood on the wheel of the gun and looked over the edge of the Alam Halfa Ridge, towards the south.

The enemy tanks and transports were still there in their thousands, black, brown and grey moulded shapes in the boundless immensity of the flat bottomlands of sand. Some of the shapes were moving gingerly forward, other, faster moving trucks, were darting about like destroyers around a convoy, leaving their tell tale trail of dust. Heavy transports, having serviced and replenished the fighting vehicles, were heading west. Watching this vast, fascinating panorama of weapons of war was like a giant sky curtain being whisked away to expose an enormous film set, unveiling an advancing armada of demoniac man-eating juggernauts programmed for butchery.

During the morning the main force of enemy tanks again moved in closer and, as the shells began to rain down on the ridge it was apparent that the tanks which had dug in underneath the escarpment on the previous day were still there.

There was a brief rest period in mid morning and I undid the webbing straps of my haversack and pulled out my pair of Zeiss field glasses that I had removed from the body of a dead German officer at Gazala.

From my hawkseye viewpoint I could clearly identify fourteen knocked out enemy tanks which had pressed forward to attack our position on the previous day, hoping to move into close quarters by hugging the base of the escarpment. They had been candidates for our guns and they squatted there, set at crazy angles, crippled and harmless like cast ewes on a barren pasture. Sunk, sterile and bereft they lay anchored and embedded on the desert floor in their own squalid killing field. They reminded me of a certain day at home on the farm when nine men with shotguns surrounded the farmyard pond.

There were about thirty wild ducks swimming about on it and diving for some rotten potatoes which had been tipped into the pond as a lure. The ducks used to fly in every morning to feed off the potatoes and, on the morning of the shoot, when they rose noisily off the water, the men shot down half of them. It was murder really because the guns had moved in stealthily, so close to the ducks which were by now half tame anyway. In a funny kind of a way those wrecked and ravaged tanks lying in their own cankered graveyard reminded me of those upturned ducks which lay dead all around the pond in the farmyard.

*   *   *   *

During the night two more regiments of artillery had moved in with us on the saddle. The whole Alam Halfa Ridge bristled with twenty five pounders and the gunners rained down shells on the Panzers down in the Quattara Depression by the thousand.

On our right flank, well secure, anchored and firmly holding the western edge of the ridge was the 2nd New Zealand Division. During the day a strong force of German Mark IVs tried to force a gap between the New Zealanders and ourselves, part of the 22nd Armoured Brigade. For fully two hours it was a battle royal with tons of hardware flying in both directions. The Mark IVs were given a tremendous pasting from our concentrated artillery and as the battle reached to the full pitch of its fury Kevin said, 'I don't know how many days of this the enemy can stand but, if we don't get the other side out soon, I think that I'll declare or call for the lemons.'

Barney Proudfoot had settled in well and was coping with the stress. He was as strong as an ox and he must have lifted and carried at least seven tons of ammunition and charges since he had joined us.

'How's it going Barney?' I shouted through the racket of noise.

'I'm getting used to it now Sarge,' he replied, 'but I didn't expect anything like this and, to tell you the truth, for the first couple of hours this morning I was shit scared.'

'You've been thrown in at the deep end Barney,' I said, 'but if we can keep the pot boiling for a little longer the Krauts will crack.'

The Luftwaffe and the Stuka pilots were having a bad day. Three times they tried to break through, attack our concentrations on the Alam Halfa and three times their attacks were broken up by our fighters. Nothing is easier to shoot down by a fighter than the slow, cumbersome Stukas and our fighters were picking them off. We noticed that the Stuka pilots were pulling out of their dives much earlier and were releasing their bombs all over the place without pressing home their attack. We were relishing the significance of witnessing the Stuka pilots who had bombed and straffed us at will for the past year and a half, becoming nervous and demoralised.

By the late afternoon it became clear that the Mark IVs attacking the ridge on our right flank had had enough and were slowly disengaging and withdrawing to the south.

Evening came, we had been breathing in lungfulls of turbid smoke and dust for two days and everyone was dog tired, dirty and played out in yawning weariness. Everything had been flung at us from armour piercing shot and 75mm shells to the perilous and highly accurate shelling from the German guns which had been lying back behind the Panzers. We all had headaches and our ears rang, but the line had held and their attack had been ground down by the weight of our artillery fire. The tanks of the 22nd Armoured Brigade had stood fast and hadn't budged. The enemy had been battled into stagnation.

Again, throughout the night hours, the R.A.F.'s night bombers pounded the Rommel Divisions. The battlefield below us was, at times, as bright as day. Parachute flares hovered overhead in a flood of light. Two searchlights were being used, intermittently, as markers. On the ground many fires were still burning and, above, the shooting stars and the night sheet lightening lit the desert night. The two weary armies lay down to sleep beside their tanks, guns and armoured cars.

Very early the next morning, the cold dawn of the third day, the persistent squeak of Panzer tracks could be heard. Captain Kershaw shouted down from the O.P. 'The Panzers are in retreat.'

Throughout the morning and early afternoon the Regiment continued to pump shells into the retreating army and when Captain Kershaw came down to the guns he found us all 'cock a hoop' with excitement.

He said to me, 'Sergeant Cooper, it's damned exhilarating.'

The relief after a victorious battle is like emerging into a bright new kingdom.

Sandy Evans came across and sat with me on the trail of my gun. He was grey faced and drawn like a pit worker from the shaft. He said, 'You know, Albert. I reckon we've got these bastards tamed at last...'

There are still many today who regard Alam Halfa as Montgomery's greatest battle.

CHAPTER THIRTY-ONE
Ross tells us about New Zealand

IT WAS EARLY September. The Regiment was back for a rest in the Nile delta. It was early evening and the Empire Club in Cairo was a bustle. Inside the club the atmosphere was like steamy treacle duff and the slow whirling action of the ceiling fans blew on to wet khaki drill. Brimming schooners of cold Stella beer were constantly on the move from the bar to the wet, shining tables. The air was full of smoke and the Fez headed Nubian waiters in spotless long, white gallabiahs and with wide red belts round their waists, silently collected the drained empties. A spruce, jolly faced scullion of a dish clout wallah shouted orders for instant meals down into the breathless kitchens. Beads of glistening sweat stood proud upon his wide forehead and they slowly merged to run in greasy trickles down his neck, 'Eggsa, cheepsa, onions, three times. One Eggsa, cheepsa, sausage.'

A noisy band of Greek singers, in belted chitons, chorus and jingle on the stage. 'Zere'll alvays be ze Inglant, Vile Inglant shall be free, if Inglant meens as much to you as Inglant meens to me.'

The soldiery applaud. They applaud everything. If Irwin Rommel walked in, they would applaud him.

A small group of artillerymen, straight off the desert were sitting round a marble topped table, in a corner furthest from the stage. Their Royal Horse Artillery, red and blue dress side hats were tucked under their shoulder epaulettes and their cap badges and buttons were those of the West Suffolk Yeomanry.

Kevin, Jock, Ross and myself had seen it all together and we had decided to 'do' the Cairo evening spots together as a subsection. Barney Proudfoot came with us. I was not supposed, as a gun sergeant, to socialise too much with my gun sub when were were back at base, but I wore one of Kevin's shirts, so what the Hell.

Although it was still early evening we were already a little drunk. Two opened packets of cigarettes lay in the middle of the beer wet table. We were living for the moment and trying to forget the war. It was good to be all together, away from the nervy twangs of battle. Kevin talked about home and his father's small-holding near Middlesham. He said that his father had now built up his flock of breeding sheep to thirty, although half of these were broken mouthed ewes.

Ross was sitting at the end of the table, his desert blackened face contrasting with his wavy mop of sun bleached hair. Kevin said, 'Tell us about New Zealand Ross, tell us about your old sheep. I think that I might head for your country after the war.'

'If you come out when this lot is over,' said Ross, 'I'll give you a job as a stockman on my high country farm and you can see how you like it.'

'I just might take you up on that,' said Kevin. 'Help yourself to a fag.'

Ross took the beer stained packet and tossed a cigarette to each of us and then drained his glass.

'If any of you come to New Zealand,' he said, 'I'll show you the most wonderful country in the world. I can show you some country, the beauty of which you wouldn't believe, with snow covered mountains and fast flowing rivers.'

'I'll bet it's not as beautiful as the Cairngorms,' said Jock, giving Kevin a light.

'Well, I didn't see your famous Cairngorms when I was in the U.K., but I shouldn't think they compare with the west coast of the South Island. There are rain forests, lakes and glaciers. You never saw such swell places as Queenstown, Skippers Pass, Milford Sound and Mount Cook. You know,' continued Ross, 'my two cobbers, Pat Morrison and Clutha McKenzie, and I, sometimes take a tent, rifles, fishing gear and jaunt along the west coast rivers, catch fish, camp and climb. You can pull out a six pounder trout anytime and we cook them over wood fires. You never tasted fish so good.'

'I thought you only ate missionaries,' said Jock, as he sipped his grog.

'Pipe down you Scottish oaf,' said Kevin.

'Sometimes,' continued Ross, brushing aside the interruption, 'we'd be away for five or six days and, on the last day, we would try and get a deer. Out there, miles from the beaten track, the birds are half tame and run about your feet and the bloody Keas will steal the rations out of your rucksack.'

'Aren't they the birds that peck the eyes out of sheep?' asked Kevin.

'They will certainly attack weakly lambs or sickly sheep,' said Ross. 'They are a kind of parrot and they have wickedly curved bills, I have known them peck the eyes out.'

'What else attacks sheep in New Zealand?' asked Kevin, 'Do you have any trouble with foxes?'

'No, we don't,' said Ross. 'There are no foxes in New Zealand.'

'I didn't know that,' I said, 'I thought that nearly all the wild life at home was to be found in New Zealand.'

'You're thinking of Australia,' said Ross. 'They've got the lot there. A Digger was telling me in Tobruk that in Australia there are thousands of wild donkeys. People are surprised when they come out to us from the U.K. to find that we have no wasps in New Zealand, neither do we have any snakes.'

'You're having us on,' said Jock.

'No I'm not. You could lay a new born down in a New Zealand paddock and there is no wild animal or insect that will harm it.'

'Ross,' said Kevin, 'How many acres did you say your farm was?'

'Thirty thousand,' said Ross.

I signalled to the waiter to bring five more beers.

'It's my shout,' said Ross.

'And how many sheep did you say you had?' asked Kevin.

'A sheep to the acre,' said Ross. 'Thirty thousand.'

'My father's small holding is sixty acres and he has thirty sheep, which is a thousand times less than your mob,' said Kevin.

'I can't see how anyone can make a living out of sixty acres,' said Ross. 'Our property in Otago is mountains, valleys, ravines and precipices and there is a damned great thirty acre lake in the middle. I can get over most of the property in the four wheel drive Holden pickup, but some of the high country tracks are one in three and only seven feet wide. When you are driving on those narrow steep tracks you don't want your belly full of "hochanui".'

'How often do you muster?' I asked.

'Only twice a year,' said Ross, 'for shearing and marking. When we muster we sometimes have as many as twenty huntaways driving the sheep off the high country and, even then, we can have a bad muster and miss out on eight or nine percent.'

'I expect,' said Barney, blowing the foaming crown off his beer,' that you live on mutton.'

'Well. We kill a hogget every two weeks, the New Zealand lambs you import into Britain are no better than rabbits but a year old hogget has got a bit of meat on it.'

'I don't know,' said Jock, rattling his box of Swan Vestas, 'here you are saying you kill a sheep once a fortnight and my poor old mum, back in Plean, was only saying in her last letter that she is only allowed a shillings worth of meat a week on her ration card, and she had to queue for an hour and a quarter for a half a pound of sausages.'

It was time for a change of scene so we drifted over to the cabaret and the hard liquor. I don't know how our stomachs and lungs put up with it all. A night out in Cairo was hard work and it played Hell with the liver.

★   ★   ★   ★

Our leave was over and we were back with the guns. There was a sizzling air of excitement and expectation. There was a stirring of the embers and the desert was coming to the boil. All the signs were that the Eighth Army was building up for a massive attack, and no one doubted that we should win the battle.

Even Jock became slightly optimistic. 'I'd no be surprised,' he said, 'if we were in Tripoli for Christmas.'

'I thought you said that we would lose this war Jock,' said Ross.

'Well I've changed my mind now that the 51st Highland Division is in the line,' replied Jock, running his finger round the rim of his mug.

'The 2nd New Zealand Division is next door to them,' said Ross, 'and they'll see that your Jocks come to no harm.' He went on, 'Come to think of it, I shouldn't be surprised if there's not a fair few twice grown Jocks in the Kiwi Division. In fact, I dare say a few of them come from Dunedin.'

'Dunedin?' said Jock, 'Where the hell is that?'

'You ignorant wee man,' said Ross with his New Zealand Scottish accent. 'You want to get back to the glens and your pawky granite hovel with its sheep droppings on the floor. Anyone knows that Dunedin is in the South Island, and do you know how Dunedin got its name?'

'I expect,' replied Jock, 'that it's the name of a Maori Princess. Every other bloody Kiwi reckons they're related to a Maori princess.'

Ross and Jock were the best of friends and were a foil for each other. 'You're talking out of the bottom of your kilt,' said Ross. 'Dunedin is named after Edinburgh and Dundee, but you're so fugging thick that you'd never work that out.'

'Get stuffed, sheepshagger,' said Jock, wandering from the issue. 'Anyway, how much did you swindling bandits pay for Dunedin? I hear that you only gave the Maoris four blankets and three fish hooks for Auckland.'

'It was a fair price,' said Ross, 'you want at least four blankets to keep out the wind up there in the North Island. I don't go over to the North Island among all those bastard cow cockies any more than I can help.'

'They tell me,' said Jock, 'that the North Island is separated from the South Island by some rough seas and a lot of jealousy.'

'And you,' retorted Ross, 'are all bull and heifer dust.'

At that moment a small N.A.A.F.I. truck paid us a rare visit and bumped up to the gun position. There were a few bottles of beer on board.

'Better let me buy you a beer,' said Jock, walking towards the truck and counting out his "ackers". 'I don't expect you cannibals understand proper money.'

'Too right,' said Ross, good naturedly, 'we usually use beads.

CHAPTER THIRTY-TWO

The Battle of Alamein

'All Commanders, from General down to junior leaders and all soldiers in the ranks, must possess determination, enthusiasm and stout hearts. In the end it is the initiative and fighting spirit of the junior leaders and the soldiers in the ranks, that wins the battle'.

General Montgomery in the Eighth Army Training Memorandum issued on September 10th, 1942.

TOWARDS THE SECOND half of October everything was being prepared for battle. The Regiment was ordered out of the line for a few days to mark out the course and run through the card that we should have to play in Montgomery's hand.

For three consecutive nights the Regiment rehearsed finding its way through our own minefields and those of the enemy. During these long, carefully planned exercises the guns and vehicles were guided through narrow lanes marked with white tape and lit by storm lanterns burning inside masked, empty four gallon petrol cans. There were three main channels through the minefield and they were named 'Boat', 'Bottle' and 'Hat'. Each petrol can had the symbol of the particular lane cut out of the tin and the lighted shape shone through towards us.

The Regiment was attached as artillery support to the 10th Armoured Division, which had a core of experienced, battle hardened, desert worthy fighting men. From the realistic rehearsals it was easy to work out that our role in the forthcoming battle would be to pass through our own minefields and those of the enemy with our guns as soon as a lane had been cleared and a bridgehead established. From the bridgehead we should lay more barrages for the army breakout to the west.

We were almost under a mystic spell and our minds were afloat as, over the next few days, we waited and watched as new squadrons of tanks, battalions of Infantry and more and more guns moved into position around us. The desert moon was coming up to the full. Throughout the hours of daylight on October 23rd, our own gun positions were tight up behind the Alamein Line.

It was ninety minutes to zero hour. The whole desert was holding its breath. It was the eve of the battle and there was a momentous, awful quiet in the Eighth Army. We sat cross legged on the brown, dry desert floor, watching the gathering dusk at Alamein. It was a strange time, saddled with an unknown and unpredictable future, a future which was near at hand and on the knees of the

Gods. There was a feeling of lawless raw edges around the tendrils of the brain in a peculiar, unearthly sensation of suspended life.

During the days and nights ahead there would be pounding hearts and racing pulses. There would be spillage of blood and, perhaps, death itself. We would be touched with spasms of fear and would be merged into a screen of fire and noise and uncertain tension. The dogs of war were again slipping their leash and we should soon be launched into the thrill of battle.

It was clearly understood what was expected of us. The escape route from the hoops of steel that were closing us in, lay straight to the west.

This could be our shining hour and, to tell you the truth, although I had been afraid often enough, in these burning moments at Alamein, I shouldn't have wanted to be anywhere else.

*   *   *   *

The night of October 23rd was a wonderful moonlit night, bright and clear, as were so many nights in the desert. The atmosphere was graveyard calm. Like a brewing tropical hurricane. At 21.40 precisely the West Suffolk Yeomanry, committed to a small patch of the Western Desert, over two and a half thousand miles from its home base took issue in the biggest barrage and concentration of gun fire since the first World War.

The massive, creeping barrage, spectacular and fearful was laid by a thousand guns. The heavens were ablaze and the sky was lit by thousands of searing flashes. The thunderous roar of the artillery was raw and deafening as, from the sea coast, across the moonlit desert, to the Quattara Depression allied artillery poured thousands of tons of high explosives into the enemy defence line. The enemy gunners were bridled and stung to retaliation and, before long, shells began to fall all around us, throwing rich glaring glows, smashing equipment and killing men.

In some outlandish and fanciful way it was like a great big dream, a dream that was diffused and had no core. With the increasing tremor that threatened to split the earth there seemed to be too much noise, too many gun flashes and too many hanging clusters of parachute flares for it to be well founded and real. Part of our night's fire programme was to lay one hundred and twenty rounds of smoke shells into the minefield to blind the enemy and to give cover to the engineers as they cleared the mine lanes. We were supporting the main attack in the northern sector and the guns on the slopes to our right were now hammering away at full bore at the faceless enemy in the invisible fastness of the night.

There was a five minute pause in the fire programme as the New Zealand Division, with the moon touching their bayonets, went on to establish lanes through the minefields and to take some of the high ground to the west.

After a sleepless and exhausting first night of the battle, dawn brought into focus the beginning of a heavy and troubled day.

Round about mid morning, Captain Adrian Kershaw and his O.P. party, were advancing in support of tanks which were working with the 51st Highland Division. Their recently acquired Stuart tank received a direct hit from a well dug in German 88mm gun. Captain Adrian Kershaw M.C., Gunner Gerald Hudson, his driver, Lance Bombardier Charlie Briggs, his signaller and Lance Sergeant Fletcher Waterman, his ack, were all killed, smashed and burned to death in a blazing inferno of havoc and destruction. The Infantry had sent the news down the blower, 'Kershaw and crew dead, send replacement O.P. party.' There was no time to brood, our minds were frothy and our thoughts in a spin. When eyes and minds are full of turmoil, we had learned to cultivate a certain, empty indifference to what was happening and to curb our emotions at tragic and heavy news.

There was more bad news in the afternoon. A forty strong, black rash of a Stuka raid, penetrated the British fighter screen and attacked our Battery's guns. The deadly black battering arm of the enemy, long range flying artillery hurled their screaming Stukas into the close patterned exploding puff balls of anti-aircraft fire. The screeching dive bombers were spiralling in on their targets through a dark sky, stained with smoke and the yellow dust of battle.

The dozens of barbarous bombs, each one creating vicious bomb burst crashed in brilliant orange and red flashes. Death was everywhere and the atmosphere lay heavy, like a dead pig. Our hearts were pounding like a Bofors gun and we were once again plunged into a situation of hazy cloudlike suspense and uncertainty.

When the danger is great, it is a moment of absolute loneliness and the awful excesses and the incomparable uproar and tearing of flames would, after a few minutes, put most people off war.

Among those killed in this ferocious, storming raid were Sergeant Harold Reeve, Bombardier Philip Underwood and four members of the crew of No. 2 gun. They said that Harold died very bravely. I think that there were five others badly wounded but, as I wrestle with my memory, I am confused and meshed with vagueness and hazy recollection. Harold and Philip dead. The stark reality must bide its time. Harold had once introduced me to his wife. She was a calm, sensible girl, utterly devoted to Harold. She would be shattered with grief, but I knew that she was not the sort of person who would cry in church and she would cope with the two children, and the rationing and the anguished aftermath.

Field ambulances and stretcher bearers seemed to have been in our area all day long. The battle had been raging for forty-eight hours and we were welded to a pyramid of danger. Although the Infantry had achieved some of their objectives there was still no sign of a real breakthrough.

Converted Matilda tanks with heavy chains on a rotating shaft flailed their way forward into the minefield, beating the ground as they advanced.

On the third day a small bridgehead was formed on the west side of the enemy minefields and this was the signal for the Regiment to follow into the breach. This was our fiery cross. We needed no passports and we required no credentials.

With painful slowness and in broad daylight the guns of the West Suffolk Yeomanry threaded their tortuous route between the tapes marking the lanes through the minefields. Vehicles and guns crazily shouldered each other in the crammed corridor. To veer a yard outside the lane could mean the detonation of an anti-tank mine and the loss of a gun crew.

We came under heavy shellfire as we edged forward, bumper to tailboard. All the time the blatant crack over our heads plucked the dry stale atmosphere with airburst shrapnel.

It took another agonising hour before we were through the second enemy minefield. From here on, there was a little more breathing space and we were able to fan out and drop the guns.

The whole area of the bridgehead was jam-packed with lorries, tanks and guns. It resembled a badly organised lorry and ordnance park. The congestion was horrendous. Our two troops of guns were only twenty yards apart and there must have been fifty guns within an area the size of a twenty acre field. It was any man's country and it seemed as if every gun in the desert was in the bridgehead.

There was the continuous shrill clamour of the German Batteries, creating flurries of shells flinging up jagged spurts of sand and flame and tearing holes in the crust of the earth and plucking off our men. Two Batteries of long nosed medium guns were adding to the intensity of thunderous discharges and another Twenty five pounder Regiment was close by on our left. We were in the eye of the storm. Lorries were only ten feet apart and it seemed that ten well placed bombs could wipe out the whole Regiment. Sporadic whirlwind 'dust devils' gusted and raged as they spun through the lines of the clashing armies.

The area was littered with dead and wounded men. Headless and limbless bodies lay between our lorries. A man was screaming in the gun smoke, he may have been wounded or perhaps he was suffering from fatigue and nervous exhaustion, submerged in currents of chilling fear.

Our blood was up and for a solid hour our guns tore and rent at the enemy positions. We knew that our bridgehead must be the prime target for the enemy on the whole of the Alamein line. We were not yet dug in, there were no slit trenches and we were set in the middle of the most juicy target since the rising of the curtain on the desert war. More than anything, we feared a dive bombing attack while we were so vulnerable and without the protection of slit trenches. To be above ground in a major Stuka attack decimated the chance of survival.

Suddenly, and it brought fear on every one of us, every anti-aircraft gun in the bridgehead opened up. This was a clear signal. We shaded our eyes and scanned the dark sky to the west. Seeming to hang almost motionless in the air, we discerned at least forty, crank winged Stukas of the Luftwaffe, heading straight for us. There was no where for us to go and there was nothing for us to do, except to lie down on top of the sandy crust of the bridgehead. We knew that these could be our last moments on earth. We also knew that the Stukas would dive straight through the curtain of anti-aircraft fire as we had seen them do dozens of times before. We felt like pinnioned call ducks and were condemned to be hanging on a finely balanced strand between life and death. Every passing second seemed a lifetime as we lay next to a gun or a lorry wheel, or curled up in a shallow shell crater. Our chances of survival would seem to be no better than ten or twenty percent. Our attention was rivetted on the Stuka leader as he began to drop over on his right wing.

'Here they come,' said Kevin.

Suddenly the Bofors and the three point sevens stopped firing and we heard the crisp rat-a-tat-tat of machine guns and the thumping of cannon shells and there, high above the Stukas, diving out of the sun were the R.A.F. Glory, glory be. So great was our surging relief that it was like a resurrection, a rallying moment of rebirth and thankfulness. At least thirty Hurricanes and Spitfires were slicing through the air with deadly purpose as they tore into the enemy formation. Within seconds the air became full of planes and crashing Stukas and we felt impelled to climb to our feet and watch the annihilation of the dive bombing attack. It was almost as if we were waiting to give the R.A.F. a standing ovation. The Stukas all released their bombs well short of us in their scrambling efforts to escape the British fighters, who were steadily picking them off. We counted eight Stukas shot down. It was a feast for our eyes. One of them, burning furiously and out of control, tore right across our guns at about a thousand feet and then crashed behind us in a brilliant and spectacular fire fed torch of destruction. Then there geysered upwards the final, thick black mushroom of smoke.

A second flight of Hurricanes were busily engaged in dog fights with the enemy's fighter escort. Two fighters fell out of the sky, Hurricanes or Messerschmitts, it was impossible to tell.

Then back to work and fresh surges of flame and thunder and the steady thump, thump of the Brens. None of us were happy in all the congestion of this tightly packed bridgehead, in this dark conflict, measured in fire and blood. We were right in front of the footlights. There was no safe ground and every yard of this God forsaken battlefield had been fought for. By the 29th of October, which was the sixth day of the battle, some ten thousand of our soldiers had been killed or wounded in the battle and there had still been no break out from the tightly held bridgehead.

During the days and nights of the 31st of October and the 1st of November, more hell was let loose than ever. Everything was happening and massed tanks and Infantry had broken through into the enemy defence sector west of Hill 28 on a thousand yard front and had won a few more yards of sand. The thunder of the guns was non stop but we were still tightly wedged into this hostile boiling garden of grim visaged warfare. Troop carriers, guns and tanks were everywhere and the whole of the bridgehead was covered in slow drifting smoke. It was an incessant racket and the desert began to stink of stale sweat and battle. The enemy guns had our range and falling shells were spurting up great showers of dust and rock. Wounded men were stumbling about in a dazed, aimless condition, like headless chickens. Two three tonners, not more than fifty yards from the guns were burnt to cinders.

It was after mid-day, we had just fired off eighty rounds per gun and the enemy were retaliating. Ross, Kevin and Jock were in a shallow trench behind the gun.

Jock said, 'What do you think of things Kevin?'

'Dodgy,' said Kevin, lighting a cigarette from his dog end. 'Very dodgy. I'd as soon be lifting swedes on a freezing cold November day.'

'They say,' said Ross, 'that this is supposed to be a crumbling operation.'

'And who,' asked Jock, 'is supposed to be doing the crumbling? For my part I'm beginning to feel very very crumbled.'

I slid into the trench besides them.

'Good afternoon Sergeant,' said Jock, as a few rounds of A.P. shot from enemy tanks whistled over our heads, 'welcome to our modest wee home.'

'I hope Jock,' I said, 'that you're not creating alarm and despondency.'

'Far from it,' said Jock. 'I was just saying to the two furriners here that I am feeling a wee bit crumbly. In fact, I would like to be a wee dormouse and curl up on some soft feathers and sleep right through the Winter.'

A breathless runner dashed up and told me to report to the Troop Command Post. 'Sergeant Major Evans wants to have a word with you,' he said.

I trotted over towards the Command Post, and had only gone a few yards when I tripped over a dead tank officer. His skull was shattered and my senses recoiled. Where he had come from and what had happened to him, God only knows. I shouted across to a burial party who were sheltering in a trench nearby.

'It's alright mate,' they shouted back, 'We know about him.'

After Captain Kershaw had been killed, Lieutenant Hester-Hewitt had been acting as Troop Commander and had gone to the O.P. Sandy Evans was temporarily doing the work of the G.P.O. in the Command Post. He was managing well. Sandy beckoned to me to come into the Command Post dug out. A man was standing by the artillery board. Sandy said, 'Sergeant Cooper, this is Mr. Straw. He is taking over as G.P.O.

I saluted and said, 'Good afternoon sir.'

Second Lieutenant Straw didn't reply. He was wearing a brand new steel helmet, well pressed shirt and khaki drill slacks and a blue and white coloured choker was knotted around his neck. He was puffing away at a cigarette and he smelled of the whisky bottle. There was a sudden swish and a loud bang as two shells burst nearby and the young lieutenant went as white as chalk. At the same time the Sixty Pounders were making a tremendous racket, pounding the enemy batteries and it was difficult to hear ourselves speak. Sandy Evans was trying to brief the young officer about our situation but the poor fellow was frozen with terror. Sandy motioned me to follow him outside and said, 'What do you think Albert?'

I said, 'It's no bloody use him staying up here. He's nearly off his rocker. I think that you'd better get on to B.H.Q. and see if you can have a quiet word with the Major.'

'I think that you're right Albert,' said Sandy. 'The poor bugger should never have been sent to a place like this with no battle experience and straight out of O.C.T.U.'

When we dropped back into the Command Post the young second lieutenant had fetched up in the corner of the dugout. His eyes were wide with fear. He was sent back to R.H.Q. that night and I never heard what became of him. I was really sorry for him. We had become hardened to battle over a period of two years but here was a young officer who had never seen or heard a gun fired in anger and who, only seven days before had been on his passing out parade. He had been pitchforked into a terrifying desperate situation where hearts were pounding and nerves were screaming with exhaustion and where, even seasoned soldiers were scared stiff and full of dread.

During the afternoon the bombardment became even heavier and we spent a lot of time in the slit trench between shoots. The whole area had become a cemetery of blazing tanks, corpses and wrecked anti-tank guns. In nearly two years of warfare I had never seen so much smoking wreckage littering the battlefield. Vehicles were mangled and twisted, water bottles, tin helmets and rifles were lying everywhere intermingled with the hastily dug graves of the unknown dead.'

'You know,' said Kevin as we were keeping our heads down during a period of hostile shelling,' my mother was something worried according to one of her letters last spring, that the sparrows were pecking her crocuses. After this lot is over I really don't think that I shall worry too much whether the bloody sparrows peck the crocuses or not.'

That night the troop put over two more long barrages and the guns thundered all round us, louder than ever. We were unshaven, tired dirty and were smothered from head to foot in grey dust. The water cart had not turned up all day. I well remember being told that before a battle it was a good idea to have a bath and then, if you are wounded, there is less risk of infection. Some hopes of a bath up here with the nearest mobile bath unit forty miles behind the lines.

The piles of empty shell cases behind the guns became larger by the hour. When morning came there were reports that the enemy line was beginning to weaken. It certainly didn't seem like it from where we were. A lot of heavy stuff and shrapnel was making us all just a little careful, I can tell you, and black coils of thick smoke drifted up into the overcast sky.

The date was the 2nd of November and the battle had been raging for nine days. We had some biscuit burgoo and two spoonfuls of chopped up Canadian tinned bacon for breakfast which we ate quickly with a spoon as there was a barrage due to be put over at 07.45 hrs. A couple of Messerschmitts had dropped a few bombs behind us and about a dozen Sherman tanks, rolling on chattering tracks had just made their noisy and dusty way through our guns to support the attack. There was a certain roused air of confidence as it was predicted that this could be the day of the break out from the bridgehead. A few shells in the ritual of the dawn chorus were coming our way canvassing for death, but nothing much to worry about.

At half past seven everything was ready and the Troop stood to its guns. The first salvos went over, dead on time at a quarter to eight. Some enemy artillery began to take a bit of interest in us, just as they had done scores of times before. Just a few plusses and a minus.

I was standing at the trail of the gun and we were about half way through the shoot when there was a loud rushing, explosion and a searing blast of heat. In a blurred second of lightening fast reaction I put up my hands and arms to protect my eyes, when I felt as if I had been hit on my right arm and my right leg with a fourteen pound hammer. The next thing I knew was that I was on the ground and my mouth was full of sand and dirt. I tried to get up but couldn't. Kevin ran over and shouted, 'Lie down and keep still Albert.'

I felt no pain, just a numbness all down my right side. I began to feel weak and dizzy and I saw that Kevin was holding a blood soaked towel. Ross was binding something tightly around my upper arm. It could almost have been happening to someone else. I felt like a bystander wrapped in clouds of blurred mist.

'You'll be O.K. Albert,' said Kevin who was kneeling down beside me, 'the M.O. will be along in a minute.'

I suddenly became aware of a searing pain in my leg and, when I tried to move my arm, it hurt like the devil. Things became very thick and hazy and I felt locked in a spinning, blinding light. I vaguely remembered the M.O. arriving and filling a syringe. I felt a slight prick in my arm then I sank into a pool of blackness. When I woke up I was lying in a soft warm bed in the 6th General Hospital in Alexandria.

*   *   *   *

The sister said, 'Sergeant Cooper! Sir Alexander Morrison is coming in to see you.'

'Who's he?' I asked.

'He's from Harley Street. One of the top surgeons in London.'

My arm was aching like the clappers and my leg felt like it would explode.

A tall, grey haired, distinguished looking man, dressed in a white tropical suit, came in and sat on a chair by my bed. He looked tired. The battle had filled the base hospital.

'How do you feel Sergeant?'

'Well I've felt a lot better in my time Sir,' I said, trying to be cheerful.

'Well, we'll soon get you fixed up,' said Sir Alexander,' and you'll be ninety eight per cent as good as new. First of all the bad news. I shall have to remove your right foot and part of your leg.'

'Above or below the knee?' I asked.

'Oh, below the knee,' he said, 'and the tin legs are very good now. Do you play any games?'

'I play a bit of cricket Sir,' I said.

'Well, you'll still be able to play cricket, but you may have to have a runner, unless you can guarantee to always hit boundaries.'

I knew that he was trying to cheer me up but I was in a lot of pain and I was beginning to feel very muzzy.

'Now for the good news,' he went on. 'The X-rays show that you have seven pieces of shrapnel in your thigh and arm, but I am reasonably certain that I can save your arm although, of course, I cannot absolutely guarantee it. It should become nearly as good as your left arm in time.' He went on. 'You'll be going down to the theatre in two hours time and I'll see you in the morning.'

I don't want to go on about my operations. They said that I was down in the theatre for five and a half hours. No wonder I felt rough all the next day. Then, every other day they wheeled me down to the theatre to change my dressings and I was glad they knocked me out for that.

After about ten days the pain was more or less under control and I began to enjoy the unaccustomed luxuries of being in a base hospital. Clean linen sheets, soft pillows, silk pyjamas, china cups and saucers and food good enough for a king. Every morning the Indian 'nappie' came round and shaved me in bed and the good ladies of Alexandria came round with fruit, books and other comforts. Christ! It was different from the fearful, raw life in the gun pit. I couldn't get used to sleeping in a soft bed and I couldn't dispel, or I imagined that I couldn't dispel from my mouth, the acrid taste of cordite.

★　　★　　★　　★

Three weeks later the Sister said, 'Sergeant Cooper, here's someone to see you.'

Kevin walked in, dressed in a newly pressed bush jacket and 'Cairo' slacks. He was carrying a bottle of whisky and an armful of fruit and magazines. On his sleeves there were three stripes.

'You old sod,' I said, 'Whose bush jacket have you got on?'

'Well, whose do you think?' said Kevin.

'Well, it's not yours,' I said.

'It bloody well is,' said Kevin. 'I got made up three days after you got hit. Someone had to keep your gun sub in order.' He carefully placed the whisky on my bedside table and placed the fruit and magazines on the chair.

'Congratulations Kev,' I said, 'sorry I can't shake hands but all this lot's in plaster.'

Kevin became serious and looked at the swathes of bandages on my stump and all the paraphanalia of slings and pulleys above me.

'When I get back on the gun we'll make the bastards pay for this,' he said.

'Have a fag Kevin,' I said, 'there are hundreds in my drawer.'

'I don't know what Julie will say about all this,' said Kevin.

'Well I've written to her,' I said, 'I'm getting quite expert at writing with my left hand.'

THE END

Postcript.

Sergeant Kevin Porter was killed two weeks later at the trail of his gun, south of El Agheila during the Eighth Army's final advance towards Tripoli.

Gunner Jock McKinley was awarded the M.M. for bravery during a Stuka attack during the Battle of the Mareth Line in Tripolitania. He returned to Plean after the war, where he took to drink and did time for knocking his wife about.

Lieutenant Ross Baraclough, after three months at O.C.T.U., joined a regular artillery unit and fought in the Burma Campaign. He later became a highly respected member of the New Zealand Wool Board.

Captain Hester-Hewitt became Lord Imray and the chairman of the directors of his family brewery.

Barney Proudfoot trained as a blacksmith and was, in time, entrusted to fix plates on the favourite for the Two Thousand Guineas. He went on to become the most sought after shoeing smith in Newmarket.

From a Dugout in Egypt

To you, my little son, my little maid
A soldier and your father, I indite
A message for the time to come when I
Am hidden far from anguish or delight,
For in that day you'll hear a 'many tongues
Bandy about the motives for our deeds.
Some will be kind, but some will utter spite
For sheer delight in malice: all such breeds
That grind the gentle hearted underfoot
And mock the just. But there'll be others too,
For whom our course is inexplicable;
Whose doubts are genuine; who never knew
the whys and wherefores of this stern debate;
Or who, perchance, from the height of after years
See more than we — the hidden quirks of fate;
The greater ironies; the jibes, the jeers
Of Destiny. Tell them our course was plain,
For we were simple men with simple views.
We were not seers, nor yet philosophers.
But facing bloody strife to win or lose
When all we loved was menaced — them and you
Violence had spread itself, with boasts, abroad,
Grinding the world beneath his iron heel,
And so we closed our ranks and drew the sword.

John Senior of Mole Creek, Australia, came across the original lines of this poem caught on a piece of camel thorn in a wadi near the headquarters of the 2/12th Field Regiment in a wadi running off the Northern Escarpment in Tobruk. It was published in an issue of the Tasmania Rats of Torbruk Association Magazine. The author is unknown.

14 years after the Battle of Alamein Lord Montgomery talks to the authors son (4th right).

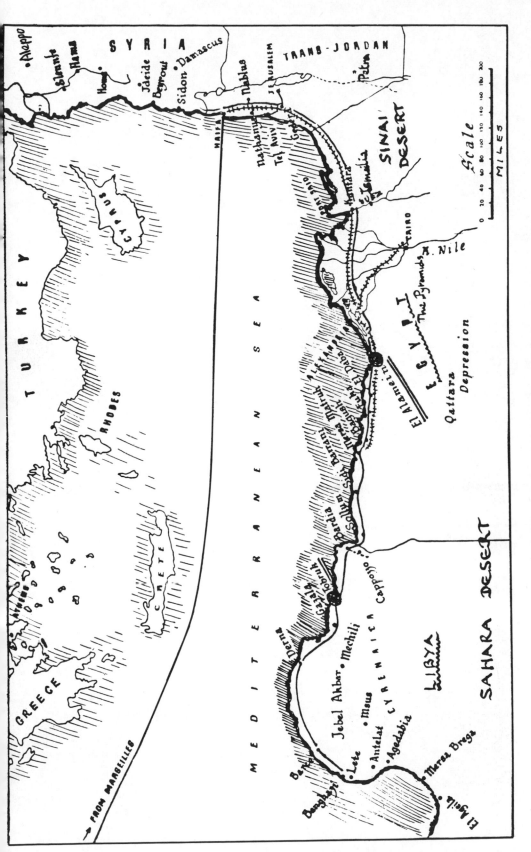

THE MEDITERRANEAN THEATRE